YIN YOGA & MEDITATION

A Mandala Map for Practice, Teaching, and Beyond

by Sagel Urlacher

YIN YOGA & MEDITATION

●○ A Mandala Map for Practice, Teaching, and Beyond ○●

SAGEL URLACHER

Tucson, Arizona
2022

Published in 2022 by Sacred Nature Press
Tucson, Arizona
United States of America
www.yinandmeditation.com

Cover and Interior Design: Predrag Markovic aka Predra6
Mandala Artwork: Rebecca Leah Designs
Yin Asana Photography: Kate Strait Photography
Author Photo: Kelly Mowrer
Illustrations: Ivana Mundja
The text of this book is set in Goudy OldStyle

First Edition
ISBN: 979-8-9856266-0-5 paperback
ISBN: 979-8-9856266-1-2 e-Book

Library of Congress Cataloging-in-Publication Data has been applied for.

Dedicated to the heart of lovingkindness within you.
One of the loveliest things about each of us, it's always
calling us home – an ever-shining goodness connecting
us to one another, and to all that is, in this rare and
beautiful moment that is our life.

CONTENTS

FOREWORD

Cultivating joy. This is the essential song at the heart of Sagel Urlacher's *Yin Yoga & Meditation*: what tools we can use to make our lives better, how we can live our lives, what are some pathways towards presence and well-being. This book's mandala map is an insightful device that can sing to both those relatively new to practice and those who have been practising for decades: "mandalas...have appeared in many traditions throughout the millennia to aid contemplation and connection to the universe within and around us." The mandala map helps us to become more conscious gardeners: "whether a weed or seed grows and blooms is up to us – that which we tend will grow."

Varied bases are covered in *Yin Yoga & Meditation*: the Yin yoga postures, potential sequences, techniques within the postures, meditation/mindfulness, energetic flows, the five elements, physical anatomy. Sagel describes possibilities of practice with poetic lyricism and practical clarity. As she asks: "So, what do you want to experience? What do you want to see?" She reminds us: "Our practice isn't something to attain, accomplish, or complete. It's a continuing journey, and it's our journey...the richness of the trip we take is up to us." Another reminding: "It works not because of what it contains but because of your intention and insight."

Sagel acknowledges roots while at the same time bringing in her own experiences so that what flourishes is both established and current. Threads from modern scientific enquiry are woven with those from much older practices and plenty of options are suggested ranging from the straightforward ("The elevating energy of the simple smile is transformative, an open secret to health and happiness") to the more complex. The principle of optionality and the importance of individuality are clearly emphasised as is the essential need for community and connection.

This is the fruit of Sagel's twenty plus years of teaching experience and practice, and her own substantial study. She reminds us again and again of the preciousness of this human existence: "You are a miracle of consciousness, a heart beating in your beautiful body, enabling you to perceive and receive this stream of sensory information with appreciation and awe." In her heart, Sagel is an optimist: "We are designed to thrive." This is a vital message in troubled times. Becoming more engaged gardeners of our own lives and this world, we can get to know what blocks and what can shift such blocks; how we can be more fully aware of within and what is around. Such crucial questions: what can we cultivate, how do we transform, what could inspire and illuminate?

I too have a long-term practice. And during my years of practising, I have read many books about practice. Some good, some not so good. Back in the early 2000s, there were very few books on Yin yoga; now there are many. This new book is definitely a very valuable addition to the growing library of Yin titles.

In the spirit of yin, there is no need to rush. Be yin within the yin... Take your time while reading Sagel's carefully chosen words. Recognise that waking up requires a lot of work. Allow yourself space to absorb the wisdom and gradually over time things can shift, stories can begin to make more sense. For practitioners and teachers, this book is a wonderful and thorough resource that I highly commend.

Norman Blair

Author of the acclaimed *Brightening Our Inner Skies: Yin and Yoga*

www.yogawithnorman.co.uk

31 December 2021

Preface

I slept and dreamt that life was joy.
I awoke and saw that life was service.
I acted and behold, service was joy.

Rabindranath Tagore

My Pathway to the Practice

Years ago, the universe abruptly did for me what I hadn't been doing for myself – it encouraged me to live more balanced days with a more balanced spirit. After completing two consecutive 200-hour Vinyasa yoga teacher training certifications, I was excited to share yoga with as many people as I could and enthusiastically took on every opportunity to teach that presented itself. I was teaching in studios, teaching private sessions, teaching at hotels, teaching in conference rooms, teaching at gyms, teaching at universities, and teaching at the beach. With mats and all manner of props stashed in bags, I was like a pack mule in yoga pants, carrying my studio on my back. From sunup to sundown and often seven days a week, I offered classes at this pace for several years with nothing close to a sense of balance.

One day, the universe responded. I arrived at a Kennebunkport hotel to teach one morning and, in a rush, reached down to grab my bag of props. WHAM! I hit my head on the massive antique wooden reception counter and nearly passed out. Following up with my doctor the next day, I learned my ridiculous rush of a schedule had actually run me right into a concussion.

A concussion or other injury can be scary and slows you down quickly. My body was physically tired and off balance. My mind was, too, for a while. I couldn't consistently tell left from right and had a hard time speaking in a straight line. Simple decisions, like choosing between paper or plastic bags at the grocery store check-out counter, were difficult, too, and left me feeling like a deer in headlights.

It was a tough time for me both personally and professionally. Although I didn't realize it right away, that experience hitting my head turned out to be exactly what I needed. Not the concussion, of course, but the permission to slow down and simply be. In our more Yang-centric society, I think this is exactly what so many of us need...the invitation to enjoy a little more being to balance out all of life's doing. As I was healing, I became keenly aware of how easy it is to become captive to our doing selves. Without even realizing it, we might come to find ourselves skimming the surface of our moments rather than fully living in the present time.

This experience was how offering Yin Yoga & Meditation became my passion, love, and life's service. This paradigm shift led me along the pathway to practicing and eventually teaching Yin Yoga, Mindfulness Meditation, and Yoga Nidra. On my journey, I've had the great honor of studying Mindfulness and meditation with Zen Master Thich Nhat Hanh and Yin Yoga with pillar of the practice Bernie Clark, co-leading retreats at Kripalu Center for Yoga and Health, and partnering with so many lovely yoga studio owners and their communities in the United States to share Yin Yoga & Meditation and Yoga Nidra teacher trainings.

Through the years, these practices have remained a powerful blessing in my life, a source of joy that supports my wellbeing on a daily basis. My yoga mat is a place of replenishment that I can always count on. Whether I'm finding five minutes in the middle of a crazy day or taking a couple of hours in extended serenity, it's a cherished space to come home to myself, no matter what the circumstances might be inside or around me. These practices are wise teachers that strengthen my capacity to thrive and continue the work of evolving into the best version of myself. They help me to live and love more consistently with greater intention and a more free and happy heart.

I offer you the following teachings out of deep gratitude for these sacred practices and all those who have so generously shared them to make my journey and this book possible. Should errors or misstatements be found herein despite my steady dedication to researching, sourcing, and representing information and inspirations, please accept these as mine.

As both teacher and practitioner, it's my hope here that you feel safe, empowered, and inspired to experiment and discover for yourself the opportunities for transformation and whole-self wellbeing these practices can offer your body, mind, and spirit as you travel along your personal and precious journey.

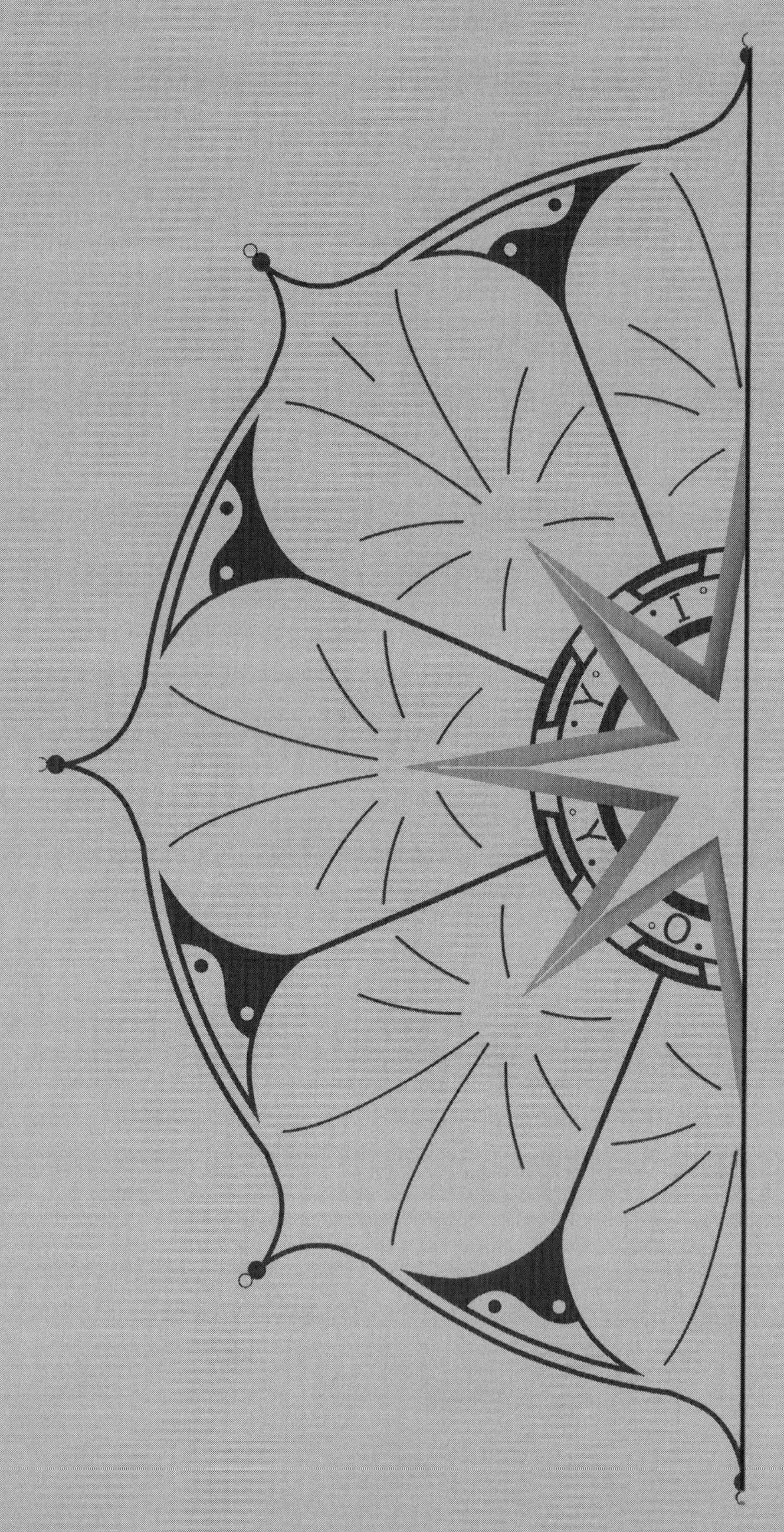

• Part One

Preparing to Journey

Chapter 1
Welcome

Chapter 2
Embracing Yin Qualities in
a Yang World

Chapter 3
Root Wisdom Traditions
of Yin Yoga & Meditation

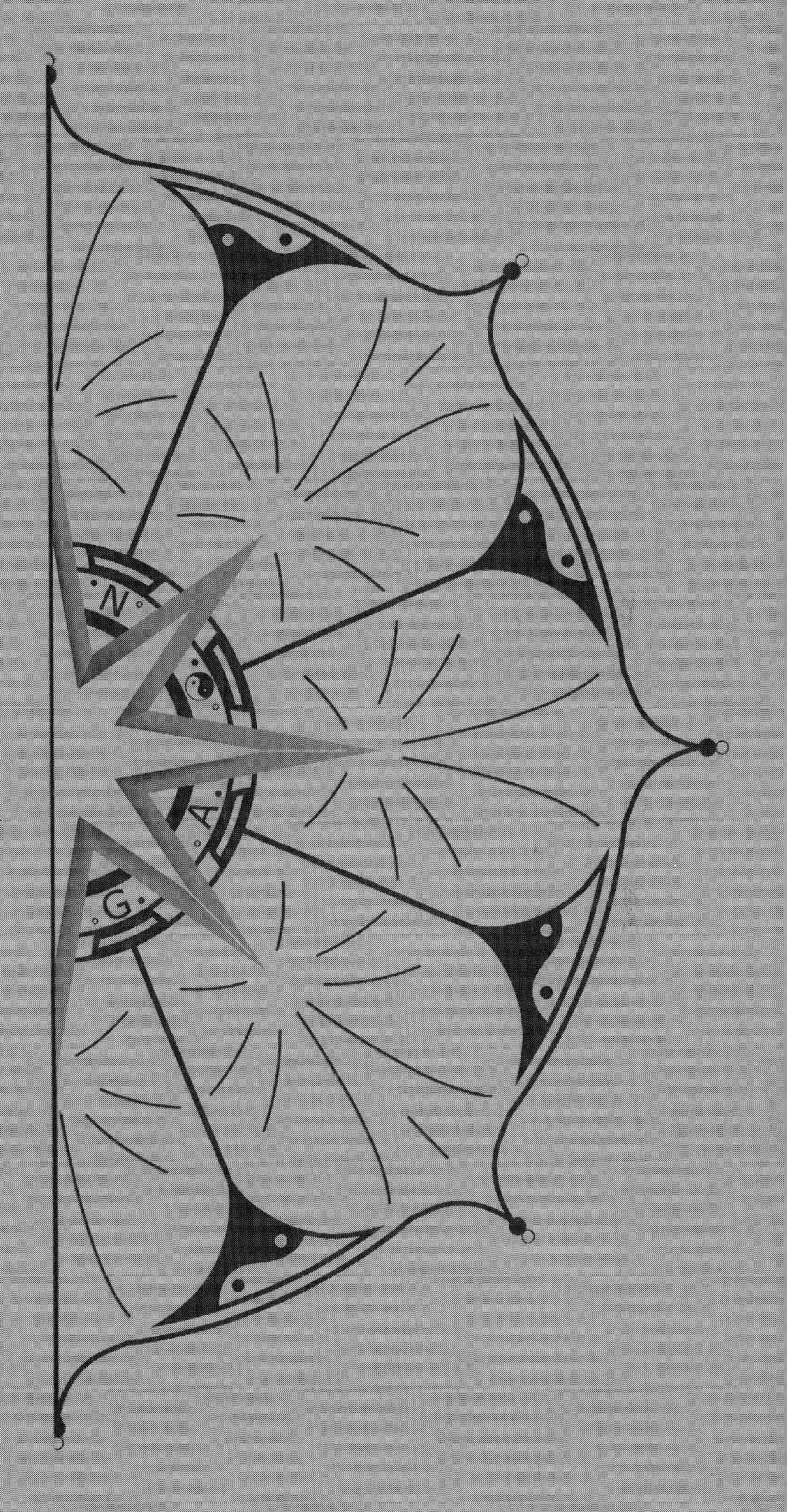

Chapter 1

Welcome

Yin Yoga & Meditation – Pathways of Presence and Wellbeing

Whether you are brand new to Yin Yoga & Meditation or a seasoned practitioner or teacher looking for some fresh inspiration and new perspectives, I offer this book to you from a heart of loving service. In the pages that follow, I invite you to embark on an experiential journey of the practice with this Mandala Map as your guide. Equal parts science and spirit, Yin Yoga & Meditation offers countless pathways to nurture, illuminate, and gain deeper insight into every layer of who we are in support of whole-self wellbeing. In this practice of compassionate presence, we cultivate mindful awareness and learn to use a variety of time-tested techniques to enjoy a safe, effective, and transformational Yin Yoga experience.

Yin Yoga exercise serves the often-neglected yin side of the body — the dense connective tissues so critical for our mobility, fluidity, and flexibility. As they strengthen and hydrate the physical body, these long-held postures also promote a balanced and harmonious flow of life-force energy through our internal energetic architecture. A powerful antidote to stress, the practice encourages conscious, consistent relaxation to soothe the central nervous system and dissolve accumulated tensions. The longer holds of the postures create a safe place to train in observing the ever-changing stream of sensations, energy, thoughts, and emotions that trace through our inner spaces. In Yin Yoga, our mat is our meditation cushion. Staying present with our interior experience, we practice noticing, feeling, and welcoming it just as it is.

Encouraging a balance between action and rest, doing and non-doing, the practice helps us reclaim our yin qualities as we soften inside and out and enhance our meditative awareness on the mat. We compassionately repattern the workings of the mind in ways that reaffirm our connection to the storehouse of joy within each of us. Attending to our whole selves, the practice brings us into better balance and grows our natural ability to stay present for the magic and mystery available in each moment. The benefits of our time on the mat extend ever outward into the rest of our days, helping us to be happier, more balanced, and more connected to those around us with a loving and open heart.

I've seen in my students how life-changing this practice can be for them, supporting wellbeing and happiness in every facet of their lives. Many value the physical aspects of the practice as critical complements to their other activities, such as cycling, running, and swimming. Yin Yoga exercise becomes an essential body maintenance program that grants greater freedom of movement and get-up-and-go. As one student put it, "I have a spring in my step again!" Others have mentioned their appreciation for how it's helped them in their healing process through pain or injury. A friend going through chemotherapy regularly expressed gratitude for how props empowered her to find variations that worked for her. Another practitioner told me how the breathing techniques he learned in our weekly class helped him better manage painful skin cancer treatments.

I've had many pregnant practitioners share how much they valued the respite and relief their practice offered week after week, while others have spoken of how it's helped them develop self-acceptance and befriend their body. A student beginning her journey of recovery from substance abuse found that prioritizing both her weekly studio Yin Yoga & Meditation class along with leading herself through shorter home sessions helped her keep making the changes she wanted for herself one day at a time.

The meditative dimensions of the practice are stabilizing and centering as we learn strategies to navigate challenging situations. Many students have shared stories of how they've benefitted from using Mindfulness tools in their personal relationships, whether learning to listen more deeply to their loved ones or pausing to take a few refreshing breaths when feeling upset. Others have shared how the skills they've cultivated on the mat have helped them in their workplace; they are able to stay energized and mentally clear during long workdays and become more confident in their public speaking skills. Students appreciate how the relaxation techniques help them sleep better, rising for their day feeling more refreshed and invigorated. One practitioner shared how connecting to gratitude and compassion helped him move more tenderly through a difficult period of grief and loss, while another approached me after class to express her excitement that learning to sense her own energy had heightened her sense of loving connection with everyone else around her. These are just a handful of inspiring examples of the positive impacts this practice has had in so many lives.

Getting Started with Your Practice

As with any exercise, Yin Yoga & Meditation may not be appropriate for everyone all the time. Students new to the practice should consult their professional healthcare team before beginning this practice to discuss what fits their body's needs. This book and any guidance herein do not consist of, or substitute for, medical advice.

Whenever we're working deeply with the body, mind, energy, and heart in holistic healing practices, unprocessed emotional experiences may begin to surface, and the Yin Yoga & Meditation practice is no exception. When there is potential for release, there is potential for personal healing and growth, but the timing might not always be right. Just like in life off the mat, the moment you encounter an emotional experience may or may not be the moment you're prepared to process it. If it isn't, that's completely OK. Everything I offer in these pages, I offer in the spirit of invitation. You are in charge of your practice and can trust your ability to make the choices that feel appropriate for you and support the experience you want to have. In your practice, you always have the option of moving your attention elsewhere, taking a break, or discontinuing any techniques that aren't serving you well. Should anything you experience feel overwhelming or unmanageable, please consider reaching out for additional guidance or professional support.

When getting started with a home Yin Yoga & Meditation practice, setting up a quiet place you can use regularly can be helpful in developing consistency. You might infuse this contemplative area of your home with peace by placing a few calming or inspiring items nearby, say, photos of those special to you that you want to stay present for, books, nature items, a painting, a journal for recording any notes or contemplations, or anything else that makes your spirit sing.

Suggested Yin Yoga Props

You'll also want to collect a few props to keep ready to hand. In this practice, props are valuable companions to help us find and maintain appropriate sensation in Yin Yoga postures. Size, shape, material, and firmness are all considerations when determining which specific props you want. For example, a soft and squishy bolster may work wonderfully in one posture but not provide sufficient support in another. My go-to bolster tends to be a full-sized rectangular bolster with firm filling and a removable canvas cover, although I find it helpful to have an assortment of styles and sizes on hand. Explore to see which works best for your body and your practice.

Yoga blocks come in a couple of standard sizes (most commonly 4" x 6" x 9") but vary in weight and material: rigid foam, soft foam, wood, cork, bamboo, and more. Half-blocks offer additional options in your practice. Sometimes a larger prop will do, while other times that half-block is just what you need. You could use some home substitutions too; for example, a stack of books could be used instead of a block in a pinch. A prop doesn't require a flashy color or designer label to be effective. It just needs to do its job, which is to help each pose in your practice be safe, accessible, and as effective as possible.

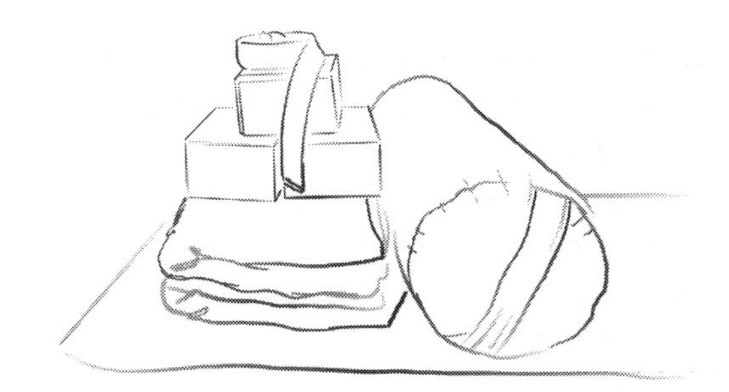

Here are some suggested prop companions to consider for your practice:

- A yoga mat
- Three full-sized yoga blocks, and one or two half-blocks
- Two or three blankets (any type will do)
- Two full-sized yoga bolsters or firm pillows/cushions (average rectangle size is 24" x 12" x 6") and one or two small bolsters or firm pillows/cushions
- One yoga strap or long belt that is about eight to ten feet long (or tie a couple of long scarves together)
- An eye pillow or kerchief
- A few feet of empty wall space, depending on the wall postures you're exploring
- A hand-held timer or app timer

Yin Yoga & Meditation Mandala Map – Let's Dive In!

This Mandala Map arose out of my love for practicing and teaching Yin Yoga, Mindfulness Meditation, and Yoga Nidra and my desire to share their unending possibilities to support whole-self balance and wellbeing. I created it to serve as a practical, accessible, and adaptable tool for anyone interested in the blend of these complementary practices.

The elements of the Yin Yoga & Meditation practice organically emerged to me as a variation of the mandala archetype, a meditative map centered in the orienting compass of our spirits. Translated as "circle" from Sanskrit, mandalas arose in Hindu and Buddhist practices but have appeared in many traditions throughout the millennia to aid contemplation and connection to the universe within and around us. The mandala is sacred space, a place to trace into the mysteries of the spirit. Illustrating our infinite wholeness and our interrelationship with the cosmos, we see in the mandala's core geometry a mirror of the shapes found throughout the natural world in flowers, snowflakes, mineral crystals, and even galaxies. Rather than presenting a puzzle to solve or a maze to get through, the paths of this Mandala Map invite you to go in and dwell in the inside spaces of your body, mind, and heart.

This book is a journey through the sections of the Mandala Map, each representing a core element of the Yin Yoga & Meditation practice. As we encounter the many facets within each element, these pages will encompass philosophical backgrounds, foundational principles, related science, ready-to-use methods, and technical instructions, including:

Root Wisdom Traditions – A brief introduction to some of the foundational philosophies of the root traditions of Yin Yoga & Meditation to familiarize you or serve as a helpful refresher.

Layers of Being – The internal terrain we travel and tend; the many layers of ourselves that offer a pathway to connecting with our true and sacred nature, or what you might think of as your most natural, authentic self.

Practice Principles – The tenets of the practice that lead us through a safe, beneficial, and meaningful experience.

Jewels of Encouragement – Touchstones of encouragement from the root wisdom traditions of Yin Yoga & Meditation. Like precious gemstones we carry in our pocket onto the mat, they help us bring personal meaning to universal experiences, supporting us as we cultivate authentic presence, happiness, and loving relationships.

The Yin & Yang Wings of Present Moment Awareness – The yin and yang sheltering wings of our natural awareness that support presence, inquiry, and understanding to help us experience the fullness of each moment.

- ☯ The yang awareness anchors help us to hold our attention steady and discern what is happening.
- ☯ The yin guardians and yin qualities assist us in welcoming what our attention beholds with clarity and compassion. Together, they

keep pointing us back to our direct experience, asking our sensing self to shine a spotlight on the present moment.

Yin Asana – The physical postures, or *asana* in Sanskrit, the most fundamental vehicles of our exercise. The Yin Yoga poses impact not just our physical yin tissues, but as we'll discuss, touch every layer of our being. Included are the many patterns and potentials, or Yinpressions, available within the postures to tailor each to best meet our bodies' individual needs.

Meditative Methods – Techniques for discovery, growth, and holistic healing to support our overall sense of wellbeing. Arising out of the root wisdom traditions, these methods ground and refine our present moment awareness, encourage relaxation, and support energetic harmony. Each of the meditative methods contains a selection of guided techniques which are ready-to-use exercises.

Yinquiry – Threads of inquiry to prompt exchanges between the elements of the practice to help stimulate personal insights. You'll find samples of Meditative Yinquiry for the Mat sprinkled throughout the book and representative words along the outer ring of the map.

Compass Rose – The compass rose, the nexus of the map, holds all elements of the practice together and embodies the internal guiding presence of our sacred nature. This is a place that can hold our intention.

In the last portion of the book, I'll guide you through how to apply what you've learned about these elements to meditatively move through the Mandala Map to craft your journey for a pose, a whole Yin Yoga & Meditation practice, or for use in your daily life. Through the meditative mandala mapping process, you'll uncover limitless options to select and blend the elements to synthesize your internal exploration and personalize your practice to serve your ever-changing needs. You can engage with them off the mat as standalone techniques, too, for contemplative inspiration or to simply be more present for others with your whole-hearted attention.

For ease of use, pages covering the core elements are indicated with a corresponding label. This multi-dimensional map is flexible and expansible, able to be used by both practitioners and teachers of any level. For anyone just getting started with the practice, this book includes easy-to-follow pose guidance, sample Yin asana sequences, and step-by-step meditative techniques to support establishing and sustaining a safe, fulfilling home practice. It can help you plumb your own depths, fostering awareness of the internal physical, energetic, mental, and emotional landscapes traversed in each Yin Yoga & Meditation session. It's a guide to help you be your own best teacher as you investigate your internal landscape oriented by your natural wisdom. Use it to illuminate the intersections of internal encounters between energy and ideas, emotions and experiences, and sensations and thoughts as they interplay throughout the vast universe within you. Over time, mandala mapping can assist you in increasingly personalizing and enhancing your mat time to meet your needs in both your home and studio practice.

For teachers wanting to share Yin Yoga & Meditation with others, this Mandala Map is meant to mirror your heart of service, helping you share what you love with caring, intentional attention. I hope you'll find it offers a fresh approach for contemplating and uniquely integrating the many elements of the practice to support you as you craft meaningful and engaging sessions for your students. Mandala mapping can spark new perspectives by opening pathways to your innate wisdom and creative flow as you continue to honor and empower your distinctive voice and serve as a guide for others. Whatever your experience level, this versatile map can spark your spirit and awaken your inner knowing, equipping you with tangible techniques, compelling inquiry, accessible instruction, and novel approaches as your practice continues to evolve.

Mandala mapping offers an opportunity to identify and consciously choose to cultivate the skills that support presence and wellbeing in the light of teachings that have been enriching human hearts and minds for thousands of years. The guidance presented here is offered to you in the spirit of invitation for your experimentation. Ultimately, it's your practice and only you know what best serves you. Explore what calls your attention and honors your needs. As a teacher and fellow practitioner, I offer this map not as *the way* but *a way* to approach the many possibilities within Yin Yoga & Meditation. The Mandala Map encourages each of us to trust our direct experience and keep listening within, sensing and feeling what's happening inside. It works not because of what *it* contains but because of the intention and insight that *you* bring to it.

A Blessing for You

Maybe you've heard the ancient Buddhist story of a one-eyed turtle living in the wide ocean who once every one hundred years sticks its head above the water to get relief for its weary body. One day, when it was time, the turtle rose to the surface and encountered a log with a hole in it floating along the surface. Quite by accident, his head went right into the hole, and thanks to that chance piece of wood, the nearly blind turtle was able to float safely for a long time, resting very comfortably held by the log.

The Buddha explained that being born as human beings is just as precious and improbable as this one-eyed turtle lifting its head above the water once in a hundred years and accidentally finding rest with this random log floating on the vast ocean. *You are precious.* Think of yourself like the turtle – in receipt of an improbable and precious gift, this human life. Please think of yourself as that log, too, a great fortune found by weary travelers in need, a place of peace, safety, and welcome for those around you. You are here on purpose – precious, powerful, connected to everything and everyone. May you remember that you deserve to nurture within you whatever needs your kind care and attention, accessing your inner resources and know-how to serve and empower the best of who you are. Joy is your blueprint and your birthright, and as you shine bright, you remain a beacon of light and love for others.

Yin Yoga & Meditation offers countless pathways of presence and wellbeing to help us honor the preciousness that we are and live happy, healthy, and meaningful lives. For both practitioners and teachers, my wish is that this map empowers and inspires you as you tap into your loving heart and intuitive insight in your practice, teaching, and daily life. I hope as you continue through this book that you'll use it in conversation with your highest wisdom in ways that support your whole-self wellness, nourish your connections with those around you, and fuel the storehouse of joy within you.

CHAPTER 2

EMBRACING YIN QUALITIES IN A YANG WORLD

Let's begin our travels through the elements of Yin Yoga & Meditation and our Mandala Map at...the beginning. What is yin? What within us is yin? How in this constantly changing, racing world can embracing and strengthening our yin qualities promote whole-self wellbeing and help us remain present for the precious moments of our lives?

Yin Is Relative

Like everything in the universe, our natural state is balanced and in harmony with everything around us. Our human form is a model of the interrelated and opposing energies of yin and yang. Ancient Chinese Taoist sages taught that the health of our energy body directly impacts our physical, mental-emotional, and spiritual health, and vice versa. When we're in balance, we're healthy, happy, and living wholeheartedly as the purest expression of ourselves. There's a sense of momentum and a feeling of being supported by our internal resources; we are tapped into the universal flow of energy.

Yin and yang are the two energetic opposites of the universe: day-night, up-down, life-death, electron-proton. Yin-yang theory describes how these opposite forces of nature are mutually supportive, interactive, and interdependent. Yin-yang aspects are inherent in all phenomena, including within us. Yang energy accomplishes; it's our strategizing, managing, and implementing side. Yin is yang's counterbalance and complement: allowing, non-doing, slowing, and yielding. Yang is outward-moving. Yin is inward-turning.

Think of yin and yang qualities not as nouns, as things, but rather as ways of describing relative states of being, as adjectives and adverbs. Yang thinks logically. Yin feels intuitively. Yang is the force that moves us out in all directions and sparks our spirit to act. Yin is the soft, warm hand of the universe that holds us, the nourishing energy sustaining and lighting our way.

Generally speaking, yin is darker, cooler, heavier, quieter, and slower, while yang is brighter, warmer, lighter, louder, and faster. In all of these examples, you'll notice the "er." Nothing is purely yin or yang. Everything exists in relation to all other things, so an object or activity may be yin compared to one thing and yang compared to another. When we describe something as either yin or yang, we're doing so in terms of one aspect in relationship to something else. Let's say we describe ourselves jogging down the street as slow. Yin-yang theory invites us to ask: We're jogging slowly – compared to what? Compared to a tortoise? Compared to a cheetah?

Imagine there are two cars traveling down a road. Let's say there's a light-colored car moving at thirty miles per hour, and a darker car driving at sixty miles per hour. Which car would you say is more yin-like and which is more yang-like? It's a bit of a trick question! In the context of color, the darker car is more yin-like in comparison to the more yang-like lighter-colored car. In terms of speed, however, the slower, light-colored car is more yin-like when compared to the relatively faster and more yang-like darker car.

Yin and yang are also equal, opposite, and complementary. Where there is a yin force or quality, there is an equal and opposite yang force to complement it. Just as there is no shadow without light, yin and yang are forever joined and make each other possible. Yin and yang require each other, just as being a sister or brother requires having a sibling. They exist only in relationship to one another, and there are no absolutes, just more or less.

Like everything in the universe, each of us has both yin and yang qualities within us. We might be more yin-like in the morning as we sip our tea peacefully on the patio and more yang-like in the evening when we're busting a move on the dance floor. Neither yin nor yang is good or bad, right or wrong. They're neutral and the proportion between the two is perpetually in flux. Everything in the universe is constantly changing, so the relationships between things are necessarily changing, too. These dynamic aspects exist in an ever-shifting, inter-transformational relationship. Like the sunny side of a hill at sunrise transforms into the shady side as the sun sets, yang turns into yin, and yin becomes yang just as the sun rises once again.

Balance and harmony are the keys - we need both yin and yang. Yin-yang disharmony and imbalance in one part of ourselves will cause disruptions, to some degree, in our other parts. The same changing dynamics are true externally in our families and communities as well.

Reclaiming Our Yin Side

For many of us, modern-day living encourages a predominance of yang qualities, making it a challenge to maintain a healthful balance. Daily life is good at keeping us moving...doing this, fixing that, planning and managing and controlling - yang bodies living yang lives, yang minds thinking yang thoughts. Whether due to an overly packed schedule to get all the kids where they need to go, or feeling like we need to produce more in less time at our jobs, we're almost constantly asked to engage our yang side in the course of the day. We might inquire, when was the last time we set up an appointment for ourselves to do nothing? In what aspects of our life do we encourage the yin side?

> In today's rush, we all think too much, seek too much, want too much, and forget about the joy of just being.
>
> – *Eckhart Tolle*

With so many things to accomplish and solve, we come to carry deep tensions and stress subconsciously in our physical body, but we can also hold them in other layers of our being, too. At times, our fight-flight response becomes over-engaged which can have a significant negative impact on our wellbeing. On top of physical consequences, this continuous yang-like state of doing disconnects us from our capacity to simply be. Relaxing becomes more difficult, even when we're trying to unwind.

With the demands of daily life, our mental attention can become dispersed and scattered: not really here, not really there, not really anywhere. A 2018 survey by Asurion found that the average American checks their smartphones roughly every twelve minutes during the day, even when on vacation! When we're out of balance in this way, our body tends to be in one place doing one thing, while our mind is in another place thinking about something completely different. At the end of the day, we may find we ended up missing the very moments we rushed to enjoy. There's an old Zen adage that advises we should meditate for twenty minutes a day, unless we're too busy. In that case, we should sit for an hour. We're not universally skilled at letting ourselves be human *beings*. Over the years, my Yin Yoga & Meditation practice has helped me realize the immense value of being, and its presence in my life remains a steady reminder. *Non-doing* has become one of my favorite verbs.

Embracing our capacity to slow down, sense, and enjoy simply being can feel like a radical act when surrounded by so many yang expectations. Everyday life doesn't necessarily encourage us to strengthen our yin qualities, but that doesn't make them less valuable - it just makes them more scarce. If we're always talking, when are we able to listen? If we're always giving, how do we receive? If we're always doing and moving, when can we rest and replenish? Embracing our yin side balances out all that doing, thinking, and accomplishing, letting us truly relax and restore, listen inward, and be more present. Honoring what is yin within us brings us back to center.

If we experience too much of either yin or yang and don't course-correct, the universe has a way of eventually intervening with more yin or yang to reclaim balance for us. Do you remember a time when you felt extra yang-like? Maybe you were working too hard, sleeping too little, or not taking the space to relax and restore? What happened as time went on like this? If your experience is anything like mine, perhaps you got Yin'd! You might have become sick or injured or you were forced in some other way to slow down and rest. Where there is too much yang, yin energy will come to the forefront to pave the return to our home state of balance and harmony. With practice and intention, we connect with and nurture the yin qualities that re-nourish the other half of our whole selves and bring us back into equilibrium.

The human brain is an analytical, creative marvel, yet our bodies are also thoroughly, majestically equipped to sense. Yin invites us to first feel what's happening in the moment rather than immediately follow the yang inclination to adjust or solve it. On the mat, we transfer our attention from *doing* to *being*. We inhabit a pose rather than perform it and practice what it means to experience a sensation rather than analyze it.

Yin Yoga exercises our connective tissues hidden deep inside. As we're slowly entering the posture, we turn our attention inward, opening our inside eyes and ears. To take good care of the physical tissues we target, we need to understand what they're telling us. Sensation is the language through which the body communicates, so we train ourselves to feel things we cannot see. In our practice, non-visual sensing becomes a new and primary way of perceiving.

Shining the spotlight of our awareness through the space of our inner landscape will help to keep our time on the mat safe, effective, and sustainable as we honor the body and its ever-changing needs. With so many external requests being made for our attention, allowing ourselves to be at rest and attuning to how things feel isn't always easy. The meditative nature and longer holds of Yin Yoga give us time to begin sensing what we're feeling on the inside. We have space to enjoy non-doing and sense the subtle physical sensations as they arise within and between the poses. When we're able to watch, feel, allow, and be fully present for our experiences without needing to reflexively change or control them in some way, we nourish our yin qualities. What yin-yang balance looks like is ever-changing, because we're always changing. Just like standing on one foot requires kind attentiveness and ongoing adjustments, maintaining balance isn't a one-time activity but rather an ongoing process. As you continue this exploration, you'll find that the yin qualities permeate the other elements of our Mandala Map, offering the opportunity to soften our approach and skillfully embrace our yin side in all aspects of our practice, teaching, and beyond.

CHAPTER 3

ROOT WISDOM TRADITIONS OF YIN YOGA & MEDITATION

The philosophies, principles, and techniques from Buddhist Mindfulness meditation, Taoist energy practices, and the deep relaxation methods of Yoga Nidra have long inspired and informed my Yin Yoga & Meditation practice and teaching. Though distinct, these sacred wisdom traditions share ideas and ideals related to the value of mindful awareness, the importance of compassion for oneself and others, the interconnection of all phenomena, and the impact of tension relief on physical, emotional, and spiritual health. In the Mandala Map framework of this book, I've synthesized some of the primary teachings from these wisdom traditions to inform a meditative journey into yourself as you travel the inner pathways of self-discovery in each pose, your practice, and beyond. Exploring these fundamental teachings within the context of Yin Yoga & Meditation offers heartening support as we nurture our ability to experience lasting happiness and wellbeing.

Though we may come to the mat for the benefit of our physical bodies, the elements of our Yin Yoga & Meditation practice have the potential to reach into all aspects of who we are. We get to experience how our inner layers interact and interplay and observe those lines of interconnection stretching outward beyond the barriers of skin into our relationships and the far reaches of the world around us.

Although the information in this section may be familiar for those who have studied these ancient wisdom traditions in detail, I include it here as a supportive resource whether it's an introduction or refresher for some of the basics underlying each philosophy. From this foundation, we can more effectively explore ways they illuminate and integrate with the Yin Yoga & Meditation practice and discover what meanings they could hold in our own lives. What follows is by no means intended to be a comprehensive summary of either their history or fundamental principles. Instead, we'll touch on the elements that enliven this Mandala Map in the hope they'll be a guiding light and source of inspiration – may their shining illuminate the wisdom in our hearts and bring immeasurable benefit to all.

TAOISM FUNDAMENTALS

You are precious, humming with energy, and powerful beyond measure. Quite simply, you're made of magic. Taoists teach that we have life-force flowing through internal energetic architecture and have the capacity to awaken and support that powerful energy, harmonize it, and cultivate it. In doing so, we nourish our intrinsic connection with everyone around us and with the universe itself. This alchemical potential has the power to help you live the life you desire and deserve.

Taoism originated in China more than 2,500 years ago and is one primary root of the modern Yin Yoga & Meditation practice. While there are religious aspects within the broad Taoist tradition, its influence in our current practice has more to do with its approach to life and coming to know the universe within and surrounding us. For Taoists, the natural world serves as both mirror and teacher of harmonious, balanced living. By carefully observing nature, we can learn to emulate it and embody its wisdom to enjoy a more peaceful, fulfilling life.

A Holistic Approach to Wellbeing

The Taoist philosophy holds that the source and design of all things in the universe is the Tao. Impossible to fully describe, the Tao is both noun and verb. The Tao is the path, and the Tao is to know. The universe was born of the Tao, and the Tao lives in all things. A Taoist seeks the truth of ultimate reality: the truth of ourselves, the natural world, and the whole of the universe. Aligning with the Tao offers us a healthy, long life and the ability to live in alignment with our intentions and purpose.

Taoism's primary text is a small book called *Lao Tzu*, or *Tao Te Ching*, written by the sage Lao Tzu, a contemporary of Confucius. Some assert that Lao Tzu wrote this short yet profound book of roughly five thousand characters in the 4th century BCE near the end of his life. *Tao Te Ching* delves into the meaning and mystery of the Tao. It explores the principles of yin and yang and ways we can live with virtue, in rhythm with the seasons, and in proper relationship with the earth.

Early civilizations perceived happenings on the earth to be the work of gods and goddesses and appointed spiritual leaders who interceded with these supernatural beings on their behalf. Over time, Taoists began to see these forces of nature as energies that existed in everything in the universe, including us. They came to believe that each of us was able to understand and harness these powers through perception and connection. Instead of interceding with a god who, for example, ordered rain to fall, all human beings have the capacity to sense, feel, and engage with the energy of water directly.

By allowing this sensing self to arise, we attune and synchronize our bodies, minds, and hearts to the powerful flow of energy in nature, communicating with our inner wisdom and higher power. When we look to nature, we learn about the Tao, and as we begin to understand the Tao, we better understand ourselves and are empowered to adapt our attitudes and actions to it. Nature's wisdom shines its light, and when we align with it, we flourish and thrive. Living harmoniously with the Tao, we harness the gifts of our inherent interconnection with all that is and experience wellbeing. This direct engagement with the energies of the universe served as the basis of Tao Yin, the original form of the medical energy practice of Qigong.

Principles from the *Tao Te Ching* are woven into Chinese Medical Theory, the ancient system of disease prevention, detection, and care that evolved over several thousand years. The *Neijing Su Wen*, or *The Yellow Emperor's Classic of Medicine*, is the foundational Taoist medical text written between the 2nd century BCE and 2nd century CE. Viewed as the first holistic medical text in human history, this book explains how to use yin-yang principles to create balance and harmony in support of good health and a long life. Both of these principal books have made their way into other Asian philosophies and cultures as well as into modern-day Western thought, albeit more slowly.

In the West, our approach to health and happiness has tended to be somewhat disjointed, with the various parts of ourselves typically treated separately by different people: heart doctors, lung doctors, feet doctors, spiritual leaders, psychologists, pathologists...the list of "health silos" is nearly endless. Classic Chinese Medicine takes a more holistic approach, treating all aspects of the individual as one seamless whole, a microcosm of the entire cosmos. Traditional Chinese Medicine asserts that all layers of our being are intrinsically connected and mutually interactive. Health in one aspect supports health in all, just as disruption or disease in one may, over time, affect every other facet.

I'm sure we've all experienced how a circumstance in one area of our lives often impacts another – the same is true inside us. A few years ago, I injured my foot on a walk. Over the weeks that followed, because one side was compensating for the other, the tension of being off balance rippled from my foot to my ankle, then to my knee, hip, spine, and shoulders, with pain eventually running all the way into my neck. What began with my foot soon became a whole-body issue. In working through this injury, I needed to honor the interconnectedness of all parts of me. Healing became a whole-body process that required a holistic physical and energetic approach.

Qi Around Us, Qi Within Us

At the heart of Chinese Medical Theory is tending the strength and flow of Qi. In Taoism, Qi is viewed as the vital force from which all life arises, the primordial energy that comprises and compels all things that exist. Also called "Heaven's Breath," Qi is ethereal, like mist over a field at dawn or steam rising from rice cooking in a pot. From the Taoist perspective, everything in the cosmos is Qi. The grass, the ocean, the air, this brick, that stick, the moon, the stars, far beyond what the eye can see...all is Qi.

You are Qi, I am Qi, and we're all a part of a larger sea of Qi, connected to each other and all that is. Not bounded by skin, the energy within flows through and out of me into the world and into you, and the same is true of the energy sourced in you. Like the inherent continuity of the breath, coming in and going out, Qi is ever-present and constantly moving, joining the whole of the universe in one vast network.

The celestial energy that forms the moon and stars is the same energy moving through our bodies. From the Taoist metaphysical perspective, we receive energy from the stars and return it to them. Qi perpetually flows from us into the cosmos and back again in a mutually sustaining and empowering relationship. We and all things exist in a beautiful, symbiotic relationship with the whole universe. We are one with all. Living in harmony with the ways of the natural world supports a healthy flow of Qi, and we are happiest and healthiest when we support and contribute to that flow.

Taoist Cosmology

In Taoist cosmology, the Tao gave birth to yin and yang, the opposite but complementary forces present in all things. Out of the tension between these two emerged Qi. The nature of Qi is to move and flow. With the earth serving as the center, Qi moved into the four directions of the compass. From these points arose the Five Elements or phases of Qi: Wood, Fire, Earth, Metal, and Water. These Elements, each a specific vibration of Qi, embody certain qualities and align with a season: spring, summer, late summer, fall, and winter, respectively. Additionally, each Element is associated with a yin-yang Organ pair and the energy channels that feed it.

Everything in the universe is a unique combination of the infinite permutations, or recipes, of these constantly shifting Qi vibrations or phases. They engage in a balanced flow, forming a natural equilibrium with constant interplay. Each of us is a unique and ever-changing manifestation of the Five Elements. The ancient Chinese sages observed that everything that exists or happens is the result of the movements of Wood, Fire, Earth, Metal, and Water, and out of this understanding arose what is known as Five Elements Theory. Materially woven into Traditional Chinese Medicine, Five Elements Theory describes the Elements and their relationships.

Fundamentally, Five Elements Theory reflects the Tao and offers a blueprint of how the different dimensions within us and the natural world interact with and impact one another. Taoists believe aligning with this framework supports the body's innate wisdom and healing power. From Water, we learn the value of relaxed effort. Wood teaches us to be strong yet flexible. Fire inspires delight and enhances the steady flow of energy in all aspects of ourselves. Earth grounds and nourishes us, while Metal encourages letting go of what doesn't serve us in honor of the transformation possible in each moment. Rooted in the reality of the Tao, Five Elements Theory offers endless inspiration to inform our practice and our life.

Flow Supports Harmony, Harmony Supports Flow

The Chinese developed Tao Yin at least two thousand years ago to generate and strengthen energy in the body based on Taoist principles. Tao Yin, sometimes referred to as Taoist yoga, includes seated poses as well as sequences of slow, fluid movements that honor and mirror the movements of animals. A primary intention of Tao Yin practice is to accumulate, stimulate, balance, and refine the flow of our internal energy and put it to use for our benefit. Although our current day Yin Yoga & Meditation practice does not generally include standing movements, our practice shares Tao Yin's focus on strengthening the quantity and quality of Qi flow within us. Both practices use gentle acu-pressure, intentional attention, and the breath to build, circulate, and balance our energy body for physical health, peaceful connection with nature, and a long, happy life.

Qi flows, and since we are Qi, our natural state, too, is one of balance and flow. The release of tensions encourages free circulation and flow of energy within the body. By clearing energetic obstacles and promoting balanced flow, we aim to restore health and vitality to all layers of ourselves joined as one continuous whole. Body, mind, and spirit become a vibrant, synergistic continuum. By bringing balance to one aspect of who we are, we balance all layers of our whole being. Nurturing the body, we heal the heart. Tending the heart, we bring healing to the body.

Maintaining a vibrant Qi flow supports longevity and prevents energetic disruptions, illness, and emotional upsets. It also bolsters our authentic and conscious connection with the natural world, which, in turn, strengthens our energetic, physical, and mental-emotional health. Indeed, the quality of our Qi determines the quality of our life. All is Qi, so if we improve Qi flow, we improve all of life. Each of us is designed with the ability to awaken and support that energy, refine it, and harmonize it as we acknowledge our intrinsic interconnectedness with all that is.

In Yin Yoga & Meditation, we learn to sensitize to Qi flowing within us and tap into that universal life-force energy surrounding us to bring balance. Because Qi is constantly moving and changing, balance is a moving target and ongoing process. There's no set recipe of yin vs. yang – we're not a chocolate cake! Like all things, we are always in a state of flux. What brings equilibrium one day may generate imbalance on another, so to generate healthy Qi flow, we need to continue developing our ability to sense what's happening within us and respond effectively and wisely. Throughout this book, we'll explore some of the treasured practices Taoists have been handing down for centuries to nourish the flow of Qi within us.

To paraphrase Alan Watts, the course that can be discoursed is not the course, of course. That is to say, to genuinely know the Tao, we need to experience it directly. To understand its power for transformation isn't to talk about it or think about it – it's to feel it, so the first step toward strengthening and balancing Qi is learning to sense it. By becoming fluent in this energetic language, we practice listening to and understanding what it has to tell us. As we sensitize to ourselves as energetic beings of magic and mystery, we identify our integral place in the ocean of Qi surrounding us, a precious piece of the universal design, and the energetic work we do on the mat naturally manifests outwardly to all we meet.

Buddhism Fundamentals

Simply by shining the light of our attention, we transform the mundane into something miraculous. Being present offers us the chance to genuinely connect with each moment and the gifts of grace and beauty waiting for us there. Present moment awareness is, at its most fundamental, an act of love.

> The miracle is not to walk on water. The miracle is to walk on the green earth, dwelling deeply in the present moment and feeling truly alive.
>
> – *Thich Nhat Hanh*

Training in Compassionate Moment to Moment Attention

The Yin Yoga & Meditation practice gives us a chance to expand our ability to perceive ourselves, others, and our experiences with wise and loving attention. As we watch with kind eyes, we practice being a welcoming witness. This compassionate observation can deliver insight into the heart of what makes us suffer and what creates inroads to enduring happiness. The skills we practice on the mat serve us when we rise, helping us be more present for the happenings of our lives and actively create more causes of happiness in ourselves and others.

Arising from Buddhist traditions, Mindfulness Meditation is a practice of awakening our moment-to-moment, open-hearted attention to what's happening inside and around us. Buddhist philosophy is another ancient map we can learn from and consider applying in the context of our Yin Yoga practice, and you don't have to be Buddhist to benefit from Mindfulness Meditation.

In the *Dona Sutta*, a short Buddhist discourse between a brahmin and the Buddha, the story is told of a priest named Dona walking the same road as the Buddha. Looking down, Dona saw the image of wheels with one-thousand spokes within the Buddha's footprints. Dona was certain this astonishing sight couldn't possibly be the footprints of a human being. He went to where the Buddha sat at the base of tree and asked him if he was a god. The Buddha replied he was not. "A deva then, a trickster, a sorcerer?" To each, the Buddha again replied he was not. "Then," the priest pressed, "what sort of being are you?"

Buddha smiled and said, "Dona, you may remember me as awakened."

The Buddha's intention was simple: he wanted us to awaken to the true nature of ourselves and of the world. His teachings center on how to live a life free from suffering and help others do the same. Asserting that we all have the capacity to be present to the realities of the universe, he prescribed a path to escape suffering that will allow us to live a life of authentic joy and freedom. The Buddha introduced many techniques to develop equanimity and openness to all of life's circumstances. His teachings support our awareness both on and off the mat to nurture peace, presence, and connection to enjoy our life as it's happening and work more skillfully with ourselves and others.

So, who exactly was this man we call the Buddha?

The Buddha's Breakthrough, Our Birthright

Born Siddhartha Gautama, the Buddha lived in India about twenty-fine hundred years ago and was born into a wealthy and prominent Hindu family. His father was the king of the Sakyas clan. One legend associated with his birth tells of an astrologer predicting that he'd be either a glorious monarch or an influential religious leader. Fearing the child would be drawn to the monastic life, his parents showered him with all the luxuries of a good life as he grew up, hoping he would choose to remain in the comfort of the palace, but Siddhartha's life took a twist.

Shortly after the birth of his son, it's said he took four journeys or, in some stories, had four grand visions. On the first, he was disturbed by his encounter with an older man, frail and helpless with great age. On the second, he saw an emaciated man, depressed and suffering from a terrible disease. His third journey took him near a grieving family carrying a dead relative to his cremation site. Stricken in his heart by what he'd seen, Siddhartha reflected on the suffering brought by old age, illness, and death. His fourth and final journey showed him a religious beggar who led a life of meditation, which was reclusive but serene. This final encounter convinced the Buddha to leave the confines of the luxurious palace and follow the path of the ascetic in order to discover a spiritual solution to the sufferings encountered in human life.

He first studied meditation with two different teachers and gained valuable skills. Meditation did not last forever, however. When he ceased his meditation, the problem of human suffering remained. He then joined a group of Brahman forest-dwellers and began fasting and practicing breath control techniques. He ate only a few grains of rice or a spoonful of broth a day. His time with these ascetics lasted six years and nearly killed him. Eventually, he came to believe that the extremes of this approach, just like the extravagant life he left behind, would not lead to enlightenment. Siddhartha was determined to find a better path – a Middle Way – that would lead to the end of suffering.

His spiritual breakthrough came one night in his mid-thirties while seated in meditation under a Bodhi tree. There he withstood a barrage of tests from the demon Mara, overcoming each challenge to understanding and enlightenment that Mara posed. All the while, the armies of Mara were shouting out that Mara was more powerful than the seated Siddhartha. Mara's final arrow, his last challenge, was the most potent yet. "And who," Mara scoffed, "will bear witness to your worth?" Essentially, Mara was asking: Who do you think *you* are to deserve enlightenment?

Siddhartha's answer was silent and simple: he reached down and touched the earth. At that moment, the very earth itself roared out, "I bear you witness!" At once, Mara and his armies disappeared, and the Buddha attained enlightenment. This moment is depicted in the Buddhist Touching the Earth mudra, one hand open with palm up in the lap, the other reaching down to touch the earth.

Buddha transformed when he acknowledged the fundamental truth of interdependence among all things – he was as precious to the Whole as the earth itself because, as Thich Nhat Hanh said, we inter-are. Nothing exists alone. Every one of us is worthy of love, connection, happiness, and purpose simply because we're here. Our value is inherent, and a joyful life is our birthright.

The affirmative nature of his teachings is so heartening. Although life brings hardship, peace is possible. The Buddha introduced what he called the Four Noble Truths. You could consider these four overarching truths as a kind of diagnosis and treatment plan.

The first truth is that suffering exists: there's a problem. We as human beings experience tension, fear, anxiety, stress, jealousy, shame, illness, and death. These things exist, and no one escapes them. No matter how well we take care of ourselves, we all will become ill, experience loss and grief, grow older, and eventually die.

The second truth shines a light on causation: suffering is caused by something, and that thing is a propensity for craving and aversion. When we chase or cling to what is pleasant, we suffer. When we resist and struggle against the unpleasant, attempting to avoid the unavoidable, we suffer. These clinging and resisting habits are often unconscious, but we all experience them.

In the *Lokavipatti Sutta*, Buddha described what he calls the Eight Vicissitudes, or the Eight Worldly Winds that blow past and through us all.

Monks, these eight worldly conditions spin after the world, and the world spins after these eight worldly conditions. Which eight? Gain, loss, status, disgrace, censure, praise, pleasure, and pain.

– *Lokavipatti Sutta, (Thanissaro Bhikku translation)*

Regardless of who we are, what we do, or who we know, the winds of gain and loss, status and disgrace, praise and blame, and pleasure and pain, will blow through our lives. Neither the positive nor the negative will remain, for each are inconstant, impermanent, and subject to change. Understanding this brings real relief and ease to the heart. We gain space to investigate with curiosity how we relate to what's happening, and we are able to pause before immediately trying to do something about it. We can't control everything that happens to us, but we do have the power to explore our reactions.

This leads us to Noble Truth number three: suffering can end. Essentially, Buddha is saying that while pain is sure to arise, suffering is not a foregone conclusion. Pain exists but suffering is not our destiny. We can choose a path of awakening and escape the grip of suffering.

The fourth of Buddha's Noble Truths points to the solution: there is a path that leads to the end of suffering. Quite insistent that people do not simply take his word for it, Buddha exhorted his followers to experiment and experience for themselves whether his teachings brought transformation and liberation. The Noble Eightfold Path is Buddha's "treatment plan."

This path lays out skills and behaviors to cultivate for use in daily life to gain freedom from suffering and experience genuine happiness. These four truths assert that, while it's not always easy, each moment arrives as an opportunity to experience either suffering or freedom, and the choice is ours. The Noble Eightfold Path to freedom includes eight affirmative approaches to open our hearts and free us from suffering. Most of the Buddha's teachings focused on aspects of this "treatment plan." These eight approaches or qualities aren't linear but rather are meant to be practiced and applied simultaneously, each mutually supportive and interconnected with the rest. I'm offering here a very simple introduction to the concepts as an applied, basic overview, and as you continue your practice and study, you might feel inspired to revisit them and consider what personal meanings these teachings may hold for you.

Wise View, or Wise Understanding – inviting curious inquiry into our moment-to-moment awareness so we see things as they are without the filters of misjudgments or misperceptions. Is there anything overlaying our perception of what's happening now and how might we see beyond it to encounter the reality of a circumstance?

Wise Intention, or Wise Resolve – holding our focus fast to the many layers of our intention as an orienting point for our efforts and attention. While acknowledging the range of our intentions, whether short-term intentions for a Yin Yoga & Meditation session or our heart's surest desires in life, how do we center and honor what we hold most dear?

Wise Speech – speaking kindly and truthfully, both in our inner dialogue and with others. We all have layers of conscious and unconscious commentary streaming through the mind. How can we invite and maintain a warm and loving attitude and tone, ensuring the words we speak help instead of hurt?

Wise Action – acting in ways that honor ourselves and others, promoting peace, justice, and love. With each moment presenting a fresh opportunity, how do we discern what actions, or non-actions, will bring the greatest benefit?

Wise Livelihood – doing what we do for a living, offering the best of who we are, working with integrity, honesty, and kindness. In what ways do we bring our heart of service to each moment and serve others with the energy of encouraging empowerment, compassion, and peace?

Wise Effort – committing to our practice, knowing each of us must do our own work. As we make a diligent effort, we know we'll encounter stumbling blocks. How do we train ourselves to work skillfully, wisely, and compassionately with these obstacles and ourselves along the way?

Wise Concentration – maintaining a deliberate focus on our object of attention, returning again and again as many times as it takes. As we practice remaining physically still, how do we continue to hone the skill of concentration in the mind so our attention remains where we place it?

Wise Mindfulness – staying tender-heartedly aware of our body, energy, emotions, and the movements of the mind. Our mat doubles as our meditation cushion as we observe the nature of sensations, thoughts, and feeling states happening inside us. How do we encourage ourselves to maintain an inquisitive, friendly awareness as we watch, free from judgment with our full attention on the treasures of the present time?

There are so many potential applications of this Noble Eightfold Path to our experience on the mat. You might, for example, consider how Wise Effort informs your pose explorations as you find the positions that suit you best. Wise Speech inspires you to notice any inner dialogue of self-judgment. Perhaps Wise View sparks a compassionate curiosity as you observe the workings of your mind during your meditative moments at the start of class. Wise Livelihood reflects your heart of service as you design and offer Yin Yoga & Meditation sessions to others or use the skills you've nurtured on the mat to bring change to the world around you. Wise Concentration can support your mindful attention as you feel for the interplay of sensations in a particular pose. Throughout this book, we'll encounter many ways to work with the wisdom of the Noble Eightfold Path.

When we're aware of what we're experiencing in the moment, we have the opportunity to encounter and investigate what the Buddha called the Three Marks of Existence, the qualities common to all phenomena: impermanence, imperfection, and non-self, or interconnection. The Buddha taught that when we fail to recognize and understand these qualities or push against them, we suffer. When we acknowledge and welcome these qualities, allowing ourselves to accept their existence in all aspects of life, we open the door to lasting peace. In the "Watch and Welcome What's Happening Inside You" practice principle, we'll further discuss these Three Marks of Existence and how we might encounter them on the mat.

In Yin Yoga & Meditation, we train our attention to become aware of what's happening as it's happening with clarity and compassion. If we don't perceive what's happening when it's happening, how do we fully enjoy the moments of our lives? Meeting our experiences mindfully, we create a positive habit for our central nervous system that helps us to simply be, rather than to immediately do. Maintaining our awareness of what's happening in the present time gives us the opportunity to show up with our whole hearts.

Pulling Weeds and Watering Seeds

In Buddhist philosophy is the idea that each of us can become a conscious gardener of the mind. Imagine the mind as a large fertile garden filled with many seeds. They are small and full of potential. Each potential thought is like a seed. In your hand, you hold a watering can full to the brim with fresh, cool water. Which thought-seed will you water? Whether or not we have a green thumb with house plants, we can all develop into beautiful gardeners of our minds by watering the seeds in us that we want to grow and manifest in our lives. We have the power to choose what thoughts and beliefs we will grow.

The essence of the teachings is this: whether a weed or a seed grows and blooms is up to us – that which we tend will grow. This is a powerful truth. Training our intention and attention on the mat, we become more and more skillful in recognizing and watering the helpful seeds rather than the harmful weeds, making our minds a magnificent garden of peace and love.

Conscious gardening is compassionate gardening. Remodeling our thought pathways takes time and patience as we uncover the many layers of mental formations. Some patterns run so deep that we're not even aware of them during a typical day. By recognizing and choosing to water positive seeds, we remove the weeds of negative, unhelpful mental cycles. Yin Yoga & Meditation is the perfect landscape to put our green thumbs to practice, pulling weeds and watering seeds in the mind as we watch thoughts, feelings, and sensations as they arise with a kind inquisitiveness.

Peace is possible. Freedom is possible. These are foundational encouragements of the Buddha's teachings. Tracing our way back to our natural self, we continue to uncover the bright and shining light that we are. This is a practice of coming home, of remembering who you truly are: a precious being on this earth, capable of enjoying lasting happiness and encouraging those around you to do the same. The skills we develop serve our wellbeing in life and help us focus on what matters most to us so we can act in alignment with our intentions.

Yoga Nidra Fundamentals

Joy is your blueprint and your birthright. Each of us, at our core, is fundamentally peaceful, loving, and free. We can accumulate tensions in life not just in the physical body, but in the mind and heart as well. Physically, emotionally, and spiritually, tension takes its toll, but we can learn to relax deeply on all layers of our being and lay down the burden of stress. Opening to the beauty and power that we are, we reconnect with our authentic selves and live each day in alignment with our heart of hearts. This is the premise and promise of Yoga Nidra.

Inhabiting Relaxed Awareness

In Yoga Nidra, we systematically uncover and release physical, energetic, and mental-emotional tensions using a variety of relaxation techniques. This softening enables us to travel into our subconscious mind and establish a renewed relationship with our sacred nature.

Yoga Nidra, or the Yogi's Sleep, is considered a profound relaxation with inner awareness. The practice of Yoga Nidra invites us to move through the layers of our consciousness to a state of being between wakefulness and sleep. This Yoga Nidra consciousness is profoundly joyful, relaxing, and empowering. Think of it as total relaxation of every part of your being as you rest in an effortless state of pure bliss. Specific techniques such as body awareness practices, directed breathing exercises, meditation, guided imagery, and visualizations work together to enable this total tension relief and reveal our underlying pure awareness, which is free from stress and connected to our highest wisdom.

Arising out of the Eight-Limbed Yogic path described by the Indian sage Patanjali, Yoga Nidra generally falls within Raja yoga lineage. A complete Yoga Nidra practice involves various limbs like Pranayama (the regulation of breath to circulate energy), Pratyahara (withdrawing the senses), Dharana (developing concentration), Dhyana (engaging in meditation), and Samadhi (super-consciousness). Moving through the multiple stages of the Yoga Nidra practice, we withdraw all of our senses except hearing, redirecting our awareness from the external world to the internal landscape as we journey deep within to commune with our most sacred nature.

Classical Indian Yoga's conceptual framework teaches that surrounding the bright light of our true nature are veils or sheaths representing aspects of our human personality. Called koshas, these layers of ourselves range from the most tangible manifestation of who we are, our physical tissues, to the most subtle, the bliss sheath lying nearest our sacred nature. They aren't layers outside of us, as you might imagine a multi-layered energetic aura, but instead they exist within us in a state of constant interplay, each impacting the others. Our physical self, the tissues of our body, affects our emotional self, our mental layer impacts our energetic layer, and so on.

In the philosophical yogic perspective, words we've heard or spoken, circumstances we've experienced, and thought patterns we have are collected within the aspects of our being as samskaras. Negative samskaras are like tensions stuck deep within us that manifest in our lives as unhelpful emotional patterns, mistaken or self-limiting beliefs, and even physical pain, all dimming the inner light of our most authentic self. The Yoga Nidra relaxation process allows these samskaras to jostle free, similar to the way Yin postures help to loosen physical adhesions and energetic blockages.

As we methodically bring rest to our koshas, we move from the more rapid, active, and jagged beta brainwave pattern predominant during our typical waking hours, into the smoother, slower, and more harmonious alpha, theta, and even potentially delta wave patterns. In the same way physical relaxation in Yin Yoga & Meditation lays the groundwork for a settled mind, Yoga Nidra is a progressively inward-moving practice, with relaxation in one part of ourselves opening the door to relaxation into the next. Once the physical body is relaxed, we move to the energetic body, freeing up the flow of our inner life-force energy. Following energetic relaxation, we rest the mind, its thoughts and emotions. Lastly, we shed unnecessary holdings in the intuitive wisdom body and the bliss sheath, opening the portal to communion with our true nature. As the body relaxes deeply, the thinking mind, the ego, is temporarily subdued, so strong emotions that keep us riled up or feeling separate from others release, giving rise to positive feelings of unity and bliss.

Relaxation Training to Empower Intention and Manifestation

One of the most empowering aspects of the Yoga Nidra practice is the remarkable efficacy of its relaxation techniques. Whether we engage them on the mat or sitting at our desk in the middle of a busy workday, we can put them to work for us. Able to be woven seamlessly into the inward-turning Yin Yoga & Meditation practice, the scientifically proven mindful breath and body awareness techniques loosen gripping muscles to open the targeted tissues and Qi channels that course through them. When practiced regularly, the collection of techniques employed to inhabit the state of Yoga Nidra is like the ultimate de-stress program, successively bringing relaxation and relief of tension to our entire being. Best of all, they're available to everyone; no experience is necessary to get started.

Because a relatively relaxed state is integral to the practice, the Yin Yoga & Meditation mat is a perfect place to experiment with some of these Yoga Nidra methods to receive the synergistic benefits this integration offers. Specific techniques that we'll discuss, including Progressive Muscle Relaxation (PMR), Autogenics, Rotation of Consciousness (Nyasa), and directed breathing practices, all assist the transition from beta brainwave patterns into the slower, more meditative states of alpha and theta. This brainwave cycle change has a direct influence on how we feel and the depth of our relaxation. Nurturing our rebalancing yin qualities rekindles the connection between body and mind. As Dr. Edmund Jacobson, developer of the PMR technique noted, "An anxious mind cannot exist in a relaxed body."

Relaxation is a skill each of us has the capacity to develop and nurture. Weaving Yoga Nidra principles and techniques into the fabric of our Yin Yoga & Meditation practice helps us train our bodies and our brains to get better at it both on and off the mat. The tensions we carry within us don't even have to be conscious to affect us profoundly. Physical discomfort, pain, and illness could result, and not just from physical tension. Unsettling emotions may have adverse effects on our body's tissues, and energetic imbalance can affect the mind. We are one interconnected whole, with every aspect of our being affecting every other. We're here to live with intention, to live on purpose, with purpose – tension is not our destiny. We are designed to thrive.

In Yoga Nidra, Sankalpa is a practice of intention setting that helps us flourish. Sankalpa is not the same as a New Year's resolution driven by willpower but rather is an ardent and enduring commitment to supporting our highest truth in alignment with our sacred nature. Sankalpa is a process of connecting with the heartfelt desires for our lives, our higher purpose, and channeling our attention and energy there.

Think of Sankalpa as your true north, the light that shines your way home to the heart. As we hone our attention and align it with our intention, we are empowered to participate fully in this powerful universal equation: Energy + Intention = Manifestation. Where attention goes, energy flows, so what we place our attention on grows stronger. Systematically releasing tensions in all layers of our being, we can plant the seed of our Sankalpa with intentional attention in the fertile soil of the mind where it grows and manifests outwardly in our lives.

As we become better acquainted with pure relaxation, we discover that rest and relaxation aren't a singular activity but an ongoing approach to living. We can train in relaxation, improve our ability to notice areas of tension, and learn to skillfully free any obstacles that dim our most authentic, sacred light. With commitment and practice, that same profoundly restful and connected state of Yoga Nidra is possible to inhabit throughout our day. We naturally begin to integrate this same restful approach into everything we do. Living in freedom each day, we align our decisions and actions more and more consistently with our intentions. We live as precisely who we are: undeniably warm-hearted, centered, and wise, a safe, loving, harmonious sanctuary of peace for ourselves and others.

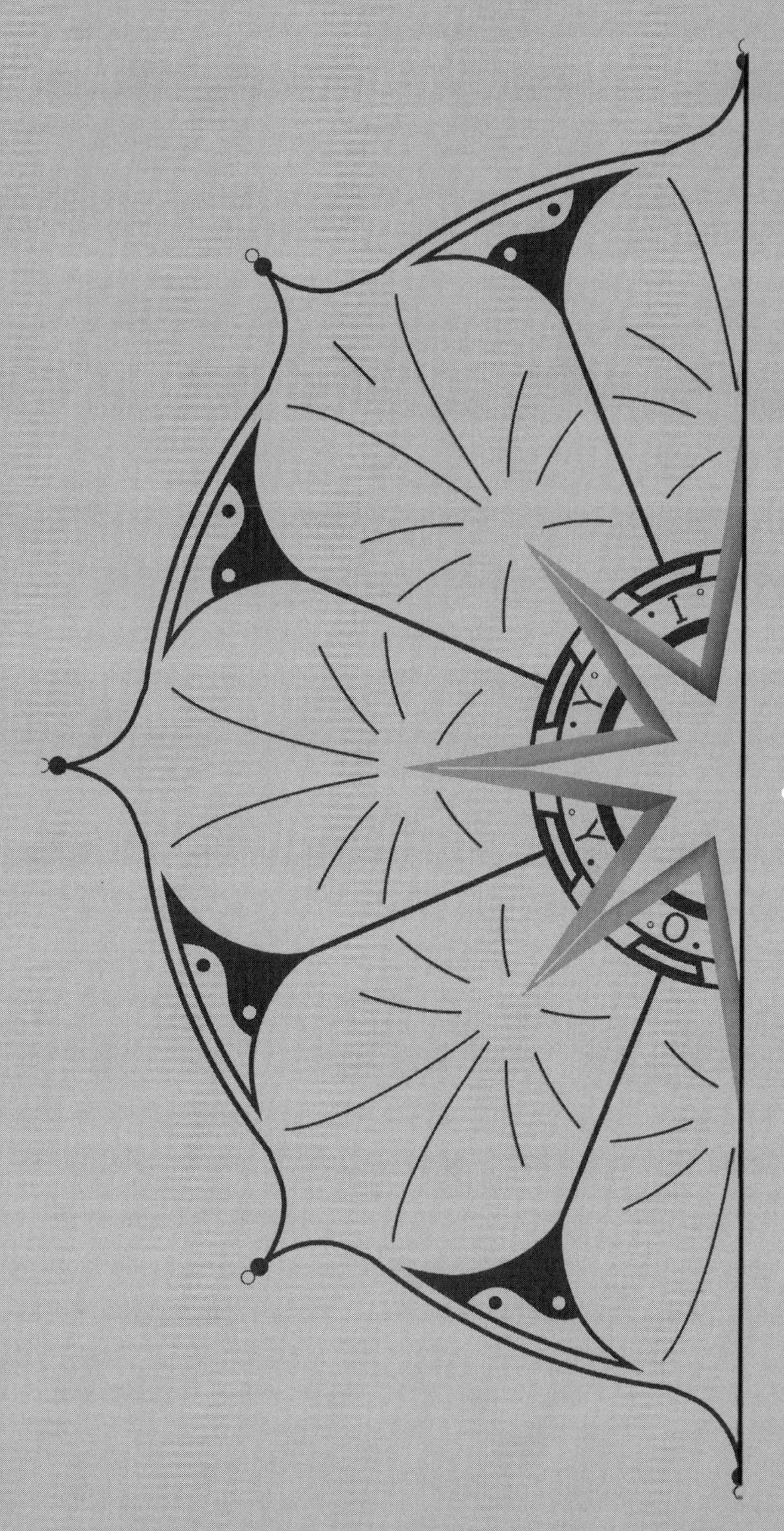

• Part Two

Into the Mandala Map

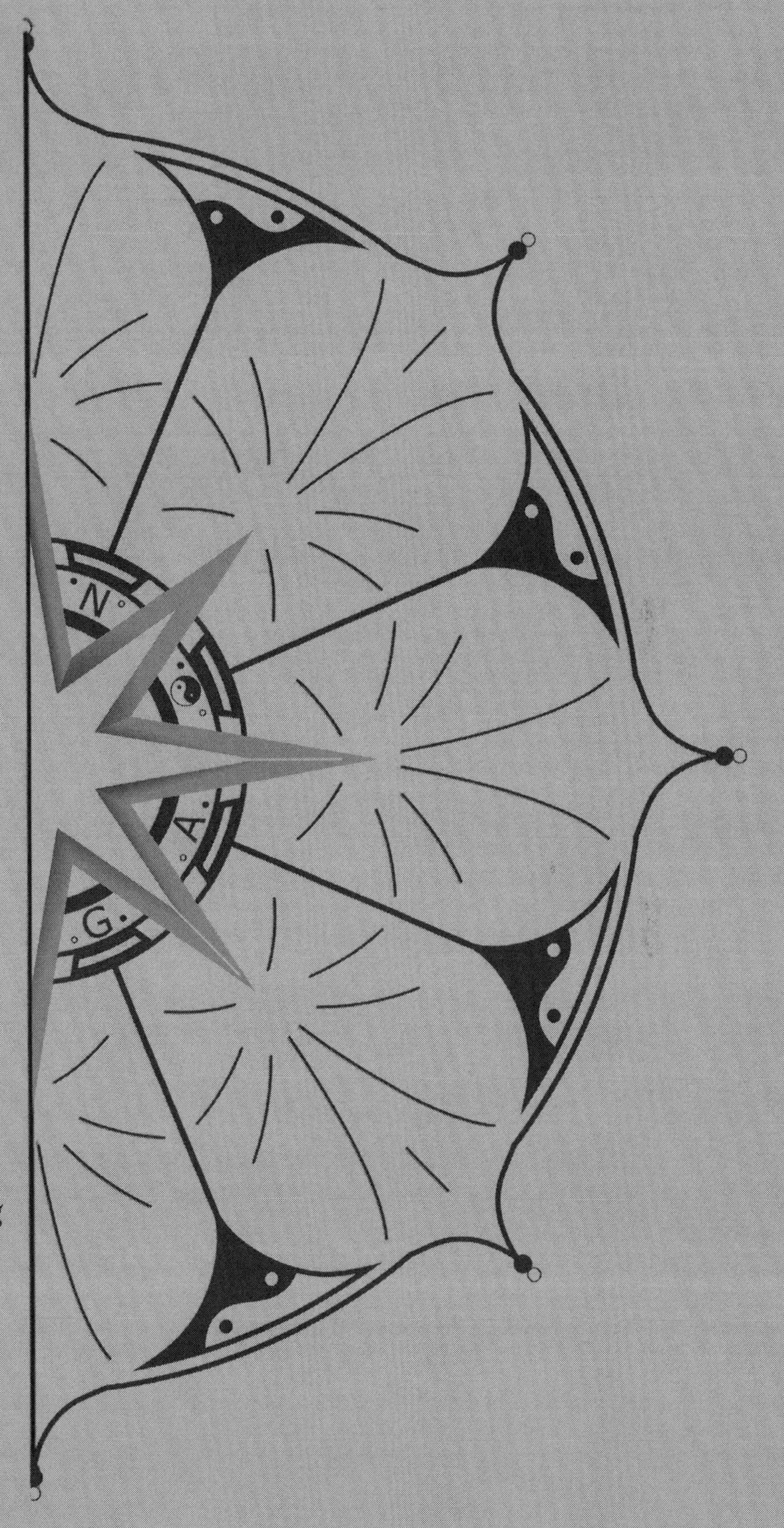
N
A
G

Chapter 4

Exploring the Layers of Our Being

Manifested on this earth, our existence is a miraculous network of tissues and biological systems, streams of energy, and an unending spectrum of thoughts and feelings. The wisdom of this practice reminds us that underneath all the ever-changing aspects that make up our human form and personality lies the unchanging steady awareness of our pure presence. As we take the experiential journey inward in Yin Yoga & Meditation, we have the opportunity to explore and serve the inner terrain of our physical body, our energetic architecture, our mental states, and our emotional selves. In this element of the practice within the Mandala Map, we'll discuss these layers of our being and how they are unique but not separate, each having their own invaluable qualities, yet are still interconnected, one beautiful whole.

Our Sacred Nature, Ever Shining

In the 1800's, the King of Thailand ordered that Buddha statues from ruined temples across the land be brought to the recently constructed temples in Bangkok, the country's new capital. One of the ancient Buddha statues brought to the city happened to be covered in stucco and colored glass. In its plainness, the statue was deemed of minor significance, but it was enormous. The monument was so colossal that they didn't have a building big enough for it, so the giant plastered Buddha was stored outside under a tin roof and soon forgotten.

Fast forward to 1955 when this unremarkable Buddha statue was brought out from where it sat under that simple roof so it could be moved into a new building that had been constructed for its storage. In an attempt to lift the statue from its pedestal, the equipment failed, and the massive Buddha crashed to the ground. In the fall, some of the stucco chipped away, revealing a glint of brilliant gold shining through the crack. Intrigued, the workers set about removing all of the plaster covering and found that this dull, insignificant statue was in fact a golden Buddha weighing five tons and determined to be worth over two hundred and fifty million dollars! The monks believe it had been covered so many hundreds of years ago as an act of protection against harsh weather and enemy aggressors.

layer

Tensions in the physical body and tensions in the mind and heart, just like the plaster over the valuable statue, can cover up or separate us from that precious and harmonious whole we are at our core. We might, at times, disregard certain aspects of ourselves or even come to falsely believe that we're made up of that covering rather than the ever-present compassionate and luminous being inside it – we believe we are the plaster and forget that beneath it there is gold.

> Our true nature is like a precious jewel: although it may be temporarily buried in mud, it remains completely brilliant and unaffected. We simply have to uncover it.
>
> – *Pema Chödrön*

Yin Yoga & Meditation gives us the chance to connect with and tend our whole selves. We take care of our body and are grateful for our body. We sense how our energy flows within us and are grateful for how it animates and activates us. We observe the vast and precious landscapes of mind and heart and are grateful for the ability to think, and for the full spectrum of human emotion that our heart makes possible. Each of these layers is bound together in this fleeting moment of time to manifest on the earth. More than just a body, more than just a mind, more than energy and emotion, we are one being, complex, compassionate, and complete. All of us arrives to our mat, infused with our purest presence.

Try if you'd like for these few moments this breath mantra of remembrance, of coming home to our whole selves:

Begin to trace the path of your breath coming in and going out.

Breathe in and out slowly, finding contentment in being right here, good company for yourself and for this present moment.

Breathing in, I see my sacred nature shining.

Breathing out, I know my true nature is peaceful, wise, and loving.

Breathing in, I am my sacred nature.

Breathing out, my true nature is love.

layer

Notice how your inhale flows so freely and then just as naturally transforms itself into your exhale — in and out, a perfect cycle, an offering of love and life. Sense here how the outer world drifts away from your attention as your awareness turns inward. Feel the steady, pure presence always shining within you, residing beyond the body, beyond the mind, beyond the flow of energy charting through you, and beyond even the movements of the heart.

Feeling the breath flow through the chest in this deepest space within, we encounter our most natural self. This is the spirit that enlivens our body's tissues, fuels the flow of Qi within, animates our mind, and serves as our compass and true north. As you breathe, imagine that precious, golden Buddha within you sparkling and shining, just waiting for your acknowledgment, cherishing, and love. Acknowledge the light of your being shining in all directions.

The Physical Layer

You are an efficient, magnificent miracle. The human body is intricately interwoven and mysterious. Rather than a collection of individual mechanical parts that fit together, we are, as fascia expert and author Tom Myers points out, much more like a plant than a machine. Taoism teaches that we are a microcosm of the universe, and like the cosmos of which we are a part, the human organism is a complex ecosystem and transportation and communication network.

We're not merely a collection of individual tissues, fluids, thoughts, feelings, and aspirations but one large, beautiful whole, a universe in and of ourselves. Supporting our health and happiness, then, is a whole-self endeavor. Caring for ourselves means caring for our entire being, every part of that interconnected whole. Yin Yoga & Meditation offers the opportunity to nourish all of who we are, from our outermost manifestation, our biological tissues, all the way down into our heart of hearts.

Inside Our Yinside

Let's begin our exploration of our layers of being with our physical form. As we journey into the inner terrain of the body, we'll practice sensitizing to the physical landscape of the yin tissues and expand our understanding of them. To help us, we'll use the pathway of an internal scan, a supportive meditative method used both on and off the mat to consciously gather information about our physical form and its needs.

As we mentally scan our tissues, we observe and investigate the nature of the physical sensations we're experiencing, how we interpret them, and what we may or may not choose to do about what we're sensing. Maintaining appropriate, healthy stimulation within our Yin Yoga poses is at the center of keeping our practice safe, sustainable, and effective, so learning to attune to the tissues and the sensations arising within them is a critical skill on the mat.

To begin, bring into focus the flow of your breath as it enters and leaves the lungs. With each conscious breath, let the awareness dip further and further inside you. As you breathe naturally, conjure for a moment in your mind's eye the image of a stone dropping through the surface of a meandering river, settling into stillness on the river's floor.

Just as leaves and twigs flow along the choppy surface, thoughts, feelings, and sensations move through us. Like that stone settled on the river's bottom, our fundamental awareness perceives these passing phenomena from a place of quiet deep within us. In this inward-turning process, we retreat from the external noise and chaos of the day and allow our attention to steady and sink, focusing on the happenings in our internal landscape. Moving the awareness inside doesn't stop whatever commotion is around us, but it does offer a little space and freedom to watch sounds and sensations inside.

If your energy or attention feels a little scattered, perhaps try a breath mantra to stabilize it as you continue to refocus away from what is moving around you to what is flowing within you. Here is a simple one offered by Thich Nhat Hanh:

Breathing in,
I know I am breathing in.
Breathing out,
I know I am breathing out.

Say these words to yourself as you breathe in and out. Allow your breath to be just as it is, flowing how it flows, nothing right and nothing wrong about it. Just let breath be breath as your mind continues to steady. When you're ready, transition your awareness to the outermost physical edge of yourself, your skin. Home to more than a thousand sensory nerve endings per square inch, your skin is a selectively permeable barrier between what is within you and what is around you. Take a few moments to sense this more yang-like outer layer in contact with your external environment that keeps you safe and supported.

Observe how your skin touches the air, noticing any sensations that are happening on your arms and also on your face, neck, legs, and feet. What do you feel? Sense the temperature of the room at this moment. We can't see temperature, but we can feel it. Concentrate on the signals the skin is sending to your brain. Does it feel warm or cool, humid or dry? Receive the sensations from your skin with gentle attention. Take this time to energize the part of yourself that's dedicated not to analyzing but to sensing and intuiting.

Let's move the awareness a little deeper than the skin now to your yang-like muscles. Stretchy like rubber bands, muscle tissue prefers exercise that lengthens and strengthens through rhythmic movements and repetitive stress. The body contains more than six hundred and fifty of these skeletal muscles, each capable of contracting and releasing, making all kinds of miraculous movements possible. See if you're able to tune into how your muscles feel as you rest here. Land your attention in your toes and slowly trace it through the feet, the ankles, the shins, the thighs, hips, abdomen, chest, back of torso, shoulders, and neck, scanning for each muscle through your body, all the way up into the head and face.

Let your attention linger long enough to explore these dynamic tissues as you scan. What do you sense? How do your muscles feel? What is their internal temperature? Are you finding any tightness or ease? If you locate any areas of gripping or holding, invite them to soften and relax. Gently contract the muscle group, holding for a few moments to feel the tension, then let it go, exhaling fully, enjoying the release. Disengaging our muscles allows the beneficial stresses of our postures to reach our yin tissues, and you can practice this right here by reminding your muscles that there's nothing they need to do right now. They only need to relax and rest.

To the casual observer, Yin Yoga probably appears rather simple with people just sitting around on the floor surrounded by blankets and pillows, but a lot is happening under the surface and out of sight. The yin-like connective tissues run throughout the body, holding us together and keeping everything in place. Yin Yoga poses target these deep tissues, stimulating them to keep them healthy. When we condition our yang musculature, the effects are much easier to observe. Lifting weights causes our muscles to grow and become more visibly toned. Although our yin side lies hidden within us, its health and function are equally important to the biological systems that keep us alive and flourishing.

Our connective tissues include bones, tendons, ligaments, cartilage, intramuscular fascia, and the 3-D fascial web extending through all parts of us. These tissues connect, bind, protect, insulate, hydrate, and separate other tissues and organs. They provide stability and flexibility and serve as a significant contributor to our proprioceptive ability, that is, knowing where we are in space. Connective tissue functions as one of the human body's major transportation and communication networks. Though we can't observe them with our eyes as easily as other tissues, we are able to learn to sense them, seeing them with our inside eyes.

Allow your attention to drift further inward now to encounter these yin tissues: the bones, sturdy and robust, with protective cartilage covering and embedded into their ends...tough tendons holding muscle tightly to bone...ligaments connecting bone to bone...a fibrous network of fascia extending all through us, providing shape, support, and order. See if you're able to begin to sense how these tissues are distributed within you. Feel for their weight and construction.

Though very different in structure and function, these connective tissues are all made from the same basic stuff: fibrous proteins and gluey liquids. Our insides are riddled through with little, sticky strands of protein, and the most abundant protein in these tissues is collagen. Collagen makes up about thirty percent of the body's protein content and is sinewy and durable. Collagen constructs flat sheets and rope-like shapes within us, with the specific formation depending on the purpose of the tissue. In addition to collagen, our connective tissues also contain a slightly springier protein called elastin. Elastin fibers are what help our tissues recover their original shape after being stressed.

While connective tissues vary in elasticity by location and purpose, they are overall much more plastic-like than muscle tissue, and are stiff and averse to stretching. Their less flexible nature means we can't safely exercise them in the same ways we exercise our muscles. This is a fundamental difference between the form and function of Yin Yoga postures and the more yang-like shapes in Vinyasa or Hatha yoga. If we treat our yin tissues the way we treat our yang tissues, we'll get hurt.

So, collagen and elastin are the sticky strands. The other important component of our connective tissues is a gooey, glutinous liquid more technically termed "ground substance." Ground substance is a crucial hydrating and lubricating fluid found within and around our connective tissues. This ubiquitous substance does not live in the limelight of our daily attention but serves many indispensable functions. This viscous, gel-like fluid consists primarily of proteins, water, and negatively-charged polysaccharide compounds known as glycosaminoglycans (GAGs). This fluid bathes the collagen and elastin fibers to keep them from drying out and overstretching, and supports their strength and pliability.

Hyaluronic Acid (HA) and chondroitin sulfate are both GAGs. HA is the most prominent GAG within us and one of the most hydrophilic, or water-attracting, molecules in nature. This slippery, unbranched polysaccharide is capable of attracting up to one thousand times its weight in water.

GAGs and proteins join to form compounds called proteoglycans, whose net negative charge draws positively charged sodium ions, which attracts water. It takes a village to hydrate! This process of chemical attraction brings water to the fibrous collagen matrix stretched within us, keeping it supple. Found throughout the tissues and even inside tiny holes called vacuoles on the collagen fibers, ground substance adds cushion and spring to our tissues. Just as we more easily compress an empty plastic water bottle than we can when it's full, ground substance acts as a shock absorber between the cells and fibers running through our body, resisting compressive forces and absorbing stresses. Ground substance also provides a barrier against bacteria, acts as an exchange medium for the diffusion of nutrients and removal of cellular waste, and stores and distributes water.

Ground substance is a bit of a shape-shifter. In its normal state, ground substance has the consistency of a viscous gel, similar to gelatin. When we apply stress to our tissues, however, it changes state and becomes more liquid. You've probably seen this kind of state change in coconut oil, which is solid when cool. If you place the jar in the sunshine, the oil softens and becomes more liquid-like. Ground substance shifts in its consistency like this when our tissues are stressed. When we remove the stress from the tissue, ground substance eventually turns back to its more viscous state. Let's explore this functioning in more detail and how the Yin Yoga practice supports this state-changing, gluey substance to keep our bodies hydrated, supple, and functioning optimally.

Cells called fibroblasts live draped on the fascial fibers and produce both collagen and elastin. These specialized cells build our fascial matrix, live on it, maintain it, and break it down, keeping it healthy and functioning well. Fibroblasts also produce ground substance.

As with all living tissues, our connective tissues require a mild amount of stress to stay healthy. Without stress, our tissues deteriorate and degenerate. Just as an unpracticed skill diminishes over time, our unused muscle tissue shrinks below a cast while healing a broken bone. What isn't used is lost, and our connective tissues follow the same fate. When we move into our Yin Yoga shapes, the stimulation we deliver to our connective tissues activates these cells to secrete the fibrous proteins and ground substance. In this way, our internal biological network maintains itself when reasonable stresses are applied regularly. This self-sustaining maintenance helps the whole of our body stay healthy and function well.

Extending through muscle tissue is a fibrous collagen matrix referred to as intramuscular fascia. A fascial sheath covers each muscle group, which is comprised of additional smaller bundles also encapsulated by a fascial covering. Yet another tube of this collagenous connective tissue surrounds each muscle fiber. This series of connective tissue tubes offer structure, strength, and lubrication. Because these tube layers are continuous, each connected to the next, intramuscular fascia allows a muscle to change shape and length as well as diffusing forces evenly throughout the tissue. The ground substance lubricates the surfaces to ensure easeful movement, allowing the fibers to slide easily over one another as the tissues stretch and contract.

Often, chronic tension felt in our muscles is not due to tight muscle fibers but rather due to the fascial sheaths surrounding the muscle becoming shortened or tightened and rigid, compressing the muscle fibers and nerves running through them. Hydrated fascia is healthy fascia, both spring-like and resilient. Consider the differences between a maple leaf growing green on a tree and a brilliant red and gold leaf at our feet, tumbling down the street on a windy autumn day. Moving the green leaf on the tree between your fingers, it has a springiness to it, a resilience. Now imagine taking the fallen autumn leaf between your fingers. How fragile it is by comparison, how easy to crumble and break. Similarly, we want our fascia to stay springy and retain its natural bounce like the green leaf.

Remember how ground substance is mutable, changing from viscous to a more liquid-y state when stress is applied? This natural occurrence is one of the many reasons incorporating regular rest is so vital for a safe Yin Yoga practice. Our connective tissues are temporarily less stable while the ground substance is in that more liquid-y state, which is OK if we're low to the ground in a non-weight bearing position. When we rise and begin to move, however, we want our joints to be steady and able to bear weight sufficiently. Rest gives our ground substance a chance to revert to its more gel-like, stable state.

Take a few moments to attune your inside eyes to the fascial matrix extending through all of your muscles. Your arms, chest, abdomen, thighs, calves... each collection of muscle tissue is wrapped in sheaths within sheaths of connective tissue, enveloped in fibrous protein right down to every muscle fiber. Sense for a few moments how one tube connects to another and creates an expansive interconnected whole.

Now, choose one muscle in your body. Glide your awareness along the length of this tissue that is covered inside and out with intramuscular fascia as it extends toward the bone. At its end are the tendons, rigid, cord-like tissues which are made chiefly of collagen. Tendons affix muscle to bone. Try to see in your mind's eye how the intramuscular fascia becomes the tendon, and the tendon becomes the bone, a blending and continuation of one tissue into the other. We're not a neat and tidy collection of distinct and separate parts as shown in a biology textbook diagram. Our connective tissues form a continuous whole running everywhere through us.

Because collagen is their primary ingredient, tendons are stiff. Once over-stretched, our tendons can't simply relax back into their original shape like muscle fibers do – another reason to take care not to approach our Yin Yoga exercise with a yang attitude. Tendons aren't a primary target of this practice, but the resulting increased blood flow and production of ground substance do support their hydration and health.

Just as the intramuscular fascia transitions into tendon, watch now as you trace with your mind how the tendon transforms into bone. Living bone tissue is a mesh of collagen and mineral salts, primarily calcium and phosphorus. Spend a few moments sensing your bones, their weight and shape as they structure you from the inside. Feeling the musculature that we activate with thought might be easier, but with practice, it's possible to sense your bones, too. Perhaps you bring your focus back to your feet and slowly scan upward through the legs, torso, and shoulders. There are about two hundred and six skeletal bones in the adult human body...can you detect their mass, their density, their heaviness? As you breathe in and breathe out, feel for their weight, their location. Where do you sense their presence?

Cells called osteoblasts live in and create bone, while cells called osteoclasts remove bone tissue. This process of making and unmaking by osteoblasts and osteoclasts is always occurring – we're simultaneously being created and disappearing. If osteoblasts lay down more bone tissue than osteoclasts absorb, the bone grows stronger. If more is absorbed than added, bone density is lost. As we age, the scale naturally tips toward more reabsorption than creation. In reality, once we pass our thirties, we begin to lose bone mass and density, making our bones more susceptible to fracture. The stresses delivered in our Yin Yoga postures stimulate osteoblasts in the same way they stimulate activity in fibroblasts, helping to keep our bones strong and stable. Do you feel in this moment their solidity and structure inside you?

Scan now along the length of your bones to the cartilage tissue embedding itself into the bone's ends. Instead of lying on top of bone, see how cartilage grows into, and turns into, bone. Cartilage is found throughout the body: in our joints, between our vertebrae and ribs, in our nose and ears, and within the cushioning intervertebral discs of our spine. Providing support and padding for surrounding joint tissues, cartilage keeps the joint's motion smooth as the components glide against each other and protects them against impact. Cells called chondroblasts create the collagen and elastin fibers that make up cartilage's structured matrix, and as they mature into chondrocytes, they help to maintain the health of cartilage tissue. The exact fibrous makeup of cartilage, as with other connective tissue types, is dependent on its location and function.

Glide your attention now through the cartilage tissue until you meet its slippery edges. Here we land into the space of our joints, where two or more bones are bound together by yet more connective tissue to allow our motion forward and backward, bending up and down, and twisting here and there. Along with our cartilage tissues, our joints are variously complex places, with ligaments holding bone to bone and bathed in fluid. Most of our joints are synovial joints, and a form of ground substance called synovial fluid within the joint capsule allows for smooth gliding and sliding through the activities of our day.

The average person has over three hundred joints where the bones, ligaments, and cartilage do their good work to support the magic of our movement. Take a few moments to let your attention wander through your body and begin to feel the placement of the joints. Start by wiggling your toes. How many joints are you flexing and extending just in these distal parts? Continue your scan bringing your awareness into the ankles, flexing and extending and circling them to exercise their directions of movement. Now moving into the space of the knees...sense as you bend and unbend your knees how their possible movements differ from that of the ankles. Notice how their size and function compare to the toes.

Like motor oil protects a car's engine from heat and friction, the synovial fluid filling synovial joints like the knees is imperative to easeful, pain-free movement. This form of ground substance also acts as an exchange medium. Chondrocytes remove waste from the joint and carry nutrition to the cartilage within the joint capsule. With age, the amount of synovial fluid we produce naturally lessens and begins to break down, decreasing in viscosity and reducing the level of protection it provides, but we can support our body's capacity to produce more. Yin Yoga postures may provide gentle stresses to the knees, stimulating the production of GAGs like chondroitin sulfate, replenishing this form of ground substance and lubricating and protecting these crucial joints.

Binding bone to bone are relatively dry and fibrous tissues called ligaments. The proportion of elastin to collagen is higher in ligaments than in tendons, which gives them the flexibility they need for their function. The exact recipe of collagen and elastin also varies within ligaments, so some are more rigid than others, depending on their location and purpose.

From the knee, move the attention now to your hip, that big sturdy joint where our longest bone, the femur, joins the pelvis. The hip is one of the most flexible joints, essential to so many of our most fundamental activities – sitting, bending, walking, and all the outdoor activities we enjoy, like hiking and biking. Sense the inside of the hip socket, how a skirt of cartilage around the rim of the cup-shaped acetabulum secures the head of the femur. Tucked within and around the hips are a significant number of ligaments, muscles, and tendons working together to provide both stability and motion.

Yin Yoga offers a wide variety of hip-focused postures to bring the hips through their many directions of movement, such as lifting the thighs toward the chest, rotating the legs in and out, and moving them toward and away from the centerline of the body. Take a few moments to explore and enjoy all the ways to articulate the hips and legs, as you consider all that they make possible in your day. Keeping our hip joints well-hydrated, pliable, and healthy is paramount, especially if you're one of the many people who spend hours each day sitting. Doing so without regular exercise and stretch breaks may cause soft tissue to tighten and shorten over time, leading to a kind of shrink-wrapping of the joint, reducing its natural range of motion.

Move your awareness now to the stable and supple spine running down the center of your back. Begin at your pelvis, moving up through the back of the abdomen, through the torso and neck, to the base of your skull. Do you feel its structure as you scan it? The spine averages thirty-three bones with twenty-three intervertebral articulations between bones, allowing us to perform actions such as twisting and bending. The sections of the spine from the base of the head downward include the cervical, thoracic, lumbar, and sacral, culminating in the coccyx, our tailbone.

This critical column and the musculature supporting it protect the delicate spinal cord and network of nerves branching from it. The muscles along the spine enable the active movement of our trunk and the rise and fall of our breath. Each vertebra has tiny bony protrusions where tendons, ligaments, and the muscles of the back and spine attach. These are the pedicles, articular facets, lumina, spinous processes, and transverse processes. Between the vertebrae lie cartilaginous intervertebral discs that lend support and absorb shocks. As you scan your spinal column with your inside eyes, imagine this sophisticated collection of tissues and how it supports the motion of your spine.

Yin Yoga poses encourage the spine to engage in all of its natural movements. The gentle, compressive stresses strengthen the vertebrae, bolster the tendons and ligaments, and activate the production of ground substance that lubricates and cushions the whole of the spinal column. Regular exercise of the spine helps maintain its natural curvature, those four distinct arcs in the spine that create a soft S-shape. Just like arcs in buildings and bridges evenly distribute forces, these curves resist and evenly transfer compressive forces through the spine to lessen the impact on individual bones and discs. Flattened spinal curves resulting from injury or poor sitting habits reduce this distribution, increasing the forces on the intervertebral discs in particular and wearing them down more quickly.

Wiggle your fingers and sense how the movement naturally spreads into the hands and wrist joints. What a wonder! Trace your awareness up through your forearms into the elbow joints as you bend and unbend them and raise and lower the arms from side to side. Continuing to move up the arms, bring your attention now into the shoulder girdles, the large and complex areas of the shoulders, each with four distinct joints that offer us a wide range of movement. Although we don't hold poses focusing on the shoulders as long as we do those targeting larger joints like the hips, Yin Yoga provides necessary stresses to their tissues and moves the joints through all of their available movements.

Our miraculous spine and the many joints in our legs, arms, and torso work together to make so many activities possible, from climbing stairs to climbing mountains. Perhaps you spend just a moment or two sending them the energy of gratitude for their brilliance and resilience. In each moment, they work hard to keep us supported and moving through the days of our lives. Our joints' health, durability, and resilience are major defining factors in our overall mobility.

When not used regularly, joint tissues may become temporarily stuck together, referred to as fixation. If you've ever been sitting in one position for a long time and heard a popping sound when you stood up, that is likely a result of fixation and its subsequent release. We all experience it at times, and movement typically relieves it. Temporary fixation could result in a more permanent fusion if we don't resolve it through movement. Our bodies are very efficient. Remember, what we don't put to use, we will likely lose. If we neglect to move our shoulder for a while, for example, as in the case of an injury, the ligaments will likely shorten and tighten. If not addressed, this atrophy can eventually limit our range of motion.

A sports therapy study found that slow and gentle stresses were more effective in producing permanent elongation for joint contracture repair than were rapid, more intense exercises.[1] The low-load, prolonged-duration stresses caused the least amount of structural weakening while supporting increased mobility. If you drive for a living or work or play in front of a computer for hours at a time, you've likely experienced a resulting stiffness and soreness at some point. Whether at work, at home, or in a car, sitting for prolonged periods isn't healthy for us – our bodies need balance. Making matters worse, sitting in the average office chair or comfy recliner often produces a posterior tilt in the pelvis, flattening out the necessary lumbar curve resulting in muscle and ligament atrophy and misshaping. Over time, this loading of the low spine may cause deterioration in the intervertebral discs.

As you sensitize to the tissues working together within the joints, consider the role of strong and fluid movements on nearly every aspect of our daily living. Whether eating and drinking, sitting and standing, walking up and down stairways, getting into and out of cars, or lifting a laughing child into your arms, smooth and stable joints make it possible! Anyone who's experienced a serious injury to a significant joint knows how restricting, even disabling, joint dysfunction can be. Maintaining joint health is one of the single most important things to do to support our continued ability to move through our lives with ease.

Allow your attention to broaden now, spreading your inner vision to encompass the whole of you on the inside. Within you, a loose web of fibers runs all through your tissues. This network stretches in every direction and into all parts of us. These fibrous proteins and the viscous, gluey ground substance exist as a sort of internal 3-D body stocking that's physically invested into everything around it like an organic, living fabric.

This continuous fascial network is everywhere - below the skin, in and around muscles and groups of muscles, nerves, blood vessels, and organs. It stitches us together, keeping everything in its correct place, including organs, blood vessels, nerves, and muscle tissue groups. Besides offering structure and support, this slippery, fibrous net helps surfaces slide smoothly along each other rather than binding. Remarkably, this fascial network even extends down into every cell, tying into the fibrous cellular cytoskeleton comprised of protein filaments linked within the cell's cytoplasm. Our fascial web transmits force evenly throughout our tissues, resists compressive forces to protect us, contributes to proper hydration, and functions as an essential communication network through which nutrients, hormones, metabolic waste, and bioelectricity flow.

Fascia researcher, bodyworker, educator, and author of the seminal text *Anatomy Trains*, Tom Myers offers the helpful analogy of an orange. When you slice an orange, you see many layers of tissue supporting and segmenting the orange into ever-smaller increments. Fascia functions just that same way. If you removed all the juice from the orange and looked at what was left, you'd have a perfect skeletal representation of the orange's structure. Similarly, if you removed all the cells and water in the human body, a perfect 3-D fascial blueprint of what you look like would remain, including the placement of your internal organs.

Once disregarded as mere "packing peanuts" by Western medicine, fascia is now understood to be one of the most enervated sensory organs we have, rivaling the skin and retina. Fascia has six to ten times more nerve receptors than muscles. Because of this, the fascial network is an integral facilitator of coordinated movement.

See if you can perceive this vast, intricate, and sophisticated network extending all through you. Do you sense how it's holding you together from the inside out and keeping everything linked and in its place? Do you sense it running from head to toe, front to back, and connecting every part of you to every other part? What happens to one part of the body, then, necessarily affects all other parts.

Let your awareness steep a few moments in the tangible miracle that is your body. From top to bottom, a collection of more than thirty trillion cells are working together - literally tied together - to keep you a breathing blessing on the earth. Just sit with your awareness in your body here, consciously connecting with your breath, and behold your beautiful self. Here is simple breath mantra to try:

Breathing in,
I am aware of my body.
Breathing out,
I cherish my body.

This short mantra pairs well with a brief mental scan anywhere, at any time. Mantras connect your mind with your body and your body with the breath, helping you remain in the present moment.

Stress Not Stretch

In Yin Yoga, our focus is applying stress to our connective tissues, not attempting to stretch them. The postures bring mild, static stresses to the tissues we've just encountered in our internal scan. We settle into a pose, letting gravity do its work, and use our attention and breath to relax the yang-like musculature to gain greater access to these hidden and often under-served areas.

The relative rigidity of our connective tissues is key for their primary function, helping us move safely and effectively, so we're not trying to stretch them beyond their natural length. This would cause instability. We must take care not to view the Yin Yoga practice through a yang lens. Unlike more active, moving exercises that target our muscles with rhythmic stretching for lengthening, our intention in this practice is not to "stretch out" our connective tissues. Yin Yoga, however, can help to regain lost space and recapture lost flexibility and mobility, should connective tissues shorten over time due to lack of use, aging, or crimping at the edges of the collagen fibers. Our focus is on reasonable stress, not stretch. Most people probably wouldn't say they show up to a yoga class to get stressed, but in Yin Yoga, mild stress is an integral part of our mission.

How do we make sure we're experiencing gentle, sensible stress and avoiding over-stimulating our tissues in a pose? Just as we learn to listen to one another to ensure successful communication, in Yin Yoga, we cultivate the skill of listening to our tissues, staying aware of the sensations that arise and responding to what they tell us. We often feel the effects of the practice continue, so we're wise to tune into what the body tells us in the hours and days after our mat time.

We have three primary applications of stress in our practice: tension, compression, and twisting. Distinguishing between them is important as we attune to what sensations are reasonable and effective, so let's talk through each type. When we twist in a pose, we apply torsion to our tissues; one part remains relatively still while the other turns in one direction or another. A simple seated twist is a great example of this: our hips stay stable on the ground while our torso turns.

Tension occurs when things pull away from each other. We often feel tension due to fascial or muscular tightness. We experience tension in a posture as a sensation of gentle tugging or tightness, pulling, warmth, or opening. The sensations of tension are felt opposite the joint's direction of movement. For example, if raising the thigh toward the chest generates sensation along the back of the thigh/glute tissue, that's tension. If you drop your right ear toward your right shoulder and you feel sensation along the left side of the neck, that's tension. When tension impedes the joint's movement, we may be able to relieve some or all of that tension over time with diligent, patient practice and application of mild, persistent stresses.

Compression occurs in the opposite direction of tension: things push toward each other, like when we press our palms together in Anjali mudra prayer hands position. If what you're feeling is compression, you'll feel the sensation in the direction of the joint's movement, in this case between the palms. Compression happens when a joint's movement is obstructed by two parts of us pressing against each other. In the example of raising the thigh, compression sensations would be felt in the front of the hip, where the bone and muscle or other soft tissues meet or where the thigh presses the torso. In the example of the head dropping toward the right shoulder, compression would be felt in the bones on the right side of the neck or should the right ear press onto right shoulder. Compression in a pose feels more like a light pressure, stuck-ness, squishy, squooshy, bouncy, coolness, stiffness, compacting, or a firm or soft resistance, depending on the nature of the tissues coming together.

We experience compression when the structure of our body meets itself, so unlike tension, compression isn't something we're able to progress past. When we encounter compression, by slightly altering the bone's angle to the joint we might sometimes find a bit of clearance to move around an inner physical boundary that is limiting us and go a little deeper. Eventually, though, one surface will meet another, and we will be stopped by the compression of our unique skeletal architecture.

The shapes of your bones are unique, as are the ways they all fit together. If your hip socket on the right side is deeply set and pointing straight ahead, you likely won't be able to move your right leg as far out to the side as you would if that socket was shallow and pointed slightly out to the right. In addition to inherent anatomical variations between people, there are variations within us, side to side. The head of the right femur might be rotated one way, while the left femur rotates in the other. As Paul Grilley asserts, "Skeletal variation is the norm, no two people are the same." The myriad differences between how the bones and bony protrusions fit together mean that we'll all meet compression differently. Your body and mine won't meet compression in exactly the same way in exactly the same place, and within our own bodies, variation often exists between the right and left sides.

Compression is not a failure of our body or our practice. Compression is simply a fact, a natural ending point in the joint's movement. We aren't able to stretch, sweat, or swear ourselves past compression. At some point, we're all restricted by compression. If we were able to work all tension out of our muscles, releasing every layer of fascial sheaths holding every last muscle fiber, eventually, two of our tissues would bump against each other, and we'd be prevented from moving further forward.

Like pain or pleasure, the structure of our skeletons isn't a punishment or a reward. The nature of our individual bones and how they're put together is sometimes a defining factor in how our posture looks. If someone can't touch their forehead to the floor in a wide-legged forward bend like Dragonfly, it might be the angles and shapes of their femur and hip socket, not the fact that they're a beginner or that their body is just "too tight." We're not able to stretch or practice our way into a different femur or hip socket. Someone else might have bones that allow them to lay their torso flat on the floor in the same pose. Skeletal layout is an anatomical fact, not a statement about our yoga abilities or personal qualities. There's nothing to congratulate or judge about our bone structure and how it impacts our practice – it's simply an opportunity to grow in awareness of and appreciation for the uniqueness of our bodies. Sensing when we've encountered compression is an invitation to accept and enjoy the body just as it is. As we'll continue exploring, our destination isn't the fullest expression of a pose but rather the mild sensation the shape elicits.

We might be tempted to tumble into the trap of believing we're not trying hard enough or something is wrong with us when our pose doesn't look like we think it should. It's so important that we stay kind with ourselves, our bodies, and our personal practice journey and use that information to our benefit. In Yin Yoga, the pose is a vehicle we use to support and serve our body, not the other way around, while we steep in the majesty and mystery of our existence.

One way to offer ourselves that self-acceptance is taking the time to learn the language of our physical tissues, the language of sensations. In a Yin Yoga posture, we inquire: *What information are these sensations conveying?* If the sensations are telling me that tension is causing the resistance in this posture, maybe there's room to stay with it and potentially go a little further into the pose over time as the body opens and releases. If, on the other hand, they're telling me I've met structural compression in this posture, and I find that no slight adjustments allow me to go any further, then this is where I'll stay, and it's OK. Gentle compression is good – it's stress, and our tissues need mild stress. This is similar to the type of stress we experience via gravity as we walk or get a deep tissue massage, and it helps to keep our tissues healthy.

As you spend time in your poses, or lead others in a Yin Yoga practice, take the opportunity to practice identifying what you're feeling and where, name the type of stress, describe it, and understand it. Notice even now as you're reading – are there any places where you perceive the sensations of tension or compression? We'll continue to delve into the details of sensation when we visit the "Move Mindfully to Mild Sensation" practice principle.

The Body Electric

The body's tissues have a crystalline-like configuration, so stressing them produces a subtle electric charge known as piezoelectricity. Think of piezoelectricity as pressure-generated electricity. The fundamental connective tissue cells we discussed earlier, the fibroblasts in the fascial matrix, osteoblasts in bone, and chondroblasts in cartilage, are activated by the accumulated charge when our tissues are stressed. The stimulation causes them to secrete the primary ingredients of all connective tissue: collagen, elastin, and ground substance.

The mechanics of this rebuilding process are fascinating. *Gray's Anatomy* (the medical textbook, not the TV series!) is a great reference if you want to dive into the details. A simplified explanation of this process is that when stress is applied to our connective tissues, these "construction worker" cells produce collagen, laying it down randomly in all directions. During this time, cells like osteoclasts and macrophages that remove collagen are deactivated. When the stress stops, like when we rest between poses, these "cleaner-upper" cells are allowed to get back to work, clearing away collagen fibers from the matrix. Interestingly, they don't remove just any collagen fibers. They ignore fibers that are aligned with the direction of predominant stress. The on-and-off collaborative effort of these different cell types strengthens our connective tissue because they retain the new fibers aligned in the direction that provides strength and support. By contrast, fibers laid down in other directions are removed. Stress and rest, stress and rest: this is the formula for connective tissue strength, resilience, hydration, and health.

Stress stimulates fibroblasts to secrete ground substance in addition to collagen, so the stresses in our practice that bolster our fibrous connective tissues also hydrate and lubricate our inner spaces. Because the stress temporarily changes the viscosity of ground substance into a more liquid-like state, nutrition, hormones, and cells travel with more ease, and trapped toxins are released and eliminated more easily, too. Like a deep tissue massage, the stresses of our practice support our natural detoxification process and increase blood flow throughout the body.

To be healthy and to function optimally, the protein fibers themselves require hydration, too. The vacuoles in the collagen fibers store water, and these vacuoles need to be flushed regularly to keep the tissues supple. Dehydrated connective tissue is brittle, crispy, and prone to breaking, which prevents water from being distributed through the tissue. Hydrated and happy connective tissue is spongy, resilient, bouncy, and creates an internal rebound effect, acting as an inner springboard. This means that hydrated fascia helps our yang movement be more efficient. Less effort is required, which reduces tissue fatigue and enhances the spring in our step!

As we age, our fibroblasts create less collagen, and the number of fibroblasts we have decreases. This natural decline means our tissues trend toward greater weakness and deterioration. Fibroblasts also start to produce less ground substance to hydrate and lubricate our tissues, causing the fascial network to become drier, stiffer, and more tangled. Metabolic wastes such as nitrogen compounds, carbon dioxide, and sulphates, as well as external toxins like smoke and pesticides, can become caught in the tangled fibers, and transportation in and out of the system becomes challenging. This kind of tightness in the fascial grid may also restrict the blood vessels and nerves running through it, obstructing their proper function and even causing physical pain. Beneficial stresses grow even more central to rebuilding our optimal strength and capacity as we get older, so Yin Yoga is a wonderfully effective body maintenance program.

Freeing Ourselves from Overactive Fight-Flight Response

In addition to incorporating regular rest, there's another fortunate invitation built into our practice: to relax. The muscles are very effective at keeping us safe and supported, which means keeping our joints locked and safe while they're bearing weight. However, when we want to deliver the exercise of mild stress to those yin tissues, we need to invite the yang musculature to relax, granting us greater access to the tissues we're targeting.

> The muscles have to relax first, and then the fascia starts to stretch and release. And that can facilitate the kind of repatterning that leads to lasting release of chronic holdings and, in many cases, a profound change of mind and body.
>
> – *Tom Myers*

Each pose offers a fresh chance to settle the yang musculature using concentrated attention and the valuable tool of our breath. Due to the mind-body connection, the physical necessity of relaxing the muscles has a ripple effect. This release generates even more physical benefits by helping to relax the central nervous system, soothing our stress response, and promoting the relaxation response. Best of all, the physical relaxation training we receive in Yin Yoga & Meditation supports relaxation in all layers of our being and its benefits extend off the mat into daily life.

Continuing your body scan now, spend just a few moments allowing your attention to rise into the space of your head. Consisting of about twenty-two bones, the skull safeguards the commander of our central nervous system, the brain. Though it's only three pounds, the brain contains more than one hundred billion nerve cells called neurons. Did you know that information passes between neurons at speeds up to two hundred and fifty miles per hour? The brain controls our interpretation of, and engagement with, the external world as well as our thinking, memory, speech, and so much more. Let your awareness marvel for a minute at the astonishing amount of work this organ performs moment to moment. Try sensing some of the internal processes it oversees...find and feel the heart, the stomach, the breath, the skin, even the thoughts, the feelings. Just sitting here, now in these moments, do you feel how very much is happening within you?

The brain is in charge of the Autonomic Nervous System, or ANS, which controls the function of many of our organs, sustaining the homeostasis, or dynamic equilibrium, of our body. The brain interacts with the endocrine system to maintain all the automatic processes that keep us alive and thriving. Homeostasis uses the endocrine system to regulate involuntary activities, such as blood pressure, heartbeat, breathing, digestion and elimination, and temperature control.

The ANS has two primary branches, the sympathetic and the parasympathetic. The sympathetic branch triggers the fight-flight-freeze response when we feel stressed or threatened, and it happens quickly, harnessing and mobilizing resources intended to help us survive emergencies. The parasympathetic branch initiates what's referred to as the relaxation response, or sometimes as the rest-digest system. Both the sympathetic and parasympathetic branches are necessary, and they're complimentary. We need and use them both based on our perception of what's happening around us. These systems have been with us since the time when saber-toothed tigers wandered the land. Daily life was rife with danger, and we needed to be able to jump up and run away in order to stay alive. The sympathetic nervous system helped us do that by immediately issuing a cascade of physiological activities aimed at helping us survive.

When we're in a fight-flight state, the sympathetic nervous system sends out a hormone stew intended to help us to either run away from danger or stay and fight for our lives. The reaction starts in the amygdala, that primal center of our limbic system that triggers our fight-flight response. In the initial receiving of sensory information, the rational, analytical mind is wholly left out – the amygdala calls the shots immediately. It sends a distress signal to the hypothalamus that kicks off the stress response activity. Based on the information it receives, the hypothalamus then decides what orders to dictate. Chemical messengers called "releasing hormones" then travel to the pituitary, and the pituitary does their bidding by releasing more hormones. Again, this is not a conscious or rational process. The triggering of our fight-flight response is automated, and the process isn't gradual. It flips like a switch.

Based on the information it receives from the senses via the amygdala, the pea-sized hypothalamus, making up less than one percent of the brain, decides if we need to enter survival mode, literally becoming ready for struggle, injury, and potentially death. When the threat subsides, the parasympathetic system comes back in charge and calms us down.

That's how it's supposed to work, and it served us quite well thousands of years ago. Fight-flight-freeze was triggered for a short period in an emergency to hopefully avoid injury and death, then we settled down, and life got back to normal when we understood that the threat was mitigated. Now, not so much. As a society, we've managed to create a modern way of life that is almost perpetually stressing us, promoting the perception that the demand of any moment exceeds our capacity to handle it with ease. The stress hormone stew that got our ancestors safely away from a tiger is the very same one that happens when we become startled, angry, or anxious today. The circumstances and severity aren't the same, but our physical response is.

Like tensions in the body, our thoughts and emotions directly affect the amygdala. The amygdala then directly influences the hypothalamus, so the tiny but consequential hypothalamus's hormonal response is influenced by what we think and feel. The decisions made by the autonomic command center of the brain are directly affected by our perceptions of what's happening around us. Said another way, a thought or emotion is capable of triggering the same biochemical response as a saber-toothed tiger!

Take a slow breath in and a mindful breath out. As you inhale, the heartbeat is triggered to speed up slightly. This activates your fight-flight response, and you feel energized and ready for action. As you exhale, your heart slows down a bit, stimulating the rest-digest response and relaxing you.[2] In its natural wisdom, your body designed your exhale to be, on average, one and a half times longer than your inhale. The overall effect of this is one of relaxed awareness rather than overactive, on-edge reactivity. Chronic stress disrupts this natural, harmonious balance and causes the inhale to be prolonged and the exhale shortened, amplifying the fight-flight effects.

On the flip side, relaxed, whole-body breathing does just the opposite. This slow, rhythmic breath enhances heart function, increases emotional stability and resiliency, and induces the relaxation response. As a result, we experience feelings of calm, confidence, relaxation, and clarity of thought. The breath is a powerful agent of information and transformation. Through it, we can learn more about what we're sensing and encourage the relaxation response to positively affect the state of our body, mind, and heart.

Becoming attuned to the breath, listening to and understanding what it tells us, and harnessing its power to help us relax and release, are all important skills for ensuring a safe and effective Yin Yoga & Meditation practice. Whether feeling its flow as a guide to interpreting sensations, or consciously encouraging relaxation to soothe the mind and heart, the breath is a masterful teacher and constant friend. As we continue to explore the Mandala Map, we'll elaborate on the many breath techniques available to incorporate into your practice, teaching, and daily life.

For now, take one more slow mindful breath in. Pause, then allow an easy breath out, lengthening it just a moment or two longer than the inhale. Offer your physical form a bow of honor and gratitude as you remain here one moment more.

Feel your breath landing you squarely into the precious moment you're living, this present time, the only time your life ever happens. Take this opportunity to enjoy the body and attention being together in the same time and space: right here, right now.

The Energy Layer

Sent into space in 1968 to document the lunar landscape, Apollo 8 astronauts William Anders, Frank Borman, and Jim Lovell had not prepared for the moment that resulted in one of the most famous and remarkable photographs in human history, the accidental image known as *Earthrise.* Borman reports that by chance he glanced out one of the lunar module windows at the precise moment the earth emerged over the lunar horizon.

> To see the earth as we now see it, small and blue and beautiful in that eternal silence where it floats, is to see ourselves as riders on the earth together, brothers on that bright loveliness in the unending night—brothers who see now they are truly brothers.
>
> – *Archibald MacLeish*

If you haven't seen that photograph lately, I encourage you to revisit it. Each time I encounter it, I'm awestruck all over again. Out beyond the gray crust of moon running along the foreground lies the earth, our own little blue-marbled miracle swimming half-visible in a sea of ink-black space, starkly demanding we remember that we have nowhere else to go. This unplanned, auspicious photo captures in such pure and breathtaking terms the magnificence and rare, delicate beauty of this planet that so generously hosts us.

The Universe Around and Within Us

Taoists believe five Elements make up everything in the universe: Wood, Fire, Earth, Metal, and Water. These fundamental Elements imbue this world with their qualities and characteristics and form the basis of all that is:

Metal – Modern science believes the core of the planet is a mixture of metallic elements spinning within this beautiful earth ball at a temperature close to the surface of the sun. Strewn throughout the earth's crust nearer the surface lie metals, precious and prized, able to be endlessly transformed by skilled hands again and again. See with your inner eye how iron, draped in flames, is shaped with endless possibilities.

Earth – Above ground, solid and scallop-topped mountains cover about twenty percent of the earth's surface. Far from passive observers as the eons pass, these massive ranges of stone host countless diverse species and provide life-giving fresh water for more than half of the earth's inhabitants.

Wood – Feel the solid rock surface under your feet as you see in your mind's eye the lush forest covering the mountain's side. Each tree's wooden flesh is a living record of its days and is full of functioning, dying, and dead cells. Sprouting from the tiniest of seeds into massive leafy towers, trees drive ever upward, gaining growth not from the base but the crown. Let your eyes follow the trunk as it rises higher and higher toward the brightness of the sky.

Fire — Feel on your face the life-giving light and warmth from our sun, the bright star sitting about ninety-two million miles away, currently burning itself as its own fuel at roughly twenty-seven million degrees Fahrenheit.

Water — Bubbling nearby, a crisp, fresh stream meanders down the mountainside, winding its way among the trees. Flowing with utter ease, following without error every bend and twist between its banks, over and around any boulder, never deterred, persistently seeking and finding its way, eventually, back to and becoming the sea.

Water, Wood, Fire, Earth, and Metal are the Five Elements, five faces of a cosmos humming with energy, comprising everything we see in every direction we look. All have their unique energetic imprint and join in majestic and mysterious combinations, always connected, changing, and shifting ever toward balance. Take a few moments to shuffle through the images of this world's wonders that you hold in your mind, whether from experiences in nature you've had, places you've traveled, or pictures you've seen. Scan with your inner eye, watching the edges and textures and colors and forms that play themselves out all around us.

The Elements, like the other constituents of Taoist energetic theory, are both literal and figurative. Each represents their material physical expression in the world as well as emotional, mental, and spiritual aspects. For example, Wood doesn't just manifest in the world as the matrix of cellulose and lignin forming the basis of an Eastern White Cedar tree, it also manifests as the underlying energies of inherent potential, adaptability, and inspired growth. Never static, the Elements are perpetually interacting with one another in ever-shifting cycles of generation and reduction to maintain their natural equilibrium.

In a creation cycle, each Element feeds another to support adequate quantities of each:

- Wood feeds Fire, as we put a log on a campfire
- Fire creates Earth, as the flames change the log to ash
- Earth generates Metal, as precious metals are found in the earth's crust
- Metal gives rise to Water, as dew forms on the surface of metal
- Water nourishes Wood, as rainwater serves as life-giving moisture to the roots of trees

In a controlling cycle, each Element restrains another, asserting an important check-and-balance toward equilibrium:

- Wood parts Earth, as roots of a mighty tree break the ground
- Earth takes in Water, as soil absorbs drops of rain
- Water quenches Fire, as rain showers extinguish a smoldering fire
- Fire melts Metal, as a blacksmith's fire forms a metal ax
- Metal breaks Wood, as an ax chops down a tree

Imbalance in these relationships occurs when an Element does not generate sufficient amounts of the other. Too little Water means Wood suffers, just as drought makes it more difficult for plants to grow. When plants die from lack of water, they become a potential fuel source for fires, so Water's beneficial control of Fire also suffers. Imbalance also manifests as one Element exerting too much control over another, and instead of offering a supportive check, it weakens or reduces another. Wood can exert too much control over Earth when plants grow together too densely, hampering the soil's ability to sufficiently nurture all the roots.

These Five Elements form all things in the universe, and they're our energies too. Imagine these continuous phases of Elemental energy as glowing lines extending through and connecting the heavens and the earth, glowing lines tying one thing to all things, and all things to each thing - and that includes you. Here we'll explore this more subtle layer or expression of our human being form: energy.

All One

You are a miracle of consciousness, a heart beating in your beautiful body, enabling you to perceive and receive this stream of sensory information with appreciation and awe. You, too, are pulsing with energy, activated by the very same Elements animating the stars. Pause to consciously acknowledge the wondrous amalgamation you are, a compilation of complex biological systems that motor your movements inside and out, persistently powering your physical and mental processes, keeping you awake and alive, brimming with potential as a being of peace and of love.

Connecting with the breath as it flows in and out, perhaps spend a few moments with this mantra:

Breathing in,
I sense I am breathing in.
Breathing out,
I sense I am breathing out.

Here you are, a breathing being on this spinning blue dot, a safe haven for human life in a universe estimated to be about ninety-three billion light-years in diameter and growing. Here we are, the two of us, connected in this moment, sitting here among perhaps two trillion galaxies, breathing this beautiful breath, intricately linked, shared energy flowing in, out, and through us. Visualize this universal energy surrounding you, flowing up the front of the body, the inside of the legs and arms, rising toward heavens, over the head, falling down the back of arms, spine, backs of legs returning to the earth. Human beings are bathed in energy as the bridge between heaven and earth, feet on the ground, spirits rising into the sky. The energies of the universe swirl in glowing lines around and within you. Feel for the same rhythm in the stream of your breath as it slides in, fills your chest cavity, then slowly releases out into the world. Take a bit of time in this breathing space to steep in this sense of connection and flow.

Breathing in,
I sense I am in the world.
Breathing out,
I sense the world is in me.
Breathing in,
I sense energy flows from me into the world.
Breathing out,
I sense energy flows from the world into me.

Many sacred traditions have theories of an energetic architecture within us. Each tradition has its own names for the various components and maps of this subtle energy body, but underpinning all of them is the basic understanding that we are more than our physical tissues. We are energetic beings in a universe composed of energy.

Living in harmony with the world invigorates the flow of energy within us. Harmonious energy keeps us healthy, happy, and living a spirited and meaningful life. Taoism offers techniques to support our capacity to actively engage with our inner energies, enhancing our ability to regulate and restore. Our longevity, and physical, emotional, and spiritual vibrancy, rely on energetic equilibrium. Because all aspects of life exist in a mutually interactive, reciprocal relationship, bolstering our physical and spiritual health boosts our energetic health as well.

Return in your mind's eye to the glowing lines extending all around you. Follow the lines as they flow down through the boundary of the skin. These glowing, flowing lines extend through the body in a defined network of channels thought to run through our dense connective tissues, including the fascial web, extending into every corner of us. Forming one large and intricate energetic highway plexus, they deliver life-force to all of our physical tissues. Also referred to as meridians, these channels run in bilateral tracks, one on each side of the body. Like rivers feeding a lake, they serve as pathways to principal energetic centers known in Chinese Medical Theory as Organ Systems (capital "O").

In the West, organs are viewed as tissues in a particular location performing a specific role: the heart pumps blood, the lungs bring oxygen into the body and expel carbon dioxide, and so on. Chinese Medical Theory recognizes these tissues and physiological processes but also ascribes additional energetic, mental, and emotional functions to them. The Organs power all physical, mental, and emotional facets of who we are.

The energetic channels take on the name of the Organs they nourish and are identified as either yin or yang in nature. The yin channels travel along the inner, or medial, length of the limbs, while their yang counterparts run along the outer, or lateral, side of the limbs. Yin channels originate from either the centerline or lower parts of the body, such as the chest and feet, and have a generalized upward and outward flow. Yang channels begin in the upper and outermost parts of the body, either the head or hands, and have an overall trajectory of inward and downward. Theoretical maps differ in their exact location and quantity but commonly acknowledge twelve primary channels, six yin and six yang, in addition to two ruling vessels. The yin Conception Vessel runs up the front spine from the pubic bone area to the mouth. The yang Governor Vessel begins in the pubic area and circles toward the back body. It travels all the way up the back of the spine to the brain, where it swings down the face to connect with the Conception Vessel. These two ruling vessels fuse yin and yang energies in a single circular course, promoting energetic balance. As you mentally trace this loop that vertically encircles you along the midline, is there any movement you can sense?

Each channel serves as a delivery stream to one of the twelve Organs recognized by Chinese Medical Theory to perform physiological functions as well as to manage energetic and emotional responsibilities. The health of these Organs impacts the health of our physical tissues, and the reverse is true, too - poor physical health affects the flow of energy within us. Organs also hold our emotions, so the health of our inner energetic architecture influences our feelings and how we experience them.

Located throughout the body both as energetic centers and functional entities within each cell, our Organs intake, transform, and transport the life-force energy that underlies our very existence. This activating energy called Qi flows within and around us, enlivening the universe itself. Existing everywhere in all things, this universal Qi gives form to the world but is itself formless. Qi is constantly transforming into many kinds of Qi, each with specific functions. Like water rippling as a fish swims through it, we sense Qi by attuning our attention to the spaces through which it flows.

Just as water manifests in many forms on the earth, from ice to liquid to steam, Qi manifests in many different forms in the universe and within us. All different faces of the same basic energy, there is Qi that nourishes, Qi that protects, Qi that fills the Organs, and Qi that flows through the energetic channels charting within us. Qi is an agent of movement and of transformation, converting food, air, and water into more energy. Qi powers the mind and empowers our ability to manage our emotions in healthy ways. Qi is also a transportation source, circulating itself, blood, and other fluids. Qi warms and safeguards the body and helps to hold all the stuff inside us in its respective place.

Think of energetic health in terms of quantity and quality of Qi. Both factors contribute to our overall wellbeing, and disharmony can arise from either aspect. Like water, Qi is meant to flow. Qi deficiency, excess, stagnation, and blockage all contribute to imbalance and, to some degree impact all layers of who we are. In Yin Yoga & Meditation, just as in life, we want to encourage our energy to flow well and with balance. We also want to enrich the quality of the Qi itself. If we have strong, vibrant Qi but its pathways are blocked, we experience imbalance. Likewise, if these tiny canals are clear but the Qi is depleted and weak, we also experience imbalance.

Suboptimal physical movement patterns, injuries, or tensions may create energetic blockages. As we discussed in "Yoga Nidra Fundamentals," tensions accumulate in all layers of our being, whether physical, mental, or emotional. When the channels are blocked, delivery of Qi is impacted and the areas behave essentially like energetic dead zones, similar to how the landscape or a building's materials block cellular phone signals. When we're healthy and balanced, we flow. Just as life feels effortless when we're in tune, our Qi is meant to flow freely. Coming back into true harmony, we feel an overall sense of wellbeing, connection, and freedom.

Chinese Medical Theory posits that we receive two primary forms of Qi: Preheaven and Postheaven. Preheaven Qi is given to us by our parents, similar to a genetic inheritance. Postheaven Qi, on the other hand, is derived primarily from food and air. Our store of Preheaven Qi is finite. The amount we have is limited and moves in only one direction: down. We want to use this Qi well because we're not getting any more of it, and when it's gone, we die.

The news about Postheaven Qi is more inspiring! We can accumulate as much Postheaven Qi as we want through nutritious food and the air we breathe, and we can also help it flow harmoniously. If we continue gathering Postheaven Qi, we'll maintain plenty of it, and have it on hand to use for our essential functions. This means we don't have to dip into and drain our precious store of Preheaven Qi. Each of us has the potential to become an expert Qi Cultivator in the Yin Yoga & Meditation practice, and the best place to start, as with so many yin aspects, is through sensing.

Feeling the Flow

Just like we're able to become more sensitive to our muscles, the weight of our bones, and the space within our joints, we can also grow more sensitive to the subtleties of Qi streaming around and within us. The more sensitive we become to our energy, the more inclined and empowered we are to keep it healthy. The conditions of Yin Yoga & Meditation are conducive to observing how it moves inside us. Bringing inquisitive, kind attention to the internal lines of energy helps sustain them, just as the physical stresses of our asana help balance and strengthen Qi flow. Continue to settle your attention toward the lines moving through your inside spaces, the physical layers that our outside eyes can't see. Try to visualize these inward surfaces.

Bring your attention now to the heartspace. The Heart Organ serves as the nexus of our energetic network. From the Heart, the general flow of Qi through the channels moves into the arms and hands, up over the head, down the back, along the spine, and to the sides of the body, through the buttocks, legs, thighs, and calves to the feet. From the feet, the flow begins its return cycle toward the heartspace, traveling upwards along the inside and front of legs. Using your mind's eye, see if you can sense this circular, cyclical pattern of Qi charting its course through you.

As you scan, follow the Qi by sensitizing to its movement. Allow your awareness to linger in places that call your attention. Perhaps there's a slight flickering or fluttering sensation, a pulsing or a vibration. Do you sense any fluctuations in temperature? Watch it with your inner eyes. What color(s) is it? Is there a texture to its flow: choppy or fluid, strong or subtle? Are there any areas where you sense constriction, where the Qi flow feels obstructed or sluggish? It's OK if you can't feel anything instantly; attuning to energetic sensations often takes time and practice. Just keep watching and scanning, feeling your way. Remain curious; there's no need to judge what you might or might not be finding. You can trust that with time and patient persistence, it will come.

Sensitizing to the flow and frequencies of our inner energies is another way to pay attention, another way to train the mind and heart in compassionately staying present with what's happening. The better we are at sensing our internal energy, the more effectively we cultivate it. Regularly engaging with it through awareness and breath improves its quality and helps us guide it more efficiently to where we most need it.

Energetic Organ Systems

Organs function in yin-yang pairs. Yin Organs are denser (e.g., Liver and Lungs) and carry the bulk of responsibilities. Yang Organs are more hollow and serve primarily as repositories (e.g., Gall Bladder) or transporters (e.g., Small Intestine) to support the yin Organs' work. Each Organ has affinities with specific colors, emotions, seasons, and tissues. The Organs also correlate with particular healing sounds used in energetic practices to clarify and balance them. The Qi channels tie the entire Organ System into one flowing unit to maintain proper Qi balance and flow.

One philosophical pillar in Taoism is inherent interconnection: what affects one affects all in the great and mysterious universe, and our internal energetic architecture is no different. All the Qi channels and Organs are united in one synergistic network. Our physical body, emotional life, and Qi network are all mutually collaborative and supportive. If we strengthen an Organ, the physiological processes and emotions it stores benefit, and vice versa. From this perspective, we are one integrated and mutually interacting whole.

Let's move deeper into our energetic infrastructure and the Five Elements within us.

Wood Element: Liver-Gall Bladder Organs

Bring your attention now to the middle of your torso, along the right upper chest just below the diaphragm. Put one hand and then the other there, resting it lightly as the rib cage moves gently up and down with the breath. Beneath your hands sits your largest internal organ, the liver. The liver manages the amount of blood in circulation; more than a quart of blood passes through the liver at any given minute. A hotbed of transformation, the liver is often called the body's chemical factory, performing more than five hundred chemical functions as it secretes bile and breaks down both the nutrients we need and the toxins we don't.

Attached to the liver is a small pouch called the gall bladder. This organ is a fraction of the liver's size, just two to three inches in total, and stores the bile the liver produces for the purposes of digestion. As you hold your hands here, send appreciation to the liver for all the excellent work it does to cleanse the body of toxins and to keep you healthy and thriving. Did you know the liver is our only organ that has the capability to re-grow itself? This fascinating fact embodies the Taoist Element ruling the Liver Organ, the Element of Wood. This is the Element of renewal and fresh beginnings.

Wood dominates the season of spring, that refreshing time of revitalization and growth when the days are longer, brighter, and filled with new possibilities. Spring offers fertile ground for bringing visions and intentions to life. After the long sleep and fallow fields of winter, Wood arises, sure of its vision and determination to see them become reality. Wood manifests itself in the world, and in us, as seeds that cannot help but burst forth.

Associated with the sensory organ of the eye, Wood enlivens the inner vision of our imagination, helping us conceive new opportunities with clear sight, empowered to give them a try. Like the young seedling that keeps growing until it breaks through the soil into the sun, we are energized by the stick-to-it-iveness of this Element to explore ourselves and this world.

As saplings sway strong but supple in the wind, Wood helps us maintain our ability to adapt to changing circumstances, responding with ingenuity and intelligence to challenges. When we bring the Wood Element within us into harmony, we are alive and bustling with the optimistic energies of a bright spring morning where anything is possible. We're inspired to keep persevering, beginning again over and over as many times as it takes, and accommodating any breeze that blows.

Wood also rules the Liver (yin) and Gall Bladder (yang), so these Organ Systems are particularly active and in need of care during the spring season. Traditional Chinese Medicine asserts that the Liver and Gall Bladder send Liver Blood to the tendons and ligaments to build durable, healthy joints. This yin-yang Organ pair thus bolsters the flexibility of our physical joints, helping us navigate our days with safety and strength.

Known as the Army's General, the Liver ensures Qi and blood both flow evenly. When this energy is out of balance, we're susceptible to getting stuck in cycles of reactivity, finding ourselves easily irritated. Harmonious Liver and Wood energies transform feelings of restlessness and irritation into resilience, equanimity, and peace, so we go and grow no matter what life places in front of us. Though its branches are tossed to and fro by strong winds, a tree stays steady with its strong trunk and roots embedded deep into the earth. Swaying but sure, a tree keeps its feet, as do we.

Both channels feeding Qi to the Liver and Gall Bladder stretch the length of the body. Starting in the big toe, the yin Liver channel crosses the top of the foot and the acupuncture point known as Liver Pt 3, or Great Rushing. To find this pressure point, touch your finger between your big and second toes and slide away from the toes along the bony ridge about an inch until you feel a slight depression. Liver Pt 3 is considered one of the most significant Qi concentration points. Massaging this area in a clockwise direction creates a tiny vortex of Qi that helps to clarify and balance the Liver, quieting the mind and draining any irritability or anger that has built up.

From Liver Pt 3, the channel continues by rising along the inner leg to the pelvis, swinging up through the Liver and Gall Bladder Organs on its way through the center body. From there, it travels up through the throat to the crown of the head. Another branch of the Liver channel flows from the eye and circles the mouth. A third branch tracks from the Liver to the Lungs.

The Liver channel is paired with the Yang Gall Bladder channel, which runs from the eye, around the side of the head to the forehead, and then drops down through the neck and shoulders. It crisscrosses back and forth across the lateral torso, and, continuing downward, it travels the length of the outer leg on its way to landing in the second to last toe.

Spend a few moments here, tracing these paths in your mind, sensing how life-force energy travels all the way up and down your body and supports your ability to envision the life you want, inhabit your capacity for growth, and foster the qualities of poise, balance, and flexibility each day of your life.

As you attune to these little glowing lines running from your toes to your head and back again, make the Taoist healing sound for the Liver, the soothing sound of *Shhhhhhh*. Take a full, quiet inhale through the nose, then exhale slowly through the mouth, making the sound *Shhhhhhh* through gently pursed lips, like the sound a breeze makes as it gently sways the tops of trees. Let it vibrate in the space below your hands, the sound of *Shhhhhhh* resonating through and filling your Liver, enlivening the Wood Element within you. As you offer this healing sound, see a deep green color filling this space and express gratitude for everything it does to keep you alive and thriving.

Just as a log of wood provides fuel for a fire to burn, in Five Elements theory, the Wood Element generates the Element ruling the long, happy days of summer: Fire.

Fire Element: Heart-Small Intestine & Pericardium-Triple Burner Organs

Slide your hands from where they sit on the liver to the ribcage center, resting them over the breastbone at the heartspace. Sensitize your attention to your palms' skin as they rest stacked above your beating heart. What do you feel as you maintain your awareness here on your palms? Maybe you're experiencing a sense of warmth where your palm sits on your chest and at the place where your hand's back meets the other palm. Perhaps there's the sensation of vibrating or rippling in the space around your hands. Maybe you're even able to begin sensing the movement of your heart in the chest that rises and falls with each breath.

Spend as much time as you'd like in this mini communion with the muscle that beats, on average, a hundred thousand times a day to keep you alive. Sitting just to the left of the sternum at the center of your chest, your heart is only slightly larger than a fist. Still, it pumps two thousand gallons of blood each day through approximately sixty thousand miles of interconnected arteries and veins, their collective path long enough to wrap two and a half times around the earth. Surrounding the heart is a protective membrane called the pericardium that shields it from invasion by pathogens. This fibrous tissue also keeps your heart fixed within the chest and provides lubrication as it contracts and expands.

Move your hands now along the path of the aorta, that large artery that travels from the heart down through the torso, landing them softly onto the belly. Coiled in the space of the abdomen lies the small intestine. More than twenty feet in length, it is the longest digestive organ and connects the stomach to the large intestine. With the help of pancreatic enzymes and bile from the liver, the small intestine breaks down food and allows nutrients to absorb into the blood stream through tiny, finger-like structures on its lined wall.

In Traditional Chinese Medical Theory, the yin Heart Organ functions in collaboration with the yang Small Intestine and is the realm of the Fire Element, the seat of enjoyment, warm connection, and love. Fire rules the season of summer, a time when yang is at its most vibrant and everything bustles with liveliness and zest. Fire feeds within us a playful delight and light-heartedness. To steep for a moment in the Element of Fire, imagine a day overflowing with laughter and play on the beach or in a beautiful park with family, friends, or a beloved pet.

Associated with the sensory organ of the tongue as it relates to speech, Fire helps us communicate with intimacy, express ourselves with passion, and build happy, healthy, and loving relationships. Fire is an Element that feeds this gentle truth: you were born to love and be loved. Giving and receiving unconditional love is your spirit's most fundamental substance.

> When all your desires are distilled, you will cast just two votes: to love more and be happy.
>
> – *Hafiz (Daniel Ladinsky adaptation)*

Fire infuses summer with activity, brightness, and movement – a lively reminder that love is a verb that is demonstrated not just through thoughts and feelings but by our words, decisions, and actions. This is the Element that helps us stay positive and aligned with our higher purpose, even when times get tough. Fire stirs our hearts and encourages us to give a smile to those who could use cheer or offer a helping hand when someone falls.

The yin Heart Organ pairs with the yang Small Intestine Organ. This yin-yang pair is also closely associated with the Pericardium and an Organ unique to Chinese Medical Theory, the Triple Burner, also called the San Jiao. The three-part Triple Burner consists of lower, middle, and upper burner areas in the torso. Though this Organ doesn't have a direct Western counterpart, it loosely aligns with the Western concepts of metabolism, temperature regulation, hormonal activities, and the lymph and immune systems. The Pericardium serves as protector of the Heart, guarding against immunological invaders and the ill effects of environmental and emotional extremes.

Of all the Taoist Organs, the Heart is most similar to its Western medicine counterpart regarding its physiological functions. Given the Organ's role in ensuring blood circulates well, the tissue ruled by the Heart is the network of blood vessels. In addition to its physical functions, the Heart has energetic responsibilities as well, serving as a principal hub for the circulation of Qi in addition to blood. The Heart further transforms nutrients sent by the Spleen into Qi for the body, pumping blood and Qi through the blood vessels to every tissue, organ, and cell.

The Heart is the primary seat of Shen, our highest consciousness and spiritual vibration, the light of our Sankalpa sparkling in our eyes. This Organ reminds us that our happiness is shared space and we're on this journey together. Free of requirements, expectations, and preconditions, a replenished Heart helps us become better at seeing all the good in ourselves and in others, too. We speak more kindly and act in ways that help others feel safe and be happy. Fire reminds us that no one goes it alone and that we're all part of the beloved human family.

Believed to be the monarch reigning over all other Organs and the emotions they store, the Heart filters all feelings. When we unblock the Heart, we show up for others and for ourselves, too. It's no surprise that the hands are seen as the Heart's motor organs. Reaching out in kindness, we rekindle our connection to one another and assert the power of unconditional love and genuine caring to transform any circumstance. Nothing obstructs the flow of love – no difficulty, no circumstance, no distance.

When the Heart is out of balance, we might fall victim to loneliness, despair, or depression, feeling like we're on our own, an isolated island in the middle of a stormy sea. We may subject ourselves or others to harsh judgments, cruelty, or even hatred. Therefore, tending to the health of the Heart is a sacred emotional and spiritual responsibility. One powerful way to restore and maintain a balanced Heart and Small Intestine energy flow is easy: laugh. A bubble of joy rising from the heart, laughter is powerful medicine, both physically and emotionally. Undeniably uplifting, its effect is tangible and immediate.

The yin Heart Qi channel nurtures the Heart. To find it, center your attention in your heartspace, letting the breath come and go as it will. Beginning in the chest, this channel has three branches. The first branch moves down to the Small Intestine, while the second branch flows to the throat, charting a course toward the eyes where it ends. The third traces the arm's full length from the underarm, through the upper arm, to the elbow, where the Heart Pt3 sits at the inner elbow. This acupuncture point, known as the Lesser Sea, supports the strong flow of Qi and blood. To find it, flex your elbow and place a finger at the base of the crease just above the bony protrusion of the inner elbow. From here, the Heart channel continues through the forearm to the wrist, where it pivots through the palm to form a connection with the Small Intestine channel at the inner tip of the little finger.

The yang Small Intestine channel begins where the Heart channel ends at the pinky finger's tip. Flowing through the palm and wrist, it traces along the arm's backside through the shoulder's back to the nape of the neck. From there, a branch descends through the heart and stomach on its way to the small intestine. Back up at the neck's base, another branch crosses the neck and cheek, rising past the eye's outer corner to end at the ear. A final segment flows from the cheek to the inner eye.

Heart's harmonizing color is a brilliant red. Visualize this color in the heartspace while practicing the Taoist healing sound of *Hawwww*, which is made through the mouth as a round, opening sighing sound at the back of the throat. Serenade the heart with *Hawwww*...made on the exhale. As you attune to its beat, feel the space around the heart soften, expand, and glow, the color red emanating from its center. Connecting to the Heart connects us to that which is eternal, awakening us to the divine grace and intelligence of the universe we live in, the great garment of which we are each a thread.

As a bonfire consumes wood and produces nutrient-rich ash which the soil delivers to growing plants, in Five Elements Theory, Fire feeds the Element of Earth.

Earth Element: Spleen-Stomach Organs

Rest your hands now onto your upper abdomen. Take your attention past the ribs to a small nook between the stomach, large intestine, left kidney, and diaphragm. Here we find the spleen, a soft and purplish tissue about five inches in length. Shaped to fit where it sits, the spleen is our most massive lymphatic tissue. It filters blood and consumes old platelets, red blood cells, and bacteria. This organ also supports our immune response by creating and activating white blood cells to help us fight infections. If you'd like, send appreciation from your hands to your spleen for how it tends to the blood supply flowing through you.

Next to the spleen lies the stomach, a hollow, muscular organ that talks to us several times a day when it feels empty, reminding us to eat. The stomach is responsible for beginning the digestive process before sending food into the duodenum of the small intestine and has a bean-like shape, comfortably holding just over a quart of food at a time.

Spend a few moments here with your hands over your spleen and stomach, considering the many ways they work to keep you healthy. These are the areas ruled by the Earth Element. To explore the energies of Earth as your hands lean lightly on your abdomen, use your attention to find all the places where your body is supported by the earth. Hold your awareness at each touchpoint for a few moments, and with gratitude for gravity, sense how Mother Earth holds us safely to her side, just as a mother pulls her child close and secure on her hip. This miraculous blue dot sliding through space in elliptical orbits around the sun provides for our every basic need: air to breathe, water to drink, and soil and sunshine to grow food. She offers us the nourishment we need to live and love, connecting us to our most profound dreams and to one another. This Element reminds us we are on the earth and of the earth, and that we belong to the earth and to one other.

Earth's qualities are the energies of mothering, nourishment, community, safety, and comfort. To embody the gifts of Earth and replenish it within you, maybe you remember the satisfaction of working on a project together with friends or colleagues, or a time you volunteered at a local food bank, community garden, or animal shelter. Feel this memory reverberate inside you, how it gave you just the recharge, nourishment, and reinvigoration you needed. Spend some time steeping in the emotions that arise as this memory resurfaces and replays in your mind, in your physical tissues, in your heart. Let yourself feel it fully.

Earth has a grounding effect, and like the soil we stand on, it offers stability and security. This Element rules the season of late summer, a time equally balanced between the active yang of summer and the inward-turning yin of autumn. Fulfilling the promise and growth of spring and early summer, this season is full of looking ahead to the harvest. Just as the ground under our feet provides food for people and animals to eat, Earth extends our ability to take care of ourselves and one another. Whether bonding with family over Sunday dinner or offering a meal to a stranger in need, Earth literally and figuratively helps us come together with love.

This Element oversees our physical digestion and emotional and spiritual sustenance, and is associated with the sense of taste, emphasizing its relationship to our wellbeing. Earth, too, supports us in hard times and tells us it's going to be OK, like the soft soothing a mother offers her crying child. Earth is the generosity that breaks the bread in half to share with the person next to us. An ancient Chan Buddhist story tells of the Buddha, asking his monks how to keep a drop of water from drying up. They considered this question carefully, but no one was able to answer. The Buddha replied, "Place it into lakes, rivers, or oceans." Earth reminds us that we are our greatest strength when we join together in caring. If Fire is the Element that shines light on the spiritual unity of all things, Earth helps us manifest and bring that beloved community to life.

In Chinese Medicine, Earth rules the Spleen and Stomach. These Organs transform nutrients into energy that motors our body, mind, and spirit. The Organ most unlike its Western counterpart, the Spleen in Chinese Medicine is like a minister of transportation, powering the transformation of food essences, Qi, and fluids throughout the body. After extracting the nutrients that form the basis of Qi and Blood from the Stomach, the Spleen sends this energy to the Lungs and transports nutrients to the Heart to help create Blood. The Spleen additionally performs the work of lifting and holding all our tissues and Organs in their place. Because of this responsibility, one tissue ruled by the Spleen is the fascial network that provides structure and support throughout the body. This tissue includes muscle tissue and its intramuscular fascia, and building and maintaining a healthy muscle tone is also part of the job of the Spleen. Its holding function also helps to keep blood contained in the blood vessels. The Stomach is an essential yang Organ, passing absorbable substances to the Spleen for distribution and forwarding those needing further processing to the Small Intestine. Whereas the Spleen promotes a general lifting up, the Stomach's function is a general sending down.

Strong Spleen and Stomach energies give us a healthy appetite for food and life in general, helping us feel energized and enthusiastic. When these Organs are functioning well, we have fewer worries and lots of get-up-and-go. Rebalancing the Spleen reconnects us to our most natural state of mind: calm, uncluttered, and spacious. Harmonious Spleen Qi helps us notice and release unhelpful mental loops and anxious inner chatter, settling a boisterous mind and clearing the way for clarity, creativity, and insight. When these systems aren't balanced, it's possible that our inner dialogue will become distracted, repetitive, or foggy. When we nourish the Spleen, we open ourselves to fresh solutions and develop our ability to nourish ourselves and our communities.

We might physically experience imbalance in these Organs as poor digestion, fatigue, or engaging in disordered eating. Emotionally, we could feel distant from our friends and family, or have difficulty offering compassion to our fellow human beings. Suffering from a lack of replenishment, we could feel a general lethargy, apathy, and a dullness of mind, body, and heart. We need nutrients and proper digestion to power us through the day, so when the Spleen and Stomach are off balance, our energy runs low. Perhaps we find ourselves slumping as we sit or stand. We know that our posture affects how we feel. As with any imbalance, one aspect feeds into another, creating an unhealthy cycle. With the Spleen and Stomach balanced, we're sensitive to the wellbeing and suffering of others. We're empathetic, interested in building each other up, and inspired to bring people together in common purpose.

The yin Spleen channel starts at the big toe and travels along the inside of the foot toward the inner ankle, where it banks upward to trace the lower inner leg. Just below the inner knee, it passes through Spleen Pt 9, the Yin Mound Spring acupuncture point. To locate this point, place your right hand over your right knee and feel where your thumb naturally hooks into fleshy area of the inner upper shin. This point is believed to help relieve low back and knee pain. From the inner knee, the Spleen channel turns toward the center of the thigh. Continuing its rise into the abdomen, it moves through the Spleen and touches the Heart channel. From there, it rises toward the surface, going through the chest into the throat and landing finally at the tongue's root.

The yang Stomach channel runs from the eye past the nose to the mouth's edge. From there, it swings up to the side of the forehead. One branch then flows down through the middle of the body to the Stomach. The other offshoot goes through the throat and torso to the groin, where it chases down the front of the thigh and lower leg to the top of the foot, landing in the second toe.

Yellow is the harmonizing color associated with the Spleen, and its Taoist healing sound is a soft guttural *Whoooooh*, like a faraway wind vibrating at the back of the throat which slightly constricts as you exhale through the mouth. With your hands over the upper left abdomen where the Spleen sits, imagine a golden yellow light emanating from the Organ as it directs nutrients and Qi all through you. *Whoooooh...Whoooooh.*

Just as metals, minerals, and jewels are encased deep within the earth's crust, in Five Elements Theory, the Element of Earth bears Metal.

Metal Element:
Lungs-Large Intestine Organs

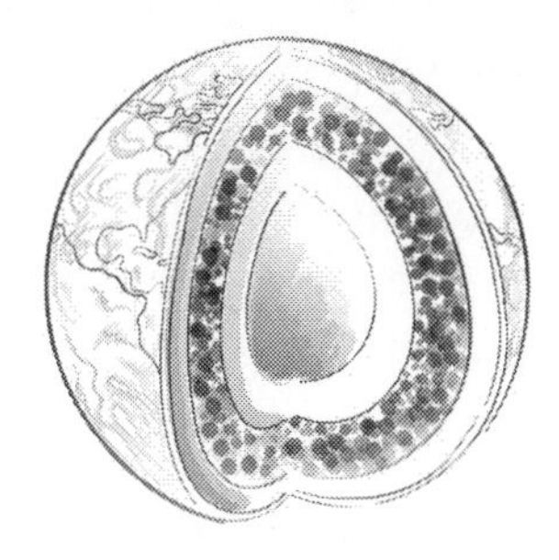

However you're sitting or lying down right now, take a moment to put your hands in an X-shape across your chest, right hand on the left chest, and left hand on the right chest, just below the clavicle. Allow your mind to settle into the space you're holding within your arms as your breath comes in and goes out at whatever pace is natural for you. Feel the breath go in and out, every inhale bringing oxygen in, each exhale expelling roughly seventy percent of all of your body's toxins through the substance of carbon dioxide. Sense each inhale as it comes and each exhale as it goes, chest expanding, chest contracting, inhale and exhale, together creating a perfect and sacred breath.

In the cradle of your arms lie the lungs, two main organs of detoxification. Made of spongy tissue, the lungs fill the entire thoracic cavity of the chest. If stretched flat, the inner surface of the lungs would fill half of a tennis court. In addition to bringing in nineteen cubic feet of oxygen for use each day, this detoxifying duo exhales more than two pounds of carbon dioxide daily.

Open your hands now, spreading all of the fingers wide, palms fully extended but not so much that you feel tension. Just find a sense of openness. Rest your right hand now onto the lower right side of your abdomen, the edge of your palm at your side body just above the arch of your hip bone and your fingers facing the midline. Mirror this position with your left hand, with the first two fingertips of your right and left hands lightly touching each other just below the navel. Draw in your mind's eye a large circle around the outer shape created by your hands. Here, you're tracing the length of your large intestine. Tracking around our lower abdomen's edges in an inverted U-shape, the large intestine is about five feet long. This tubular organ functions as the final stretch of our food's digestive journey. In addition to eliminating waste material, it absorbs vitamins, electrolytes, and about a quart of water each day.

These Organs are believed to be overseen by the Metal Element, the master of letting go and the keeper of all that is precious. Metal helps us reclaim our preciousness and self-worth, honoring our inherent beauty and value as a spirit on this earth. Like gold, silver, and crystals hidden deep in the earth's crust, each of us contains precious wonders to cherish. Metal helps us hold ourselves dear.

Metal also rules the season of autumn, a time of extraordinary transformation when nature lets go of the abundant, outward-moving energy and activity of summer and begins to turn inward. As the days grow cooler and the nights lengthen, nature's innate intelligence signals the chemical messages telling the leaves of trees to pause production of chlorophyl, the green pigment that captured sunlight to fuel their growth in the warmer months. The trees eventually surrender the leaves themselves to the soil below. Metal is connected to the sensory organ of the nose. You might spend a few moments recalling the scents of an autumn afternoon as the fallen leaves tumble at your feet.

Each autumn, about forty percent of all bird species take to the cooling skies to begin their annual migration, while many of those who remain undergo a physical transformation. The yellow feathers of goldfinches fade to brown in the fall, while the tiny hippocampus of the black-capped chickadee expands by a third, allowing the bird to better remember where it stashed the seeds of summertime. This is the quality of Metal, the energy of metamorphosis. It mirrors metals in the earth that can be shaped and reshaped over and over again.

The Metal Element oversees the Lungs and Large Intestine Organs. Known as the Chancellor of Qi, our Lungs perform the essential function of bringing oxygen and Qi into the body from the external environment and delivering them to the bloodstream and Qi channels for internal distribution. The Lungs transform oxygen into life. With each exhale, they do the work of releasing the unnecessary carbon dioxide and making room for the next inhale. We perform this breath cycle of taking in and releasing more than six million times each year.

In addition to the Qi they derive from the air, the Lungs also accept nutrients transported by the Spleen from the food we eat, transforming them into Qi to be circulated. Where Qi goes, blood goes too, so in this way, the Lungs also support healthy circulation of blood and bolster the function of the

Heart. As the only internal Organ to interface directly with the atmosphere around us, the Lungs represent our inner courage and must be actively watchful, not allowing any external pathogens to enter. The Lungs distribute Qi and bodily fluids to the skin's outer layer to support this protective tissue. Because healthy Lungs boost our immune system, a Lung imbalance could result in us falling ill more frequently.

The better we breathe, the better we feel. The inhale builds up our internal Qi, and the exhale brings release and relaxation. Deep breathing energizes our tissues and settles the central nervous system, strengthening Metal within us. Emotionally, the Lungs and Large Intestine Organs help us access and embody Metal's gifts, supporting and reaffirming what is valuable and letting go of what is no longer needed. Working collaboratively as a form of energetic inhale-exhale, the Lungs bring in and direct Qi through the body, and the Large Intestine sends away that which holds us back from thriving in the present moment. Metal allows us to let go of anything that isn't helping, creating space to bring into our lives that which benefits and sustains us. With it harmonized and strengthened, we summon the capacity to meet and accept the moments of life as they arise, rather than being held back or weighed down by persisting grief, old disappointments, or past experiences with loss which are outside of our control.

Letting go of deeply held sadness is not always easy. We'll all face times of loss; some are sudden and unexpected, while others are achingly, excruciatingly slow. Grief and loss are universal experiences, whether we lose loving family members and friends, a job or a home, our health, or a sweet and constant pet companion, though each of us experiences them in personal ways. Metal helps us manage these heartbreaking times of change with stability in spite of our sorrow, accessing the courage we need to allow ourselves to feel and heal. Metal energies support us as we let go of what's leaving and lovingly accept what arrives in its place.

Disharmonies in the Lungs and Large Intestine make it difficult for us to accept the impermanent nature of all things, making it challenging to fully let go of the losses that the seasons of our lives inevitably bring. We might feel trapped in feelings of sadness or hampered in our ability to accept certain realities, clinging onto the past or pushing away the present moment. Potentially we may find ourselves keeping things we don't need, whether physical possessions or mental-emotional patterns.

To make room for all of the goodness that wishes to come, we need to access our willingness to shed that which no longer serves us. The Lungs and Large Intestine invite us to discover anything we want to release and inquire: *In this area, would letting go feel like freedom?* Metal reminds us that transformation is possible in each moment. We are built with this energy and designed to live each moment in freedom and peace. Embodying this Element's confident courage, a balanced Lungs and Large Intestine work together to give us the fortitude to stay present with life as it comes, able to better weather its cycles of gain, loss, and change. We balance Metal when we harmonize the energies of these Organs, so exercising the tissues surrounding the energetic channels that feed the Lungs and Large Intestine strengthens and balances its qualities in all aspects of ourselves.

The Lung channel travels through the upper body. Beginning in the abdomen at the solar plexus, it drops down to touch the Large Intestine, then rises up through the stomach and diaphragm, before rising again to encircle the lungs and trachea. It then moves into each shoulder and traces down each arm's inside, finally landing to rest at the thumb's tip.

The Large Intestine channel begins at the tip of the index finger then moves along the finger toward the thumb's base, passing through the Large Intestine Pt 4 acupuncture point. This point is said to ease headaches and other forms of pain through strong Qi and blood flow, but please note that manipulation of this point is not advised during pregnancy. To find it, trace the back of your index finger from its tip down into the space between the thumb and forefinger. From there, the Large Intestine channel climbs through the wrist, forearm, elbow, and upper arm. Flowing over the shoulder into the neck, it rises from the jaw to the lip, then wicks around the nostril to end beside it.

Imagine a bright light of purest white shining now within your chest. As you breathe in and out, the white light grows brighter and brighter. Explore making the Taoist healing sound for Lungs, the sound of *Sssss* created on the exhale. To make this sound, as you breathe out, press your teeth together and let the gentle sound of *Sssss* happen as the air moves past your lips through closed teeth. Sense how this restful sound resonates softly in the bright, pure, white light as the tiny air sacs in your lungs empty, and any sluggish energies harmonize into flow. Like Metal, we too can change and transform. Our spirits are inherently dynamic, engaged in the process of continual change, meeting life as it comes with presence, appreciation, and acceptance.

In Five Elements theory, Metal is believed to generate the Element of Water, just as water condenses and collects on a metal object's surface or a pot collects and carries water.

Water Element: Kidneys-Urinary Bladder Organs

Place your hands along the back of the rib cage so that your elbows point out, your fingertips fall along your back spine, and your thumbs reach around toward the frontside midline. With the ribcage encompassed by your hands, let your fingers spread wide along your spine and back ribs. Slide them down, tracing the surface of the midbody until your fingers feel the lower edges of the ribcage at the lumbar area of the back. Held within you beneath this spread of your fingers and protected by your lowermost ribs, lie the kidneys, one nestled on either side of the spine.

The kidneys are bean-shaped organs that serve as filters, removing metabolic waste and excess fluid from the blood. Fluids do the essential work of transporting nutrients and waste to and from our tissues and organs, so by their nature, the kidneys serve every cell. Every minute, more than two pints of blood pass through them. The kidneys determine how much water to include with the waste material transferred through tubes to the urinary bladder, which expels it as urine. Because they also keep the proper phosphorus and calcium levels in the blood, the kidneys support healthy bones. The urinary bladder is a flexible pouch connected by tubes to the kidneys that stores and eliminates urine through the urethra. It lies several inches lower in the pelvic cavity just above the pubic bone.

Take a minute with your hands spread around your middle to hold your attention on these extraordinary organs. See if you sense these biological filters cleansing and clearing the two and a half pints of blood that pass through them before sending the waste to the urinary bladder.

The most yin-like Element, Water, has a drawing downward and inward quality, flowing with the ease of a wandering stream into our mysterious inner landscape, home to our intuition and inner knowing. Like the purest of its physical manifestations on the earth, Water is yielding, able to travel around obstacles. Supremely pliable, Water is inherently unbreakable, no matter how it twists and turns about. How effortlessly it flows ever onward, neither pushed nor pulled, propelling itself at its own pace and guided by its own wisdom and grace.

Nothing in the world is as soft and yielding as water. Yet for dissolving the hard and inflexible, nothing surpasses it.

–Tao Te Ching (Stephen Mitchell adaptation)

This Element reflects a calm, quiet determination, a sense of hibernation and easeful persistence without effort. This is Water: mighty yet still, yielding yet irresistible. Viewing any canyon, Water reminds us that just as a river cuts straight through rock, softness is often much stronger than any hard, sharp edge. Indeed, as we look at our lives and to some of history's greatest change makers like Rosa Parks, Mahatma Gandhi, Nelson Mandela, and Rev. Martin Luther King, Jr., we find that in the end, love proves stronger than any aggression, kindness more potent than any weapon of war.

Winter is ruled by Water. The most yin-like of all seasons, winter is the coldest and darkest time of year. Days are short, and much of nature has drawn into itself, lying dormant and recharging until the spreading light of spring. After the prolific growth of summer and bountiful harvest of autumn, winter is a time for introspection. With Water energies internalizing the awareness to reduce distractions, we more easily observe and respond to our internal happenings and can discover everything this Element wants to teach us. The sensory organ connected to the Water Element is the ear, representing our ever-present ability to listen inward. Imbalance of Water might feel like we're not quite up for challenges we encounter. When we nurture Water, we more easefully trust our inner wisdom and inhabit a willingness to keep on with steady perseverance.

The Water Element oversees the Kidneys and Urinary Bladder. Serving as a storage and delivery system of our fundamental energetic essence known as Jing, the Kidneys are the flame that powers all other Organs, and they support our overall vitality, our spark of life. If this raw fuel is low, all other systems suffer. We're capable of replenishing this essence through our Yin Yoga & Meditation practice, good eating and sleeping habits, and harmonious living. These Organs store our basic essence, converting it to Qi as needed and supplying it to the rest of the body so the whole Organ network has sufficient supply to perform its physical, emotional, and energetic functions. When the Lungs take in Qi from the environment around us, the Kidneys exert a holding function to store it. This essence is used to regulate our physical growth and maturation, and promotes aging with grace and wisdom.

Chinese Medical Theory asserts that the breath roots in the Kidneys. Harmonious Kidney function supports deep, full breathing, and vice versa. If Kidney energy is out of balance, the breath may become shallow and eventually impact our wellbeing. The abundance of Taoist deep breathing practices speaks to the significance of the energetic storage responsibilities of the Kidneys. They manage the use of water and regulate the quantity of fluids in circulation. Once absorbed by the stomach, Qi and fluids are sent by the Spleen to the Lungs. Directed by the Lungs, the fluids flow to the Kidneys for filtering. The Kidneys then direct the clean, healthy water to the Lungs for distribution throughout the body. The impure waters move to the Urinary Bladder where they are transformed into urine and eventually eliminated.

The Kidneys rule our bone tissue, and the Jing stored in the Kidneys is the basis of a substance referred to as Marrow. Marrow is believed to be the energetic foundation of bone tissue and the basis of the brain and spinal cord. In Chinese Medical Theory, the brain is called the Sea of Marrow. Marrow is responsible for several key functions, including ensuring our bones' strength and sturdiness, hydrating our joints, and supporting healthy brain function, including the proper balance of the stress and relaxation responses.

In addition to contributing to our physical constitution, the Kidneys fuel our willpower, determination, and personal power. When harmonious, they give us confidence in our abilities to inhabit our present and future aspirations. The Kidneys shine a spotlight on our inherent potential and the foundational wisdom we arrived to this earth carrying in our hearts. When the Kidneys are out of balance, we may develop a disposition for fearful or panicky behavior. We might lack confidence or feel listless and unmoored. This lack of self-trust delivers further injury to the Kidneys' energy, and a problematic cycle develops. Imbalance has the capacity to affect us physically, too, potentially resulting in disrupted growth patterns and reproductive abilities as well as brittle bones. One of the most considerable impacts of energetic disharmony in the Kidneys is a dysregulated stress response because the Kidneys are linked to the adrenals.

Rebalancing the Kidney energy and Water Element in us sets aside feelings of paralysis and beliefs that we don't have what it takes to meet the challenges at hand. It ignites our sense of resolve, allowing us to be secure in our ability to keep moving in the direction we want to go. Similarly, because the Urinary Bladder supports a strong back, these Organs hold us upright with an absolute assurance in who we are and our ability to take decisive action to experience the life that we want.

The yin Kidney channel starts at the tip of your smallest toe and moves into the foot's sole, the lowest and most yin part of the body. Here where we contact the yin energies of the earth, we find Kidney Pt 1, the acupoint known as the Bubbling Spring. Functioning like a portal to draw energy from the earth, activating this acupoint through acupressure settles the stress response, returning a sense of groundedness.

Looking at the sole of the foot, we find this concentration point below the second and third toe. Curl the toes slightly inward to locate a small depression formed a few inches down from the base of the toes. First, engage with this point by simply placing your attention on it and allowing your awareness to rest there. Let the sole of your foot rest upon the earth, and sense the grounding earth energy surging into this point of your foot. Gently massage this point with a light circular motion for a few moments then pause to feel any aftereffects.

Follow the flow from Kidney Pt 1 as it travels through the foot, circling the ankle and then rising up the inner legs through the sacrum to the lumbar area of the spine. Sitting between the second and third lumbar vertebrae, just behind the navel, is a significant acupuncture point known as the Door of Life, sometimes referred to as the Gate of Vitality. The Door of Life is the entry to where our original life essence is held in the Kidneys. Here we access the inner life fire that keeps us warm, powers our digestion, and imbues all Organs with Qi. Steep your attention in this influential spot.

The channel then tracks further up to the adrenals and the Kidneys, those pilot lights which support all other Organs and their functions. One branch touches the Urinary Bladder then skates upwards through the Liver, landing in the clavicle. The other branch rises from the Kidney to the Liver and then ascends through the diaphragm and into the Lungs. From there, it traces up the throat into the base of the tongue.

The yang Urinary Bladder channel flows in two parallel branches. Both tracks run from the top of your body at the crown of the head, route through the brain and then down along either side of the spine, through the backs of the legs, and all the way to the tip of the pinky toe. A small branch breaks away in the lumbar area to connect the Kidney and Urinary Bladder. One of the only channels that enters the brain, the Urinary Bladder channel is intimately connected to the autonomic nervous system and our fight-flight response. Clearing and balancing this channel releases stored tension, both physical and mental, and helps us respond to life with quiet confidence and ease.

Bright, brilliant blue is the color of the Kidneys. Take a moment to see in your mind's eye the area of the Kidneys glowing with a gleaming blue, infusing the space around them like a light mist. On your next exhale, make the healing sound of this Organ, *Chooooooooo*. Purse the lips as you exhale, touching the tip of your tongue to the front top of the mouth to create a nearly silent breathy sound as though saying the beginning of "choose." *Chooooooooo*...soft, soothing...changing the energies of any anxiety or fear into tranquility. *Chooooooooo*.

Jing, Qi, and Shen – The Three Treasures

As we've discussed, there are many different forms of Qi manifested from the same universal Qi. Chinese Medical Theory recognizes three treasured kinds of Qi that enable and preserve human life: *Jing (essence)*, *Qi (energy)*, and *Shen (spirit)*. Each of the Three Treasures is a distinct phase of Qi, just as ice, liquid water, and steam are all H_2O. These invaluable, subtle essences are held in an energy center in the body called a Dan Tian, or elixir field, until the body requires their use.

The densest Qi of the three, Jing is the life-sustaining essence that builds our physical tissues, supporting our physical vigor and nourishing the health of our flesh and bones. Jing is the substance that fuels the construction and growth of the temple of our body. Inherited from our parents like our DNA, Jing is known as the Seed of Life and is the necessary force behind our growth, maturation, healthy reproduction, and aging.

Take your attention to the low belly now, perhaps placing your hands on your abdomen just below the navel. Focus wholly on the area under the palms of your hands. Sense the journey of your breath as it is reflected in the rise and fall of your belly. This place that moves up and down with the breath is the center known as the Lower Dan Tian, also called the Sea of Qi. It holds Jing. The Lower Dan Tian is like a battery, storing the essential energy that powers our very constitution. This space, the cradle of our essence and keeper of our most fundamental substance, is the focus of many Taoist energetic practices and meditations due to its prominent role in our health and longevity. When we power this internal battery, the battery powers us. The Kidneys are important neighbors of the Lower Dan Tian, working together as an energetic feed and spark for our Organs and the body as a whole.

In addition to the Jing we inherit, we receive additional Jing through the food we eat and the air we breathe. The Spleen and Lungs are integral to this process, transforming Jing into Qi, the second of the Three Treasures. This form of Qi is the specific form of energy that powers our human physical and mental day-to-day functions. This phase breathes life into the structure of our body's tissues, and through the work of the Organs, sustains our mental and emotional functioning as well. Qi circulates with blood through the channels, fueling cellular metabolism and physical movements, the healthy experience and release of emotions, and the proper functioning of our brains. Qi impacts how we feel, think, and act. A candle is a common image used to describe the relationship between these energies. The candle's wax and wick represent energetic substance and potential of Jing, while Qi is the flame.

Rising from the Lower Dan Tian, Jing is transformed into Qi, and although Qi is stored in various Organs, its primary generation and storage center is the Middle Dan Tian. Move your hands to the center of the chest where the Middle Dan Tian lies. Below your hands, the Heart and Lungs are doing their beneficial work of transformation and circulation, sending Qi to every Organ and cell. Situated between the Lower and Upper Dan Tians, the Middle Dan Tian is considered the bridge between physical matter and our spirit, the final and most refined of our Three Treasures.

Spirit is the essence called Shen. The transformation of Qi into Shen as it rises toward the head completes the energetic cycle. Shen is our highest consciousness where the heavens meet the earth, the divine spark in our human form. Just as the flame of a candle burns wax to offer light, Shen is this radiance within us, the brightness shining in our eyes. Shen moves through the body within our blood vessels and resides in the Upper Dan Tian, which is in the brain behind the space of the third eye center. Bring your attention now to the place between your eyes and let it travel inward toward the center of the brain. Let your body relax as you focus more and more on this space. Allow all tension to release from your legs, your arms, your shoulders, neck, and face. Easeful yet attentive, open your awareness to any sensations, visions, or emotions that arise.

Shen is also held in the Heart, governor of the mind. Because of this, Shen is sometimes referred to as the heart-mind. Heart-mind energy is associated with refined self-awareness and the sense of intimate unity and interconnection we share with others and all of the universe. Let your awareness linger for some time in this intuitive place, opening into the endless expanse of our shared reality and collective destiny.

These Three Treasures animate all aspects of who we are, and as we work to protect and cultivate them, we aid our natural, internal alchemy. Supporting the refinement of these energies by moving them through the three Dan Tian reservoirs is a primary aim of our energetic enhancement practices. Through our physical postures, mindful breathing, and meditation techniques, we have the opportunity to support the natural cycle of transformation of Jing into Qi and Qi into Shen.

Yin Yoga & Meditation Creates Flow

While our internal energetic architecture may seem somewhat hidden and mysterious, the basic premise and foundational principles we put to use in Yin Yoga & Meditation to tend it are relatively uncomplicated. Harmonious flow is helpful; stagnation, deficiency, and imbalance are not. When an obstacle disrupts a Qi channel, flow becomes sluggish just as falling boulders could turn a mountain stream into a trickle. Eventually, physical discomfort, pain, or even illness may arise. Because the Organs are the home of our emotions, this kind of energetic imbalance can also impact our ability to express our feelings and cloud our perception. Within us, these energetic boulders can come from conscious or unconscious tensions, anxieties, and hurts tucked within us. When our subtle energies are re-invigorated and evenly distributed, physical health improves and the accumulated Qi flows in support of our overall wellbeing. Tending our energetic selves tends our physical body, too, so bringing balance and flow to our energetic architecture before problems manifest physically becomes a preventative practice.

On our mat, we get to become Qi cultivators. We encourage energetic flow and freedom by sensing, moving, and clearing Qi along its channels to promote replenished flow to our Organ Systems. Yin Yoga & Meditation offers us the opportunity to develop our Qi sensing and harnessing skills and to send energy where it's most needed, restoring it to its natural, balanced state. In the postures, we apply the acu-pressure of physical twisting, bending, tugging, compression, and decompression to our connective tissues to gently nudge our Qi channels open and create space for energy to flow where it's needed. Our awareness serves as an assistant to guide and gather energy into areas that feel stuck, tense, or congested. In energy worker circles, we hear the phrase, "Energy flows where the mind goes." In other words, our attention is like an energy magnet and with it, we're able to help bolster and harmonize the flow of energy within us.

> Inhale when we're born, exhale when we die...all the breaths in between determine the quality of Qi, the quality of life.
>
> – *Taoist adage*

The way we breathe also impacts our subtle energy body's workings. How encouraging it is that such an effective tool for longevity and transformation is always at our disposal! Using a variety of ancient Taoist and Yogic techniques, we'll be learning many ways to work skillfully with the breath to accumulate, cultivate, and circulate Qi through the channels. For example, we might choose to employ our breath as an energetic broom, sweeping away blockages so Qi moves more freely. Relaxing and releasing the body, we support a robust, even flow, which also creates space for any related mental or emotional tensions to jostle free and patterns of holding to rise and release. Joining the acu-pressure of our postures with compassionate awareness, mindful breathing, and Yoga Nidra relaxation techniques, we help clarify and strengthen our Qi to ensure it reaches all the Organs as they do their indispensable work. Striking a balance between this more conscious engagement with our subtle energy body and space for us to simply *be*, we allow the natural wisdom of the body to continue the process of harmonizing and optimizing the flow of Qi within us. The "Taoist-Inspired Energy Cultivation Methods" section includes a sampling of Yin asana flows with posture sequences and guided techniques to support balance and flow within each of the yin-yang Organ pairs.

Perhaps you turn your attention inward once more. Allow yourself to take in your magnificence in this moment: you are alive, breathing, humming with energy and light on a planet that is rare beyond comprehension. See within yourself the little rivers of energy flowing. With your gentle gaze, paint each Qi channel with a golden light shining, top to bottom, bottom to top, shining, shining, until you are lit from within, thousands of tiny rivers flowing balanced and strong. Let yourself steep with reverence and reverie at the astonishing being of light that you are. Appreciate and celebrate the goodness of these glowing lines running to, through, and all around your heartspace. See the glowing lines within you traveling outward, joining the lines of the others in your home, in your neighborhood, your country, and all through the world. Keep seeing the lines extending outward and outward, joining the lines running from everyone else, from all that is. Feel in this moment how you are in the world, and the world, too, truly is in you.

The Mind Layer

As we continue to explore the mysteries of the layers of our being, we're now entering into the territory of the mind. Auspicious questions like *What is consciousness? Where is the mind?* and *Who am I?* have occupied great mystics and thinkers throughout history. We're certainly not going to answer all these questions here, but as we proceed with this scan, let's continue to engage with them through our inner experience. Allow your inside eyes to rise to the sophisticated and surprising space of the mind, the place where incoming information from the external world is received and remembered, processed, and transformed into thought, word, and deed.

Yogi Achala has told the story about standing next to the Mississippi River one day with his young child. Looking at the river as it slowly flowed by, his son asked if the river was polluted. Kneeling beside him, Yogi Achala explained that the river was pure, it just carried the pollution. Like the waters of the Mississippi, our mind carries thoughts but is not made of them. We needn't identify ourselves as our thoughts, no more than we'd identify the river as any impurities flowing within it.

Rolling as though carried by a river through our mind, our thoughts are influenced by and responsive to both the sympathetic and parasympathetic nervous systems. Sometimes placid and peaceful, sometimes rough and roiling, thoughts are nearly ever-present companions in our internal landscape, narrating, judging, solving, evaluating, and instructing.

The Movements of the Mind

> One of the most compassionate and revolutionary breakthroughs we can have is to realize we are not our thoughts.
>
> – *Tara Brach, Ph.D.*

Think again of how the river's surface carries a twig along, bouncing and bobbing, tossed about by the current's flow. Let your attention fall downward through the commotion at the surface, coming to rest in the stillness of your fundamental steady awareness. Just as we trained the attention on the interior physical tissues, let's shift our focus now to the waves that thoughts make as they move through the waters of the mind.

For the next two to three minutes, commit to noticing what's traveling through the river of your mind. Each time a thought appears, tag it by giving it a name. Let the thought come, name it, and then let the thought go. Keep your tagging simple: *worrying thought...happy thought...remembering thought...anxious thought...wondering thought.* If it's too challenging to find a specific name right away, that's OK. You may give it a generic tag instead: *thought... thought... thought.* See if you can detect each thought without being swept away by it or getting entangled in it. Try to avoid any tones of impatience or judgment as you're tagging, staying gentle instead. After a few minutes of watching your thoughts, take note with curiosity which thoughts appeared, how many there were, and if there were any patterns.

Acknowledging and naming thoughts is a valuable process because each time we label a thought, we become aware of it as a thing that's happening within us rather than believing that it is who we are. We understand that it's separate from us. We recognize, for example, that if we're thinking an impatient thought, that doesn't mean impatience defines us, nor that we are an impatient person.

Realizing this, even stormy thoughts that are wild with emotion and energy begin to lose their power over us and we're able to maintain better emotional control of ourselves. With awareness comes the opportunity for choice and change. Our intention in thought-watching is not to prevent thoughts from happening but rather to train ourselves to pay attention to them on purpose, to give them our intentional attention so we become more adept at working with, rather than against, the movements of the mind. In seeing the transient nature of our thoughts as they come and go, we're coaching the mind to more consistently and reliably reside in the present moment. Thich Nhat Hanh called this process "shining the light of mindfulness."

In our meditative approach to Yin Yoga, we hone our natural ability to become aware of each thought as it arises without being derailed by it. There's a joking expression, "I've been through some terrible things in my life, some of which actually happened." This is a good reminder that although thoughts are real things, they aren't necessarily facts. Watching the mind closely with curiosity will allow us to discover that much of what we worry about never actually happens. Yin Yoga & Meditation gives us practice in climbing down out of our heads and coming home to our bodies to inhabit each moment with as much pure presence as possible.

The brain is designed to think and generate thoughts. Whether our thoughts happen to be peaceful or problematic, they're natural visitors in the landscape of the mind. In Buddhist circles, we encounter the term "monkey mind," a particularly apt image for the unsettled, restless, and capricious way our thoughts sometimes swing through the mind like monkeys jumping from one tree branch to another. The extent of the internal conversations we have with ourselves is almost comical at times. Maybe you've seen the cartoon showing a man driving a car through what appears to be a vast expanse of featureless desert. To the right there's a highway sign reading, "Just you and your own tedious thoughts next 200 miles." I'm guessing we're all familiar with that feeling!

No matter how raucous or cacophonous our mental chatter becomes, we can practice shifting our intention to watching. Noticing the movements of the mind further matures our attentional muscles and our capacity to perceive the stream of thoughts without blindly believing everything they're saying. Like a talkative companion, the mind has a propensity to comment, judge, and tell all kinds of stories. We don't need to remove or vanquish all this narrative critique, but we can recalibrate our relationship to it.

As we've learned, we all have the capacity to be conscious gardeners of the mind. The more we pay attention to our thoughts, the more we recognize our mind's behaviors and become aware of patterns. Our mental habits aren't things that just happen to us. Allowing our intention to lead our attention is a transformational decision as we garden with purpose. Thought watching then becomes another pathway of discovery as we continue to learn about the workings of our mind. As we observe the stream of thoughts moving through us, labeling supports our awareness as well as the inquiry process. You may reflect mentally or journal directly after thought-watching meditation exercises as a helpful way to record any insights that arise, inquiring:

- Do I notice the same thoughts are on repeat in a habitual pattern?
- What will I do, if anything, about what I'm perceiving?
- Are there any other circumstances in which I might benefit from consciously acknowledging my thoughts?
- Is there anything else here for me to discover?

We don't always get to choose the thoughts we think, but as we improve our capacity to observe them, we have more choices as to how we want, and don't want, to respond. The more regularly we steady our attention, the easier the steadying process will become. As we practice identifying and observing untrue thoughts, we continue to lessen their power to produce more like them, just as weeds plucked from the roots can't multiply. Over time and with diligent effort, we receive the fruit of our practice and increasingly experience ourselves as a place and purveyor of peace.

The mind has many moods, and its activities are perceptible in our predominant brainwave patterns at any moment. As you remember, beta waves are the waves of our conscious mind in daily life: rapid, active, jagged. The senses are engaged, and we're acting and reacting. We include some moments to simply arrive at the beginning of the Yin Yoga & Meditation session because there's a tendency to bring those choppy beta brainwaves with us when we come to the mat. There's no need to judge or fight against an active mind. This is an opportunity to appreciate the brain's natural, sharp responsiveness and give it a chance to quiet so we can focus on our inner landscape.

As the mind begins to quiet and stabilize, it moves into alpha brainwaves, which are slower, less erratic, and more synchronous. Experiencing alpha waves, you're still aware of the external world, but you're not quite as reactive. Instead of driving a race car, it's more like you're sitting contemplatively under a beautiful tree in the park, happily watching the world. This brainwave is typical during light meditation, and interestingly, this is the dominant brainwave pattern we experience as children: calm, creative, and content.

As we move into more profound relaxation, we experience theta brainwaves. Theta waves are even slower and smoother yet. Our senses become more internalized, as in a deeper meditative state. Theta waves don't have any pesky editors or censorship, no *don't do this* or *don't think that*. With theta brainwave patterns, we get those *aha!* moments of intuitive insight, sudden answers arising seemingly out of nowhere as gifts from the subconscious mind. Albert Einstein said he came up with his theory of relativity in what sounds like a theta wave moment, as he imagined himself riding a sunbeam.

As you observe thoughts, to help settle the attention onto the flow of the mind, you might try a breath mantra which makes use of a river image:

Breathing in, mind like a river.
Breathing out, thoughts always flowing.
Breathing in, I climb out the water and sit on the riverbank.
Breathing out, letting the river of thoughts flow by.
Breathing in, I'm aware of my thoughts.
Breathing out, I appreciate my thoughts.
Breathing in, mind like a river.
Breathing out, letting the river of thoughts flow by.

As we compassionately observe the mind sliding from thought to thought, we climb out of the stream and watch with clarity and tenderness the magnificent miracle it is instead of twirling around with every swirling thought. When we begin to recognize the thoughts we're carrying at any moment, we're able to inquire: *Is this thought helpful? Does it serve me? Will I believe it or chase it? Does this thought define me?* Giving ourselves the space to inquire brings clarity to what's moving through the mind.

Thoughts happen in the mind, but we also feel them in the body. Therefore, as we watch the mind, we benefit from observing the body as well. The Yogis and the Taoists teach us that layers of our personality engage and interact. The state of the body affects the mind, and the state of the mind affects the body. Many studies have indicated that holding specific postures increases confidence, responsiveness, and positivity.[3] If we're feeling a little blue, we might slump in our chair and curl inward. Our breathing might also be affected, becoming more shallow. By investigating how thoughts feel in our bodies, we experience the intimate interplay of this interconnection. Identifying what's happening in our physical tissues can shed light on what's happening in our minds.

Whatever We're Doing, We're Training in Something

Just as the Yin Yoga poses help to remodel our connective tissues, meditation helps to remodel the mind. At the heart of Mindfulness teachings is a simple yet profound truth: whatever we're doing, we're always training in something. This is true in everyday activities we regularly perform, and it's also true of the thoughts we repeatedly think. Once considered static in structure, we now know the brain's tissues and circuitry grow and change based on training and environment. The brain generates new brain cells and creates new neural connections. We call this neuroplasticity, and it means we can rewire the brain to follow new thought and response patterns.

Meditation is literally a brain-changing practice, priming brain cells to fire together in patterns that strengthen areas involved with decision-making, memory, and emotional flexibility. A 2005 Harvard study showed that Mindfulness Meditation thickens tissue in the prefrontal cortex, an area of the brain associated with cognitive and emotional processing and wellbeing. Other studies showed meditation caused growth in the hippocampus, the center of memory and learning, and shrinkage in the amygdala, the region that initiates our stress response.[4]

Neuroplasticity expert and author of the best-selling *The Emotional Life of Your* Brain, Dr. Richard Davidson points out that all this research is ultimately very encouraging. Meditation remodels the brain to strengthen the qualities of happiness: resilience, equanimity, calm, and compassionate connection with others. Davidson explains, "There's fundamentally no difference between well-being and learning to play a musical instrument. If you practice, you'll get better." We can use Mindfulness Meditation as that training. Through meditation, we strengthen our natural ability to be present for all of the magic of life and for each other, even in the tough spots.

All of us adopt certain habits of thinking and behaving, and as we might come to recognize, they're not all helpful. The heartening news is that with awareness, we learn to more skillfully identify and strengthen positive thought patterns and release negative ones. Once aware of our mental patterns, we can consciously select those we want to reinforce and dismantle those that aren't helpful, replacing them with new, more positive habits. Think of a wire that runs from a light switch to a light fixture – it exists, but it's not permanent. If we were to remove that wiring, the light wouldn't turn on, no matter how many times we flipped that switch. Similarly, a trigger in life might occur and flip that switch, but if we've dismantled the thought wiring, the lamp won't flare.

A dear friend once shared a story about her father's work as an electrician, which has stayed with me as an inspiring image of the brain as a connected network, able to be shaped and reshaped. She spoke of how entranced she was as a little girl with the intricate, colorful networks of electrical wires throughout the walls and ceilings of houses. She loved the way they streamed into hidden places to carry the invisible magic of electricity. She saw her father as a Magician Electrician of sorts, amazed at how he knew what went where, which tangles needed to go, and how to put new, more organized wiring in place.

She remembered going with him to one old farmhouse with particularly chaotic wiring and asking him why the owners had made it that way if it didn't work. "Well," he said, "sometimes people start with things one way, and they work OK at first, but over the years, as the house grows, the wires keep adding up following that same messy pattern, and it ends up like this," inefficient or even dangerous. Then it takes a Magician Electrician like her father to come in to reclaim order, re-lay the wires in ways that help the house rather than hurt it.

The neural networks in the brain that power a thought or behavior are just like this. The more often we think a thought or behave in a certain way, the more likely we are to repeat it because neurons that fire together wire together, even if the thought or behavior pattern harms instead of helps us. But unlike those old farmhouses, we don't have to call in an expert. We can be our own Magician Electrician. Through time tested meditation techniques and a commitment to mindful choosing, we can begin to dismantle the tangles that keep us from living the life we want and create new and more empowering connections in our brain. As though standing in a dark room, we get to decide: where do we want the electricity? Our thoughts create the wiring. We're always surrounded by many potential pathways to happiness, and our journey continues intentional step by intentional step.

So, what do *you* want to experience? What do *you* want to see?

Compassionate Repatterning

A young monk went to his Zen Master to bemoan the fact that another monk had criticized him. "Master," he said, "how could he call me foolish? He has no right to call me a fool! How dare he call me a fool. I'll get back at him for calling me foolish!"

The Master put his hand on the young man's shoulder and asked, "My son, do you know what you've just done?" The monk shook his head. With kindness, the old man said, "Why, you've just allowed your brother to call you a fool four more times."

By repeating his brother's insults, the young monk not only relived their sting, but he also began creating the thought wiring that might convince him the words were true. The movements of our minds create mental patterns, both positive and negative. The more often a pathway is used, the more likely it is to be repeated. In the foothills behind our house, mule deer take repeated journeys following the same line through the landscape, brushing desert scrub away and creating a well-worn path in the ground that aids easier travel. Just like the deer wearing a pathway through the hill, we wear grooves in the mind. Meditation exercises offer us the chance to practice identifying what tracks the mind is pacing and to choose: *Is this the groove I want to tread, or is there a new pathway I'd like to tend?*

Many of our thoughts are not only repetitive, they're also unconscious. This is why the work we're doing to awaken to our thoughts is so powerful and important. When we grow quiet, it's amazing what we might hear! While on retreat with Thich Nhat Hanh at Blue Cliff Monastery, the bulk of our time was spent in sacred silence, so we all enjoyed the evening discussions led by the monastics. Our small group circle was led by Brother Phap Dung and Sister Hy Nghiem. Both leaders were so warm, humble, and insightful as we circled up and processed our experiences from the day.

My group was filled with fellow educators, and among them was a bright-spirited woman in her sixties who was blessed with a special way of making everyone smile. One evening, she shared that spending most of the days in silence had highlighted for her how much inner commentary she had that she'd never really heard before. Even more, as the days spent in silence went on, the initial mental chatter had quieted and revealed yet another hidden layer of self-talk. "I'm noticing so much judging commentary babbling on," she exclaimed, "I had no idea how judgmental I was!" All of us in the circle nodded in recognition, having been experiencing the same thing ourselves. Brother Dung and Sister Nghiem encouraged us to stay kind and take the opportunity to be a caring friend to ourselves. It's good guidance for us all. As we continue to awaken to the workings of our minds, we remember – thoughts might be real, but they're not always true and they're certainly not the whole of who we are.

As we get better at listening within, we begin encountering more subtle layers of conversation that we might not even realize are there. It may seem easier said than done, but being a compassionate witness to the words that are flowing through the mind allows us to pause and consider if a particular conversation loop we've identified is helpful or not. Perhaps we find an opportunity to pull a weed and plant a positive seed, for example, replacing a nervous thought with an encouraging one. Once we've identified these inner conversations, it's up to us to decide which thought loops are worth nourishing.

Silence can be a difficult place because often it's there that we meet habitual thought patterns, mistaken beliefs, and judging commentaries. We don't have to join a week-long silent retreat at a monastery on top of a mountain to encounter this space of silence. We uncover it in the still space of our posture or inhabiting the pauses inherent in our breath. Wherever you find it, bring kindness to the streams of thoughts you encounter, resisting any temptation to immediately ignore or judge. Remember that like the Mississippi River, our most natural self, that pure awareness underlying all of who we are, is separate from what it carries.

Beginning with a Beginner's Mind

In the beginner's mind, there are many possibilities, but in the expert's mind, there are few.

– *Shunryu Suzuki Roshi*

It's said that a university professor visited Zen Master Nan-in to inquire about Zen. Nan-in brought out some tea, and while filling his guest's cup, he poured the tea up to the brim and then just kept on pouring. Watching tea spill onto the floor, the professor cried, "The cup is full, sir! You can't put any more in!"

Nan-in replied, "Just as this cup is full, so too are you full of your own thoughts and judgments. How shall I teach you Zen unless you begin by emptying your cup?"

When we allow ourselves to let go of what we think we know, we can learn a lot. Thich Nhat Hanh encouraged us to write three very important words on a piece of paper and put them on a wall or a mirror where we'll see them every day. Those three words are: *Are You Sure?* Asking *Am I sure?* is an easy way to empty our cup. *Shoshin* is the Zen Buddhist concept of beginner's mind, a willingness to take on a not-knowing attitude, free from preconceptions and set-in-stone notions. When we ask ourselves that question, we drop expectations and come out of mental autopilot mode, allowing us to open with a child-like curiosity. *What is this? Do I need to do that? Is this assumption accurate? Is what I'm saying to myself true?* Practicing not-knowing helps us offer ourselves and those we love a refreshed perspective, and in the end, experience a truer perception of our experiences.

The mind has a way of solidifying around past stories, opinions, and beliefs. The brain wants to fill in the gaps of any story or experience, just as it instantly fills the gaps of missing letters in a sentence on a page. However, it isn't always adept at cracking those beliefs or stories back open for reevaluation when new information or inspiration arrives. This tendency isn't something to judge or feel badly about, it's simply a fact of how the brain functions. Understanding this helps us approach our training in present moment awareness with greater clarity, compassion, and patience.

In his book *The Mindful Brain*, Dr. Daniel Siegel explains that the brain's prefrontal cortex is layered like the bark of a tree, with six layers in all. Sensory stimuli enter from the external world through our senses. The information then travels through the midbrain at the base of the brain into the prefrontal cortex in the frontal lobe. Here's the catch: while the incoming information is traveling upward from the midbrain, a message is sent downward from the top layer of the prefrontal cortex to identify what is being sensed. The external information rising up joins the data coming down, and voilà, we have a perception. Unfortunately, perception is not always necessarily complete and correct! When these two streams of information meet in the middle, the brain stops processing the new message, falling short of fully perceiving the new external stimuli. Said another way, our autonomic biological processing of external stimuli slants, or weights, our perception toward what used to be true. By default, we perceive the present through the filter of the past.

Therefore, in each moment, our perceptions of our partner, child, colleagues, as well as situations and surroundings are influenced by *what they used to be* rather than simply *what they are now.* Evolved for efficiency, our brains think they have enough information about a person, so although we look with our eyes in the present time, we may not always see each other truly as we currently are. When we intervene using practices that help the brain receive each moment with a newly found freshness, we improve our ability to interact and connect with the person as they are, or the situation as it is, in the present moment. Through Mindfulness practices, we train the attention to stay in the here and now to better overcome that biological default and allow ourselves to encounter each moment and each person anew, freed from the filters of previous conditioning.

With practice, we get better and better at perceiving new information and new possibilities. Thich Nhat Hanh's suggestion is a useful place to start: *Am I sure?* For example, have you ever arrived to your mat with a preconceived idea of what your body was able to do or not do that day? At work, have you ever gone into a meeting already convinced of what the response was going to be to a new idea, or entered into a conversation with a loved one already certain of how it would turn out? Science tells us that certainty might just be our brains recycling past information. In Yin Yoga & Meditation, we can use a variety of meditative exercises like Mindfulness concentration techniques to nurture a sense of receptivity and wonder. I've included many examples in the "Meditative Methods" section and hope you'll enjoy experimenting with them and experience their abundant benefits for yourself.

The Heart Layer

As each of us experiences day after day, the range of human emotions is nearly infinite, and the human heart is home to them all. Able, abandoned, absorbed, addled, admirable, affable, affectionate, afraid, agreeable, aggravated, aggressive, amazed, ambivalent, amused, angry, annoyed, anxious, apprehensive, ashamed, astonished, awkward...these are just a handful that happen to begin with the letter A!

At any given moment, we're likely having at least one emotion, even if we're not necessarily conscious of it. Whether delightful, neutral, intriguing, or distressing, emotions almost perpetually wander through the vast landscape of the heart, and each is deserving of our loving attention and acceptance.

A Friendly Host

Welcoming the arrival of each emotion like a friendly host, we cultivate our natural capacity to open the door of our hearts with curiosity, warmth, and generosity. If you'd like, begin to take notice of the state of your heart right now, free of evaluation, judgment, or commentary about it. What feeling is here with you? Is it joy, contentment, sadness, worry, or something else? Try to feel this emotion in its entirety, all around its edges. Refrain from attempting to contain it or fence it in; there is no need to crowd it with thoughts, movement, or resistance of any other kind. Sense some space opening around it and enjoy these few moments, just being here however you are, breathing safe and relaxed on this good planet.

As you settle in with whatever feeling state is manifesting within you, consider how you might greet some friends who stopped by your home. You'd likely receive them warmly, invite them in, sit with them to listen and share, maybe serve some tea. After you'd spent some time together and they were ready to leave, you'd walk them to the door and send them off with a smile, right? Try imagining the feeling you're experiencing as this visiting loved one. Perhaps say the name of the feeling to yourself, or quietly speak it out loud: *Contentment, hello, thank you for being here. Worry, I see you. Gratitude, I'm glad you came to visit me. Tiredness, I feel you, it's OK that you're here. Joy, I sense you arising within me, welcome, welcome.* Breathe peacefully as you offer this emotion permission to exist in this moment, just a visitor and here for a short time.

> *Breathing in, I recognize this feeling is visiting me.*
> *Breathing out, hello my friend, I see you.*
> *Breathing in, I will call you by your name.*
> *Breathing out, dear friend I welcome you.*

Stay mindful of your breathing as you continue to expand your perception to encompass the flow of your breath. Sometimes, depending on what we're feeling, our breath becomes constricted, restricted in depth and duration. If you find this is happening, direct some gentle attention to the chest space to provide the lungs with more places to expand when they inhale, relaxing, relaxing. Breathe all the way in...give more freedom to the lungs to empty entirely when you exhale completely. Sense how giving more room for the breath can also offer more permission for the feeling to be exactly what and how it is.

With each breath, relax more and more. Releasing any tension in the body or in the mind, let your energy flow freely into every part of you. Expand the awareness further through you. Notice if the feeling is also making itself known in the tissues of the body. Offer this area of your body a gentle reception. As you observe your body, remain attentive to any ripples of emotions or physical sensations that follow. Here, we've settled into the final layer of being we'll explore in our Mandala Map, the heart.

Our Vast Emotional Landscape

> The best and most beautiful things in the world cannot be seen nor even touched, but just felt in the heart. Every day I find out something which makes me glad.
>
> – *Helen Keller*

The height, breadth, and depth of our emotional landscape is expansive. Some feelings are barely perceptible, while others blaze like a five-alarm fire. A 2015 study by Trampe, Quoidbach, and Taquet showed our everyday life "seems profoundly emotional," with participants reporting they experienced, on average, at least one emotion ninety percent of the time.[5]

Perhaps you'll try this brief reflection exercise. Take a few moments to jot down any emotions you felt today. Next, think further back to the last week. Add to your list the names of any feelings you remember experiencing within the last seven days.

Here are just a few possibilities to ponder: acceptance, anger, appreciation, boredom, curiosity, craving, confusion, compassion, calmness, disgust, envy, excitement, embarrassment, empathy, fear, gratitude, guilt, hope, helplessness, inspiration, joy, love, loneliness, nostalgia, pride, sympathy, satisfaction, sadness, or triumph.

Next, place a check mark beside each emotion you've listed to tally the number of times you remember experiencing that particular emotion within the last week. Take a few moments to look at what you've jotted down. Is the overall list surprising in any way? As you review your inventory, are there any specific entries that draw your attention? As you continue to reflect on the feelings you've listed, is there anything to discover?

In the Trampe et al study, would you like to take a guess as to which emotions the participants reported experiencing most frequently? Joy rated first, while love and anxiety rounded out the top three. Interestingly, they found not only were people experiencing an emotion almost all the time, but that people also reported often experiencing more than one feeling at a time. In fact, participants reported noticing at least one positive and one negative emotion simultaneously thirty-three percent of the time. Of these "mixed emotions" documented, the most common co-occurrence of positive and negative feelings was with anxiety and love.

Return to your list momentarily. Do you recall any instances where you noticed more than one emotion occurring simultaneously? Were there any times during the week when you experienced mixed emotions, a positive one intermingled with a challenging one?

This and other studies, such as one published in 2017 by Cowen and Keltner, suggest that not only are our emotional lives varied and variable, but that they are also a collection of fuzzy gradients rather than discrete and delineated occurrences.[6] Feelings blend into one another much as our tissues turn gradually from muscle into tendon and from tendon into bone.

In her book *A Stroke of Insight*, Dr. Jill Bolte Taylor writes that the average emotion lasts just a minute and a half from the time of its chemical conception in the brain until it processes itself through the body. The average feeling, whether it's confidence, irritation, loneliness, gratitude, joy, or despair, lives for just ninety seconds. What manifests in the mind *will* fall away, which means we're able to trust that even the most difficult emotions will pass when they're allowed to follow their natural course. Positive feeling states will also slide away, so we can take this as encouragement to cherish and spend time savoring them.

On the Yin Yoga & Meditation mat, we get the chance to watch our emotional landscape with care and can practice choosing to let our feelings live their natural, transitory existence without insisting on immediate intervention. When we notice an emotion, can we acknowledge it and then let it go in its own time? Training in recognizing each emotion and allowing it to be without judgment or reaction teaches us we're capable of embracing all of the feelings that are a part of our remarkable human experience. If we're feeling especially relaxed and happy, we can practice simply allowing those feelings to be there and to enjoy them while they are. We can offer the same allowing attention to less pleasant feelings too, letting them be how they are for as long as they are.

Because emotions are embodied, each feeling we experience will likely elicit some level of physical sensation in the body. Growing in body awareness helps us detect what emotions are emerging. If you're experiencing contentment or joy, for example, do you also feel a sense of warmth or buoyancy arising in your body? If you're feeling worry or anxiety, do you sense any tightening in the belly or the chest or any influence on the breath? Where does the feeling of generosity or inspiration manifest in your body? What about mischievousness or optimism?

Whatever the feeling is, we can train in inviting it in with friendliness, abiding with it as long as it lasts, free from judgment. Call it by its name using a soft tone. Stay present to feel it, then watch as it glides away, making room for another. As we practice being mindful of feelings in this way, we observe how fleeting each feeling really is, living for just a few moments in this expansive space of the heart in this precious span of time that is our life. We're reminded, too, that even when a feeling is strong, it's possible to experience it without becoming overwhelmed by it.

Feelings come and go like clouds in a windy sky. Conscious breathing is my anchor.

– *Thich Nhat Hanh*

Thich Nhat Hanh spoke of feelings as weather systems that move through our internal landscape, sometimes subtle and other times powerful. When the heavy winds of feelings blow, he encourages us to become like a tree. The top of the tree sways back and forth in the wind, and the branches and leaves toss and flutter. Looking at the tree, we see it also has a very stable trunk that is rooted deeply in the earth. Although the top of the tree shifts back and forth, the tree remains grounded and safe because of the trunk's stability.

When emotional storms come, we might find ourselves getting tossed around by those feelings, but just like the tree, we also have a strong core that is rooted and secure. We don't have to live our lives high up in the branches that sway and swing. To help us find our stable base, Thich Nhat Hanh advised that when the winds of feeling gather speed, we should get low to the earth and bring our attention to the place just below the navel. Following the movement of the abdomen as we breathe in and out, we recognize we're more than any single emotion that travels through us. Held with sureness on the solid ground, we remember the way back to our strong trunk, the core of calm that helps us weather the storm and not get taken away by it. He says that when you practice like this, your emotion will not be able to destabilize you anymore.

A Gateway to Healing the Heart

Theories like Somatic Experiencing© and Body Memory Theory hold that emotions may be stored outside the mind and captured in the cells and tissues of the body. Perhaps you've encountered the idea through the term "issues in the tissues." Researchers such as Peter Levine Ph.D., Bessel van der Kolk, M.D., and Pat Ogden, Ph.D. have explored these concepts in their work. Whether or not emotions and experiences have the capacity to be stored external to the mind, it's useful to consider the physical associations of memory and how certain memories and experiences sometimes settle into patterns of physical holding.

Emotions are finite chemical reactions in the brain. We feel them in the moment, and we feel them as memory too. Specific sights, sounds, or smells have the ability to acutely resurrect very specific emotions from a certain place or time from the past. We might experience some physical reaction to a difficult memory, maybe hunching the shoulders in a protective response, holding the abdomen with our hands as though we have a stomachache, or the tightening of facial muscles into a frown. These habitual responses may, over time, become chronic physical patterns.

The body of research on trauma and its ongoing, chronic impact on our physical body and mental health is growing. Dr. van der Kolk asserts that trauma narrows our window of tolerance for challenging emotions and could prime a person to have the fight-flight response activated on an ongoing basis by seemingly minor stressors. Trauma, he believes, results in the erosion of a person's ability to experience not just challenging emotions but *all* emotions, even positive ones. His studies highlight how engaging the physical body has the potential to help us regulate our emotions and repair our mind-body connection.

In a similar vein, Dr. Levine believes the healing of trauma to be mainly a biological rather than psychological process. In other words, working with the physical body becomes a gateway to healing the heart. His Somatic Experiencing© method offers techniques to retrain the central nervous system, helping the patient locate where the fight-flight patterns have become engrained in the tissues of the body and release them. As the body invites, patterns of tension unwind, and stored stresses may release.

In Yin Yoga postures, as we meet physical thresholds in the body, we may also be meeting mental, emotional, and spiritual boundaries. Mindfully maintaining mild sensation is an act of caring, precaution, and potential healing. Striving or moving too quickly could be harmful, not just to our yin tissues but also to any emotional ripples in that area. The body, mind, and heart are like intersecting universes. What happens in one creates impressions in the others. Listening inward and remaining responsive, we allow the tissues of the body to point us to the inner places that need nurturing. Areas of tension or discomfort have a lot to tell us and can begin to untangle when we're able to maintain compassionate awareness, rather than avoiding, ignoring, or judging them.

The physical tightness that often accompanies difficult emotions can, if sustained, develop into an accumulated armor of musculature and fascial patterning. This may, to some degree, restrict the flow of Qi within us. The pressurization of tissues in a Yin Yoga posture may elicit a particular emotion near areas holding energetic blockages. Imbalance in the Kidneys, as we've learned, is linked to feelings of fear and apprehension, so postures such as Dragonfly that stimulate the inner leg line tissues through which the Kidney Qi channel flows could therefore initially generate a feeling of anxiousness as energy harmonizes and strengthens.

As we practice Yin Yoga & Meditation, we naturally will feel all sorts of things, some which may not always be physically or emotionally comfortable. By releasing judgment or other forms of resistance such as distraction or disregard for what we're feeling, we can offer the emotion the room it needs to be there. Relaxing the musculature allows any holding in the tissues to loosen, and any emotion ready for release can surface when it's ready. Feeling can contribute to healing, so we work mindfully and tenderly with ourselves in this practice. We can choose to back away from any boundary if the time isn't right.

If in your practice a feeling becomes overwhelming, or if additional resources would be helpful in working through anything you encounter, give yourself the permission and encouragement to reach out to a friend or professional counselor for added support. You can always invite yourself to rest in the peace of simply sitting on the earth, held steady in this present time, appreciating the flow of your breath. Trust the wisdom of your body and that you'll know when the time is right.

The root wisdom traditions of Yin Yoga & Meditation tell us that to fully understand one thing, we must be able to understand its opposite. To know sunshine is also to know shadow. You might think of everything as one side of a coin: happiness and sadness, heat and cold, near and far, apathy and inspired commitment. Chances are you've heard the Zen saying, "No mud, no lotus" that speaks to how the beautiful lotus flower requires its uglier counterpart, mud, in order to grow. This is both a botanical fact and a metaphor for how the soil of suffering has the capacity to grow joy and happiness. Human beings have a tendency to desire positive, happy feelings and avoid more difficult ones. Not something to judge, this is simply an inheritance from our ancestors who required it for daily survival. However, if we allow our capacity to feel difficult emotions to diminish, we might also dampen our ability to fully cherish positive ones like joy, contentment, and gratitude.

In this practice, we hone our ability to be an unjudging, welcoming observer of whatever feeling arises, whether pleasant or unpleasant. We experience first-hand the changeable nature of emotions and embodied sensations, and, over time, become better at managing difficult feelings and situations and more consistent in treasuring and embracing the uplifting ones. We understand that whatever we're feeling, it won't last forever. Recognizing the impermanence of all emotional states reminds us how important it is to savor all the good things we encounter and let them be a buoy and a light.

In the "Yoga Nidra-Inspired Methods" section, we'll explore an exercise called "Greeting Opposites for Experiencing Both Sides of the Coin" to help us gently investigate any unconscious reactions to certain experiences or feelings and develop our ability to welcome whatever emotional guests arrive. Being able to pay attention, acknowledge our experience, and sustain an open and welcoming presence allows us to pair yang activity (noticing) with yin receptivity (allowing). We see that our feelings have a right to exist, and each will, when left to its own accord, fade away. As we cultivate a welcoming relationship with them, our emotions – even challenging ones – begin to transform into insightful teachers and even friends.

Connecting with the Compassionate Heart Within

We all have some hard-wired tendencies that may, at times, challenge our ability to respond compassionately. Have you heard of the theory known as the bystander effect? The body of research around it is remarkable and unsettling. The bystander effect posits that people are less likely to help someone when they know or believe other people are present. Additionally, the greater the number of bystanders, the less likely a person is to offer help.

Beginning in 1968, psychologists John Darley and Bibb Latané conducted a set of experiments to discover why people fail to act on behalf of others even in scenarios where the person may be in danger. In one of their studies, the subjects were led individually to a room purportedly to engage in discussions related to urban life. However, while the subjects waited for the discussion, the actual study began. A heavy stream of smoke was made to flow from a heating vent in the conference room, accumulating in the air enough to even obscure their vision. Some of the study subjects waited in the smoke-filled room alone, while others waited among various actors recruited to play the part of fellow participants.

Can you guess what happened? Seventy-five percent of subjects waiting alone in the room reported the smoke quickly. When joined by two or more people privy to the experiment, however, only ten percent of subjects reported the presence of smoke, even though the smoke caused them to cough, rub their eyes, and open the window. That statistic is astonishing, and unfortunately, Darley and Latané found it wasn't an anomaly.

These two researchers performed additional experiments of the same type, including one where subjects were greeted by a receptionist who then went behind a curtain and noisily climbed onto a chair as though to pull something from a high shelf. Hidden out of sight, the receptionist played a tape featuring a loud crash and cries for help, complete with moaning, "Help...my ankle...I can't get this thing off of me!" Nearly three quarters of solitary participants checked on the receptionist, but when staged actors were present with them in the room, that figure dropped to a mere seven percent. Many variations on these kinds of experiments have been done, and the findings have largely remained the same. As psychiatrist Joel Dimsdale put it in his book *Anatomy of Malice*, "In social situations, there is a diffusion of responsibility. If a bystander sees that other witnesses are doing nothing, then he or she will also do nothing."

We can take heart, though - seven percent is not our destiny! A 2015 study by Lim, Condon, and DeSteno found that Mindfulness Meditation improves our ability and willingness to offer our fellow human beings caring assistance in times of need.[7] In this experiment, half of the study participants with no previous meditation experience met regularly with a master teacher who offered training and guidance in Mindfulness Meditation. The other half of participants, serving as the control group, received none. Eight weeks later, both groups were invited to come back in for cognitive testing. However, the real test again happened in the waiting room.

When participants arrived one at a time, they found a waiting room with three chairs, two of which were occupied by actors associated with the study. As expected, the participant took the third chair. A few minutes later, in hobbled a young woman on crutches with what appeared to be a broken foot. With nowhere left to sit, she sighed uncomfortably and propped herself against a wall, cringing in pain. The actors, as instructed, ignored the woman, while the researchers waited and watched for the participant's response. Would the participant give up their comfort to try to relieve her pain or stay seated and ignore it? In the answer lies great hope. While just sixteen percent of the control group gave up their chair to the woman on crutches, the proportion increased to half among the participants who had spent the last eight weeks practicing Mindfulness Meditation.

Those weeks of meditation increased the odds of acting to relieve another person's pain by threefold; this is all the more striking given that there were bystanders, which would typically attenuate such behavior. This study is the first to clearly show the power of meditation to increase compassionate response to suffering, even in the face of social pressure to ignore it. Offering a loving, open awareness, even for just a few moments, begins to soften the tougher edges inside us and around us, too. Looking with kindness crumbles the walls between us, even barriers that might initially feel impenetrable. Like the sunshine slowly, necessarily evaporates the morning dew, compassionate acknowledgement and response can change the world one heart and one interaction at a time.

You might now reorient your inside eyes on any feelings that are manifesting in you. Close your eyes if you'd like as you turn your attention once again to the center of your chest, the heartspace. Notice again what feeling tone is sharing this present moment with you. Where is it demonstrating itself in your physical tissues? Trace a line from your heart to that place in your body, a pathway of communication and caring. Quietly name the feeling to yourself, saying lovingly: *Hello dear feeling...I see you and I welcome you here with me right now.*

Chapter 5

Yin Yoga & Meditation Practice Principles

The practice principles of Yin Yoga & Meditation work collaboratively to awaken our internal wisdom and ensure our practice remains safe, effective, and inspirational. A practice guided by these principles offers a beautiful space to explore the who, what, how, where, when, and why of our being. They form a core element of our Mandala Map, because when the practice principles inform our approach, each pose and each moment can be an enlightening journey into ourselves. By observing them, we bring benefit, strength, and flexibility to our physical body and nurture ourselves as energetic, emotional, and spiritual beings.

In these pages, we'll cover the fundamentals behind each principle and how they serve us in our practice. Each helps us honor the natural structure and needs of our own unique bodies and consistently bring the greatest benefit to the whole of who we are. They form the basis of a holistic Yin Yoga & Meditation practice, so I encourage you to take your time with them and reflect on how you integrate them into your practice. If you teach, inquire how you share them with your students, whether experientially, through verbal prompts, visual cues, or any tangible techniques you build into a class session.

Practice Principle 1: Arrive to the Mat

I stood some years ago at the front of the Great Togetherness Meditation Hall of Blue Cliff Monastery in Pine Bush, New York, looking up at giant banners hanging over the altar which read, very simply: *I have really arrived...I am truly home.*

> The practice of mindfulness, of bringing the scattered mind home, and so of bringing the different aspects of our being into focus, is called Peacefully Remaining or Calm Abiding – this is a returning to our fundamental nature.
>
> – Sogyal Rinpoche

Taking a few breaths in and out, consciously and in peace, I invited myself to truly arrive. It was the first day of a week-long silent retreat with Zen Master Thich Nhat Hanh and the monks and nuns of his order, and the seven days that followed changed my life.

Throughout the retreat, Thich Nhat Hanh offered daily dharma talks, and a primary theme he repeated each day was the importance of arriving to the only place life ever happens: now. Most everything about the retreat was designed to help participants do just that, arrive with freshness into each moment. From signs on each step ("A mindful step"), to calligraphy on large boulders near the walking paths ("Go like a river"), to little notes with mantras called "gathas" near faucets ("Water flows from high mountain sources. Water runs deep in the Earth. Miraculously, water comes to us. I am filled with gratitude"), reminders to come home to ourselves in the present time were everywhere.

These messages weren't just written. During the course of each day, one of the monks or nuns would ring a massive "bell of Mindfulness" hanging in the courtyard three times. The instructions were that when the bell rang out, we should pause whatever we were doing and take three slow, conscious breaths, arriving back home to the now. This deliberate stopping to arrive is a foundational practice of presence, squaring the mind and body into the same place. I found that these moments of stopping opened so many possibilities in each moment and have regularly incorporated a bell of Mindfulness into my days ever since.

Thich Nhat Hanh's gatha for "Hearing the Bell" is so beautiful:

Listen, listen
This wonderful sound
Brings me back
To my true home.

The Practice Starts When We Stop

I learned a lot about myself on that retreat, from my unconscious habits of movement to the value of practicing the skill of stopping. Everyone was assigned to a small group of participants or "dharma family" for evening discussions as well as to perform work each day in support of the retreat. Our dharma family was assigned tea cart duty, so for about an hour every afternoon, we would clean and refill the tea carts with hot water and an assortment of teas. One afternoon, I apparently was really into my tea cart work and, lost in my head and lost in the task, I didn't hear the colossal Mindfulness bell ringing out less than ten feet away. Although hundreds of people surrounding me had stopped what they were doing to rest in silence with their breath, good little tea cart worker me continued to obliviously arrange the tea boxes! I still laugh imagining my face when I finally realized the world had stopped around me.

"Arrive to the Mat" is the first practice principle we explore in our Mandala Map. To begin our Yin Yoga & Meditation practice, we first have to stop and invite our attention to come into this new Now - which is sometimes easier said than done. Maybe you've heard the Zen joke about a man on a horse. The horse is galloping quickly, and it appears that the man on the horse is going somewhere important. A passerby on the road shouts, "Hey, where are you going?"

The rider yells back, "No idea, ask the horse!"

With so much to do each day and so little time, it's easy to understand how we might develop a tendency to stay on the move. The Yin Yoga & Meditation mat invites us to climb down off that galloping habit horse and pause, allowing our arrival to our practice to become a doorway into deeper concentration and insight.

Three Acknowledgements for Arriving

Arriving into the present moment draws a line through spacetime, a threshold we cross to enter the sacred space of Now. Taking a few meditative moments at the start of our Yin Yoga session offers the chance to steady the mind before beginning the Yin asana. Bringing a stabilized attention with us into the poses helps us stay safe and pay close and consistent attention to the sensations we feel.

Keeping the mind in one place can be challenging, and when we first arrive to our practice, our brain is likely in a beta wave pattern. As you'll remember, the smoother, more synchronous alpha wave pattern is more supportive of a relaxed, concentrated attention. The process of intentional arriving helps us learn to mindfully decelerate from the rush of the day as we land onto the mat, so stopping becomes important transitional training for the brain.

Touchpoints for the body, mind, and heart, these three acknowledgments can help us transition from what was to what is with a more precisely attuned internal awareness:

- Acknowledge that you're here.
- Acknowledge how you are.
- Acknowledge your intention for being here.

Acknowledge – I Am Here

When arriving to our practice, we can begin by simply acknowledging where on the good earth we are and the mat we're on. Perhaps you take a few meditative moments to acknowledge where you are in this moment using this guided technique for arriving:

Find a comfortable seated position.

Sit tall, allowing your strong back to support an open chest and heart.

Let go through the shoulders.

Rest the hands easily on the lap and feel the jaw and face soft.

Bring the mind to the body and the body to the earth.

Find the touchpoints where your body meets the ground.

Release tension in your muscles and allow yourself to be held by the solid points of the earth beneath you.

Feel yourself here in this space, settled onto earth, grounded in your body, grounded in right now.

Allow your breath to naturally flow. Enjoy this time of sitting and feeling the breath flow.

Alive, breathing, being right here on this earth.

Breathing in, I feel my body.

Breathing out, I know I'm here.

In, I feel my body.

Out, I know I'm here.

As your body settles, notice: Is there something tugging on your attention that you could let go of just for now, maybe a meeting or conversation from earlier in the day or anticipation of something coming later? If so, take a few slow breaths in through the nose, out through the mouth, and let it rest to the side for now...

Honor the effort you made to be here in this moment, your dedication to learning and growth. The dedication to taking good care of yourself.

Acknowledge the fact that you're here, right now, in this place.

The only thing that needs you is this slice of time.

Aware only of the present. For now, not looking to the past, not worrying about the future.

Enjoying it, here, just as it is.

As we locate our body in the Now, we also find our mind. As Thich Nhat Hanh said, "A miracle happens when the mind and body are in the same place." Did you know the word miracle is derived in part from the Latin *mirari*? *Mirari* means to be astonished and behold with rapt attention. When we arrive, we can behold this marked moment with wonder – we made it to our mat. With all the other things we could have chosen to do, here we are. The act of recognizing the effort we made to arrive honors our commitment to our practice.

Acknowledge – How Am I?

> The day you start your practice, your true progress will begin.
>
> – *Swami Kripalu*

The next acknowledgement invites us to notice how we are. You might try an internal scan of the body, mind, and heart to get a sense of how you've arrived here, tracing through all the layers of being. Whatever you find will be the perfect starting point. Even when we're not feeling how we necessarily want to feel, how we are is how we are, so that's where we start.

Perhaps you continue your arrival, allowing your attention to settle more deeply inward using the following brief guided scan:

As you breathe, invite your awareness to slide a bit more internally.

Letting external sounds fade away, attune to the sounds within the body now.

Listen for the sound of the breath, the sound of your heartbeat, the sound of the blood flowing through your body.

Take some time here to observe yourself, allowing things to be just as they are for now.

Notice – how are you feeling? Is there any information to gather or something to learn right now?

As you check in with yourself, offer the permission to be and feel however you're finding yourself, greeting yourself like you would a friend.

Start with your physical body. How do you sense the state of your body?

Move the attention briefly through the body from the feet up through the legs, the hips, torso, shoulders, and neck to the crown. Allow your body to communicate any areas that feel good, vital, healthy, as well as any areas that may need some release, healing, opening. Breathe softly as you scan.

Move now to the movements of the mind. What thoughts do you feel flowing? Are they moving quickly, or do you sense space between?

Slide your attention now to the space of the heart. How is your mood? Are there any emotions making themselves felt right now?

However you're finding yourself right now is a fine way to start. Whether the internal weather systems are quiet or stormy, or your physical tissues feel tight and tired or open and at ease, they're all good places to begin. There's no perfect physical, mental, or emotional state we need to be in when we arrive, no condition except the one we're in right now.

Here on the mat, we have the opportunity to encounter ourselves and truly honor whatever we find. In these pages, you'll find a number of scanning techniques for you to use to support your arrival to the mat.

Acknowledge – What is My Why?

The most important thing is to find what is the most important thing.

– *Shunryu Suzuki Roshi*

principle

Maybe you've heard the story of an aging king who was childless and seeking an heir. This ruler was a good man and wanted to make sure his kingdom was well-cared for after his death. He was also reasonably egalitarian, so he decided to allow anyone who was interested to apply for the job and invited everyone to arrive at the same time. To ensure no one would appear more impressive than another of lesser means, he granted access to the royal wardrobe and everyone was allowed to wear whatever they wished for the evening.

The day of the royal interview party came, and the king waited upstairs with his ministers while the applicants prepared for the interview. There was a huge feast laid out for them, and everybody was thrilled at the potential of being king or queen. When they arrived, they used the royal bathhouses with special soaps and spent hours dressing and talking and flirting and admiring each other, enjoying lots of food and wine and entertainment, solving puzzles, and playing games. It was quite a raucous affair!

Hour after hour, the king and his ministers waited for the applicants to come upstairs for the interview. Finally, the king sent an attendant to the banquet hall to see what was taking so long. The attendant soon returned and reported, sadly, that everyone had left...and carried with them the rest of the food, all the royal clothes they'd tried on, the jewels, and even the silverware. Becoming full and tired, they went home, forgetting why they came.

As we arrive to Yin Yoga & Meditation practice, it's helpful to remember why we came. What brought us to the mat today? Which pathway led us to our very first practice? What do we need right now? Is there anything we want to nurture, strengthen, or remember while on the mat? Is there something specific we'd like to release, create, energize, or offer as a result of our practice time? These are questions that let the mind trace back to our intentions and what's most important to us.

Your practice intentions might be broad or refined, consistent or ever-changing. For example, perhaps an overarching intention is to practice in support of your whole-self wellbeing. You might set session-specific intentions which could change each time you come to the mat depending on your needs. Strengthening and opening the physical body might be an intention one day, for example, and calming and clarifying the mind the next. There's no right answer or one perfect reason to practice. What's most important is remembering what's most important.

Let's continue our arrival with the third acknowledgement prompting us to inquire with sincerity: What's important right now?

Settled on the earth in this present Now and content to feel however it is you feel, ask yourself: What intention might I like to set to support my attention for today?

Maybe this serves as an inspiration as you continue in your day.

As you sit, let your intention rise to the surface. Honor whatever intention presents itself.

When you're ready, you might close these moments by holding hands at your heartspace and cradling the answer between your palms. Maybe you feel led to place your hands onto your heart and allow a kind awareness to embrace it in a moment of recognition.

Remember your intention serves as an anchor for your attention. Return to it, reflect on it anytime you need to. Intentions gather our attention. If the attention is scattered, our energy is likely scattered too, making it trickier to do the things that bring us peace. When we stay focused on what's important to us, we conserve our energy and progress toward what we want and most need.

Choosing Your Arrival Posture

Whether you're taking just a few moments of arrival to reflect on the acknowledgements or want to enjoy a more extended meditative exercise, there's no single correct position for arriving to your mat. We'll explore a couple of arrival postures below, and as you go through the "Yin Asana Spotlights" section, you might experiment with a variety of other postures that could work for your time of arriving and sitting meditation. There are many alternate positions available, depending on your intentions and the varying needs of your body, including seated, kneeling, side-lying, supine, and prone. The best arrival posture is the one that feels accessible, helps you maintain a relaxed yet alert awareness, and does not cause pain or strain. As you try out the various postures, give yourself permission to use as many props as necessary to make the position supportive and sustainable. If one posture doesn't feel right, play around with the different options until you find one that works well for you.

Acquainting with the Orientations of the Pelvis

When choosing a seated arrival posture, you'll want a balanced and stable base to help you feel well-supported from the ground up. The position of the pelvis is essential for a good foundation because it impacts the position of the spine. A neutral pelvis helps to recapture the natural curvature of the lower back, serving as a foundation for aligning the rest of the spine. Although we sometimes hear the phrase "a straight back" in instructional yoga cueing, it's a verbal shortcut of sorts. In reality, the back doesn't want to be perfectly straight. As we've discussed, the spine has a gentle S-shape, four natural curves that absorb and distribute loading to maximize efficiency and avoid injury. Preserving the spine's natural alignment helps maintain a relaxed, upright posture. When aligned, the spinal muscles provide the central axis of support and allow the other muscles of the back and spine to become engaged with less effort, preventing back pain or strain.

Whether setting up for your seated arrival posture or any seated Yin Yoga posture, it's important to first establish our spine in its natural position. Familiarizing ourselves with what a neutral pelvis feels like and how to find it allows us to approach the posture from a place of awareness, stability, and strength. This body awareness is beneficial for us off the mat as well, for the overall health and vitality of our spine. Let's play with a couple of simple ways to get acquainted with three general pelvic orientations: anterior (forward) tilt (Fig A), posterior (backward) tilt (Fig B), and neutral (Fig C).

Fig. A

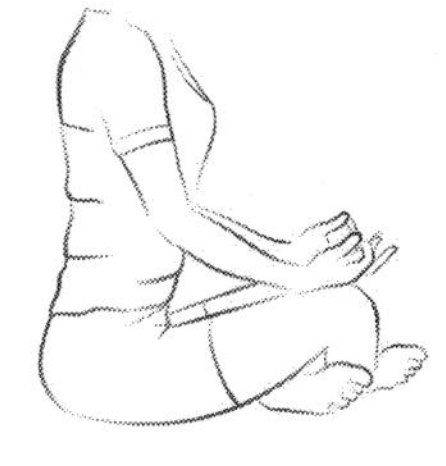

Fig. B

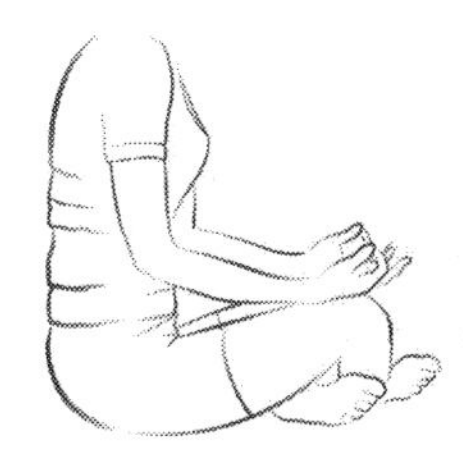

Fig. C

For this first example, position yourself on your hands and knees in Tabletop. Take a breath in, and on your exhale, gently round the spine and dip your tailbone downward, arching your back into Cat pose (Fig D). Cat moves your pelvis into a posterior tilt. Feel for this as you pause. On the inhale, move into Cow by dipping the belly toward the earth and tipping the tailbone upward toward the sky (Fig E). Here in Cow, the pelvis reverses and enters an anterior tilt. Do you sense the difference? Do this Cat-Cow breathing for a few rounds to sense the nature of the anterior and posterior pelvic tilts and their individual effects on the lower spine in each position. As you continue, see

principle

if you can find the middle point along the continuum between these two pelvic extremes. Feel for the position in which the pelvis is tilted neither too far forward nor too far backward (Fig F). In this neutral pelvis position, you'll also notice the lumbar spine finds its natural slight inward curve.

Fig. D

Fig. E

Fig. F

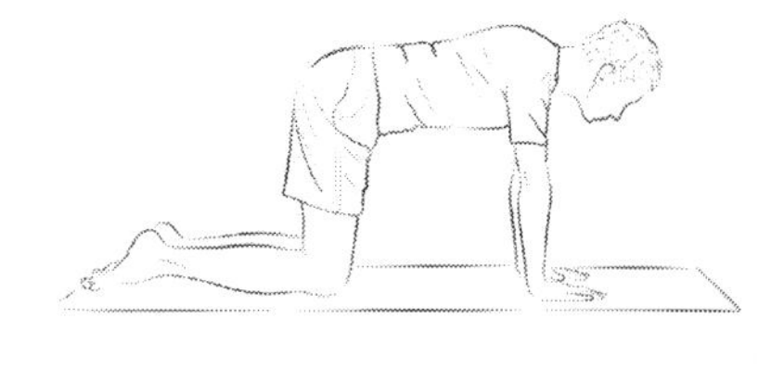

principle

For a second way to become familiar with your neutral pelvis position, lie on your back with knees bent and feet on the mat. Imagine your pelvis as a small bowl of water, full to the brim. Now, gently tip the pelvis so the front hip bones roll forward, recreating Cow just as you did above but this time while supine (Fig G). Notice the effect on your low back. Which direction would the water spill? With this anterior pelvic tilt, the water would spill forward toward your legs. Next, slowly un-tip the pelvis back to its starting position and then roll the frontal hip bones back toward you a bit, slightly tucking the tailbone recreating the Cat arch as you did above (Fig H). With your pelvis in this posterior tilt, the water would now spill backward toward the chest. Notice also the flattening effect on the lower spine. Continue to experiment with this a few times, gently tilting the pelvis forward and back, imagining how the bowl of water would respond. Next, use the extremes to help you find the middle position between the two where the water levels within the bowl (Fig I). When you find it, pause. Do you sense how this neutral pelvis position reestablishes the natural curvature of your lower spine?

Fig. G

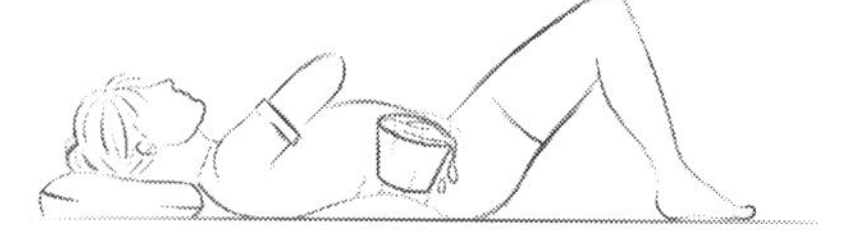

Fig. H

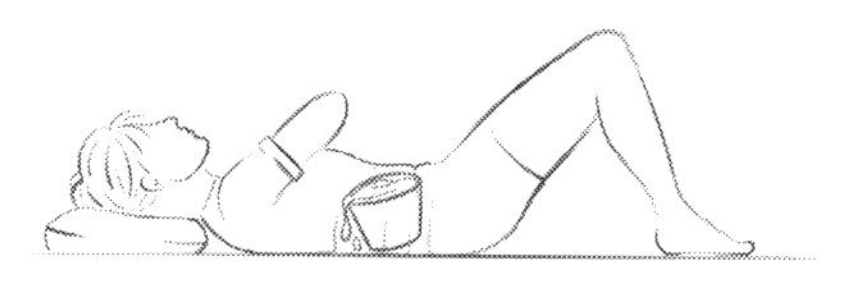

Fig. I

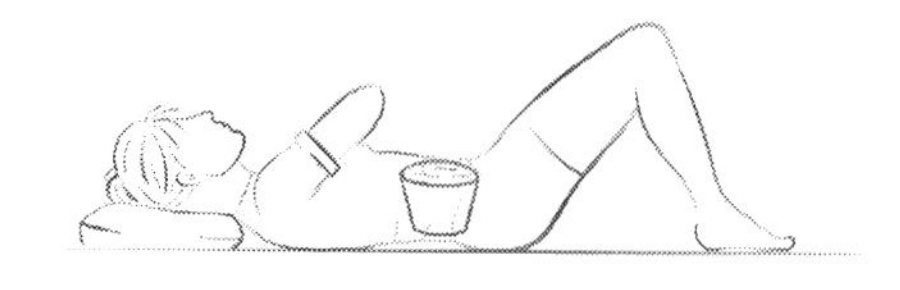

Establishing a Neutral Pelvis in Seated Postures

Now that we're familiar with how a neutral pelvis feels, let's explore some basic steps to help us recreate this balanced position while seated. We'll use Sukhasana pose as an example because it's a relatively accessible posture commonly used as a sitting meditation position, making it a good candidate for a class-opening arrival posture. These guidelines for establishing a neutral foundation also apply anytime you set up for a seated posture, so please feel free to revisit this section when a refresher would be helpful.

To begin, place a single-folded blanket onto your mat. Sit on the blanket and extend your legs straight in front of you. Check that your hips are above your knees. If they're not, add more height under your seat. Positioning the hips slightly higher than the knees will help take undue pressure off the knee joints and bring the pelvis toward its more neutral position. This will help release the *iliopsoas* and allow the spinal muscles to be more at ease, supporting a neutral spine. Next, tune into your sit-bones, also known as the ischial tuberosities, the triangular-shaped bony protrusions located at the base of the pelvis. Sit so that you're sitting slightly more on their front side rather than their back.

Check in with your pelvis to see if it's in its neutral position, tilted neither forward nor backward. If the frontal hips are tilted too far backward, you'll feel a slumping or rounding in the lumbar area. If this is the case, try elevating your seat further with additional props. Should the hips be tilted too far forward, removing some of the props from under you may help restore a neutral pelvic position. Adjust your seat height until you sense the balance point of the pelvis and natural curvature of the lower back. This position should allow you to sit with relative ease. If the knees happen to be suspended above the ground, see how it feels to place a block, rolled up blanket, or bolster underneath each outer knee to encourage the leg muscles to release more.

To proceed into Sukhasana pose (Fig J), bend your knees and cross either leg in front of the other with your feet positioned at a comfortable distance in front of you. If you're working with a sensitive spine, you could try Sukhasana with your back against a wall to bring ease to the spine. Over time, the support of the wall can help train the back muscles to stay upright with less effort and more comfort.

Fig. J

Another option is a simulated angled kneeling bench (Fig K). To build the bench, place a block at its lowest height under the back of a large firm bolster so the bolster angles downward toward the front of the mat. Place a blanket on top of the bolster to get a little more height under the hips as necessary to find a neutral pelvis. Straddle the bolster with knees on either side and rest your sit-bones onto the bolster.

Fig. K

Once you've established your seat and are sitting well in your upright posture with the pelvis in neutral, let your arms be comfortable and positioned in a way that doesn't pull your upper body forward or cause you to lean backward. Rest the hands onto the thighs with palms facing up to generate receptivity or facing down to feel more grounded. You could also choose to stack your palms in your lap on top of one another with the tips of thumbs touching. This hand position is known as Zen mudra.

Begin with a slight swaying of your upper body side to side, front to back, or circling around to help you find your center of gravity. To further settle, feel your neutral, strong spine letting the head, chest, and shoulders sit directly over your hips. Imagine there's a thread dangling down from high above, attached to the crown of the head, and flowing down through the center of the spine to your tailbone, rooting you to the earth. Sense it helping to keep you lightly suspended upright from your base to the crown while the rest of your muscles drape freely from its support.

Soften the tops of the shoulders away from the ears and let the shoulder blades slide slightly down the back and toward one another to invite the front of the chest to open, creating more room for the breath. Enjoy an easy, full inhale through the nose, then exhale slowly through the mouth. Release any tension in the jaw and allow the muscles of the face to relax by opening the mouth wide and gently jiggling the jaw side to side.

Choose to have your eyes opened or closed, whichever helps to best steady your awareness on the present. If you're not sure, experiment with both and notice any differences. If the eyes are open, see how it feels to half-close them and lower the gaze a few inches in front of you. This slightly downward angle may help block out external distractions. If the mind feels very busy, bring the gaze to watch the gentle rise and fall of the body as you breathe. If your eyes are closed and you start to fall asleep, you might find yourself falling forward a bit. To invigorate your attention, try opening the eyes and take a few deep breaths to reenergize the mind with fresh, oxygen-rich inhales.

Feel free to experiment to see which arrival postures benefit you. The answer may change just as our needs and circumstances change day to day, so stay curious and flexible. Choose what best serves your intention and needs. We'll explore many types of meditation exercises throughout the book that you might incorporate while arriving to the mat: breath awareness, lovingkindness practices, internal surveys to explore the happenings in the body-mind-heart, and Taoist energy circulation and visualization methods to support the flow of Qi through the body.

Though not always easy, intentionally taking the time to stop, to come home to this moment we're inhabiting and allow ourselves to really be in it, invites calmness and a clearer perception. Imagine taking a photo of the mountains from the passenger seat of a moving car. You'd get quite a blurry shot. What if, instead, you pull over, get out of the car, and place the camera on a tripod before pointing it at that beautiful vista? This shot will look very different, all the nuances of color and shape of the craggy cliffs well-defined, a feast for the eyes. Now, imagine life as a series of these photographs. Would you choose to live the blurry ones? Yin Yoga & Meditation gives us a chance to stop, get out of the car, and set up the tripod to see and feel with clarity what's happening inside us.

Our lives, our bodies, our minds, and our hearts are always changing, so you might consider arriving as an ongoing process from moment to moment. Whether starting a Yin Yoga practice, entering a room, or entering a new pose, have a marked time of arrival to check in...*Where am I? How am I? What's my intention?* Arriving grounds our energy, supports our awareness, and allows us to fully inhabit this precise moment in our precious life.

Practice Principle 2: Move Mindfully to Mild Sensation

In Yin Yoga, there's no perfect pose, no such thing as one shape fits all, and no ideal posture that we strive to attain. What a relief! In this practice, we take a mindful journey toward mild sensation. The ever-changing acu-pressure of each Yin shape offers gentle, healthy stimulation to help keep our connective tissues supple and strong. We prioritize function over external form and aesthetics, focusing on *what we feel* rather than *how we look*.

In Yin, We Go In

Don't go outside your house to see the flowers.
My friend, don't bother with that excursion.
Inside your own body, there are flowers...
One flower has a thousand petals.

– *Kabir (Robert Bly translation)*

Here, we go into the hidden parts of the body and sensitize to the physical sensations we feel in our postures. Letting the thinking mind rest, we turn our attention inward and watch with a kind curiosity to discover how our body is responding to each pose. Sensation is the language of the physical body, and in our second practice principle, "Move Mindfully to Mild Sensation," we learn to interpret what's being communicated moment by moment to maintain a safe and beneficial practice.

With the attention internalized, it's essential that we ease mindfully toward the inside edges of the shape until we feel mild sensation. As we've learned, the yin tissues are plastic-like in nature and prefer gentle, long-held stresses, so you'll want to find a level of sensation that you're able to stay with for a while. Pressing the body too far or too quickly into a posture risks damaging the very tissues we're serving. In a culture where faster is often conflated with better, moving slowly may feel like a radical act. Here on the Yin Yoga mat, though, there's no rush. Watch with your inside eyes, and slowly feel your way forward into each pose much like you'd feel your way through a dark room.

Maybe you've heard the old story about Sufi sage Mullah Nasruddin losing his keys. One night, a passerby found him combing through the dirt under a streetlamp in front of his house. The man asked what he was doing, and when Nasruddin told him he'd lost his house keys, the man got down on his hands and knees to help him look. After an hour of fruitless searching, the man asked, "Mullah, are you sure you lost the keys around here?"

"Oh no," Nasruddin said, "I dropped the keys inside my house." Incredulous, the man asked why, then, they were looking outside. Nasruddin replied matter-of-factly, "Because this is where the light is!"

Often, we're trained to look outside of ourselves for information and answers, but Yin Yoga & Meditation reminds us the light of wisdom shines brightly inside us, too. As we embrace and reclaim our yin qualities, we strengthen our ability to perceive and interpret the physical sensations arising within, illuminating our direct experience.

Function over Form

The outward appearance of a Yin posture isn't a desired end point, it's a means, a vehicle used to bring beneficial stimulation to a desired area of the body. There is no external standard that we should meet in a pose. What should a particular pose look like? The answer lies not in the exterior shape but in what we're feeling, where we're feeling it, and how intense the sensations are. We're asked to lay down the weight of expectations, come home to the body, and focus on how the pose feels internally. Attuning to the ever-changing sensations in each pose is our first job on the mat.

Giving your full attention to the sensations rather than to the appearance of the pose might feel like unfamiliar territory at first. Getting used to this approach may require a pivot of perception, especially in Western culture where external appearance often takes precedence over internal sensing. Yin Yoga has relatively few physical alignment cues compared to yang-like yoga styles, which may spur some uncertainty, especially for those newer to the practice. This emphasis on function over form is one of the most fundamental points to learn and apply. "Does this look right?" is one of the common questions I hear from those just getting started with Yin Yoga. Consistent and steady reminders that what's right is what feels right on the inside build confidence and empower practitioners to trust what they're feeling in the pose and adjust as needed to meet their body's needs. While the teacher is there as a guide, only the practitioner knows precisely what they're feeling.

Sensation-ful but Stay-able

Understanding the language of the body is an ongoing process that requires patience, curiosity, and a willingness to make a change if the body is asking for it. We want to use the posture to find and maintain a mild level of sensation. The shape should be sensation-ful but stay-able; the sensations are diffuse and detectable but not pronounced or too concentrated in a very small area. There should never be any indication of pain. It's natural for poses to sometimes be a touch uncomfortable but they should never hurt you.

It's no secret that in the U.S., we live in a culture that champions the slogan "No Pain, No Gain." When the going gets tough, we're often encouraged to suffer through it no matter what the cost. This messaging is one reason we might not be clear on what exactly constitutes pain versus mild discomfort and reinforces the criticality of practicing this principle. Our ability to have a safe and effective practice relies on our being able to sense and understand the difference. When we characterize the sensations arising, we're able to knowledgeably adjust based on what we're feeling. If sensations are too strong, we need to ease out of the shape a bit. If they're too faint, we have the option to ease forward a little more.

Healthy tissue stimulation in a pose will generally feel like a gentle, spread-out opening that is stretchy and expanding, a slight tug, light pulling or tightness, spaciousness, or a bit of release. These qualities of sensation are typically characteristic of stresses caused by tension between the tissues as they're gently being pulled away from each other. Compressive sensations may manifest as a light massage-like feeling with slight, dispersed pressure. Resistance could also feel like a smidge of rigidity or as a softer, spongy-squishy sensation when tissues press against each other. Sensations should feel spread out, extending relatively evenly throughout the tissue area being stimulated. If any sensations are too centered in one small part of your body, feeling like they fit within the size of a guitar pick, this indicates pain and needs to be avoided.

If you detect sensations in your body that feel nerve-y or electrified, sharp, stabby, hot, burning, throbbing, prickly, hurting, jabbing, stinging, or very pointy, these all fall into the category of pain and require an adjustment, as well as any other sensations that feel like red flag warning signs to you. Additionally, with so many blood vessels and nerves threading through the body's intricate construction, numbness and tingling may arise while in our postures. This prickly-tingly feeling, like the area is falling asleep, may indicate a nerve or blood vessel is compressed and warrants an immediate adjustment.

Another potentially useful way to help you or your students identify the level of intensity that you're feeling is applying a scale of zero to ten, where zero is sensation-free and ten is painful. In Yin Yoga, we aim for a three-ish, that is, something, but not too much. Whenever in doubt, go for the option that lessens the sensation. As we move through our practice, we honor the yin quality of non-striving. Yang energies animate many aspects of life, but while on the Yin Yoga mat, overly yang energy could lead us to ignore the body's wisdom and push past mild stress and our limits for physical safety.

After finding an appropriate degree of sensation, become attentive to the breath as it goes in and out. Notice, is it remaining calm and smooth or is it jagged and labored? If it's difficult to breathe easefully and intentionally, this is another sign we need to ease out a little from the pose. Even in poses that feel more challenging, we need to be able to breathe well. Think of the breath as a valuable indicator of how your body is receiving the shape. Strained breathing is often the body communicating that we've moved beyond mild sensation and our tissue's natural limitations and should soften our approach. Whenever we're unable to find a modification that resolves the painful sensation, we should exit the shape to try an alternative posture or enjoy a few moments of rest.

Internal body scans are simple but effective techniques that help us sensitize to and concentrate on the physical sensations that arise by taking the attention on a slow journey through our inner layers. Begin by identifying the strongest sensations first and pausing there, taking time to feel them fully. Stay curious to find the location and intensity of the sensations and inquire: *Is what I'm feeling reasonable and mild? Does it allow me to breathe well?* Without hurrying, allow your awareness to float to the next place of sensation in the body. Once you've scanned the inner landscape from toes to head with your mind's eye, it's helpful to reverse direction and sense your way back down from the crown to your toes.

While surveying your physical experience, try to maintain a beginner's frame of mind. The body differs from day to day and even from one side to the other, which makes preset notions of what it can or should do on the mat relatively unreliable. Each time you approach a posture, you have the opportunity to enter with fresh eyes and stay attentive and responsive to your needs in that moment.

Encouraging inquisitiveness, internal body surveys help a wandering mind stay present and tune in to what the body is experiencing at a given time. The more closely we listen to the language of the body, the more we learn what its messages mean in our practice and in life. Throughout the book, you'll have a chance to try a variety of body scans to traverse the vast inner physical landscape and honor what flows through the mind and heart as well.

Props Create Possibilities in Your Pose

The possibilities in a pose are as varied as the people doing them. As we know, all human bodies are designed uniquely, with countless individual anatomical variations between them and within them. Because the nature of the Yin Yoga practice is slow, low, and relatively non-weight bearing, it inherently offers us plenty of time and space to safely explore a wide variety of posture alterations and options. Important companions for practitioners of all levels, props expand the range of choices available in our poses and help us mindfully tailor our time on the mat to serve our body's individual needs. Props create possibilities!

Used creatively, props may help to make a posture accessible. For example, sitting on a block might allow you to safely forward bend without loading the lumbar spine. Using a strap lengthens the arm and may enable you to reach a part of the body without straining the neck or shoulders. Props also hold the weight of the body and aid muscular release. A bolster under the upper body may be just what's needed to provide a stable base to help the muscles relax more.

Props may also create a safer space to practice with specific physical concerns. A knee or ankle sensitivity could cause painful compression on a hard floor, so practicing with a soft blanket spread across the mat offers welcome relief. We can use props to nurture one part of the body in the interest of benefiting another. Sliding blocks under the knees, for example, may relieve pressure in the knee joints and open access to the hamstrings. Like so many others, I've worked with injuries in my practice and have experienced how valuable it is to be equipped with plentiful options, pose variations, and supportive modifications.

Although there might be a misperception that props are like training wheels to grow out of, props are supportive when trying to lessen sensations but also when you're wanting to amplify sensations. By sitting onto blocks, for example, we make room underneath us to go deeper in a forward bend.

Injury, age, and parts of the body we do or don't want to exercise all contribute to how we choose to employ props. As teachers, we want to offer the information and permission students need to honor their body's needs with kindness in alignment with their practice intention. Ultimately, as a practitioner, you are your own best teacher. Only you know how a shape feels on the inside. Each of us has our individual pathways to finding mild sensation, and because we're always changing, props help us experiment with our postures to discover how to best serve our body each time we come to the mat. For these reasons, we'll look more closely in the "Yin Asana and Counterposing" section at creative ways to consider employing props in the postures to maintain reasonable sensation.

Understanding this foundational principle and the characteristics of safe and appropriate sensation ensures we're able to make informed decisions in real time on the mat. Rather than pushing quickly toward a specific destination, "Move Mindfully to Mild Sensation" reminds us to internalize our attention and approach the poses slowly, easing ourselves toward a sustainable threshold of sensation. By connecting with the yin qualities of sensing, yielding, and acceptance, we move into each shape steadily and with gentleness. Once we meet a mild level of sensation, we've created space to continue to sensitize more and more to the landscape of our internal experience. After all, Yin Yoga poses aren't a destination. They're a process and place we inhabit to serve our bodies, hearts, and minds with intelligence and love.

Practice Principle 3: Relax and Remain in Relative Stillness

Engaging in more flowing, yang-oriented exercises, our muscles perform a dance of contraction and relaxation to move us, bending and straightening limbs and supporting our joints to avoid injury. In Yin Yoga, the muscles don't need to work so hard, letting go of their responsibility to keep us upright as we settle low to the ground. Our next practice principle, "Relax and Remain in Relative Stillness," emphasizes the importance of letting go of muscular gripping and allowing ourselves to simply *be* while the posture does its good work. We release the effort of the muscles and surrender the weight of the body to the earth, allowing gravity to hold us as we rest for time in stillness.

Generally, postures are held an average of three to five minutes, although some practitioners will hold them longer, sometimes even up to twenty minutes, depending on their needs or experience. More delicate joints like the shoulders typically require less time in the exercise, closer to one to three minutes. A newcomer to the practice or students who are pregnant, hyperflexible, or returning from injury will often benefit from shorter hold times. Anytime you're not certain, a good rule of thumb is to start slowly by holding the posture for a shorter period, remembering to exit the pose anytime the sensations grow too intense. In "Yin Asana and Counterposing" section, we'll look at additional suggestions and specific considerations for pose hold times.

Relative Whole-Body Relaxation

Yin Yoga & Meditation offers supportive space to train our ability to relax ourselves, even in times of challenge. Our bodies gather unconscious tension, and when exercising hidden areas of the body, we might encounter some discomfort as we move into places that are tight or untended. Staying easeful when meeting sensation is a powerful training, valuable in our practice and the rest of life. As we've learned, Yin Yoga is a practice of relative whole-body relaxation. Each pose offers an opportunity to scan with warm curiosity through our inside layers to see if there are any tight muscles to target for release. Instead of judging any tensions we find, we can practice recognizing them and inviting the tension to relinquish its grip. Sometimes, simple awareness is enough to release a tight tissue.

Tension has the ability to keep the breath captive, so as we consciously relax the body, we allow the breath to flow more freely. Symbiotically, as we invite the breath to travel with ease, our physical tissues respond and soften their resistance. Harnessing this mind-body connection provides a reliable pathway to relaxation on the mat. As we rest in stillness while holding a posture, we might practice using our breath to mingle with the mild sensations we're feeling. Bringing our internal gaze to inside places of tightness, we smile with gentleness...breathing in, acceptance...breathing out, release. Later in the book, we'll look at some specific directed breathing techniques you might wish to experiment as you experience sensations in the poses.

As we mindfully sense our way through our inner landscape in this way, our central nervous system gets the message that everything's OK. This letting go process encourages us to approach our experiences not as something to reflexively fix but as something to first feel and watch before deciding if and how to respond. The mind and body are interconnected, one serving as a conduit to the other. If the body is tense, it transfers its tension to the mind. A troubled mind creates tension in the body. Likewise, if the body is relaxed, that same peacefulness is impressed onto the mind. When we stay with slow, seamless breathing, conscious of each cycle in and out, it signals to our spirit: all is well, all is well. Body and breath awareness practices allow us to more consistently replace tension with relaxation, so the relaxation techniques used in Yoga Nidra are wonderful complements to Yin Yoga & Meditation. We'll explore a number of these in the "Yoga Nidra-Inspired Methods" section.

As we experience in the rest of life, there are no absolutes, and the same is true in Yin Yoga. For example, although easeful, mindful breathing slightly engages our core muscles. Like everything else, our body's level of muscular engagement exists on a continuum, and on the mat, we lean toward complete relaxation. Sometimes our muscles resist as a way of protecting us, so stay attentive to tension as another measure of intensity. If you consciously invite the muscle to let go, and it continues to hold, the tension could be communicating that you've tipped the balance and pushed past what's reasonable. Retreat a little and see if that helps the sensation become milder.

Remaining Relatively Still

Be a bud, sitting quietly on the hedge...
Stand here. There is no need to depart.

– *Thich Nhat Hanh*

Once we've moved into a posture to the point of mild resistance and consciously relax the muscles, we commit our body to stillness. As you'll recall from "The Physical Layer," our yin tissues are more plastic-like, so they require gentle, static stresses to remain safe during our exercise rather than the rapid and rhythmic cycling preferred by muscles. Connective tissues also need time to remodel, so we stay in the pose while remaining relatively still to receive the benefits of the stimulation. Just as a mile is walked step after step after step, gentle, continuous pressure applied over a period of time is the way of yin.

Relaxed stillness opens passage for the acu-pressure of the poses to go into its intended focus, the connective tissues. The fascial network running through our body stretches and contracts much more slowly than muscle fibers, so to exercise it as effectively as possible, we need to hold our postures at least a minute or more. Fascial research shows that once muscles have had a chance to relax into a sustained stretch, the intramuscular fascia interwoven through the tissue begins to release. In this way, the static holds of the postures prompt a repatterning that can provide real relief for recurring tightness. As we've learned, the body's viscoelastic ground substance also requires sustained stimulation to liquefy and support the natural hydration and detoxification processes. Just as we wouldn't expect braces on our teeth to remodel them overnight, in Yin Yoga postures, we relax with patience and trust, knowing the beneficial stresses will bear fruit over time.

While holding the poses, it's important that we remain willing to make mindful adjustments when necessary to ensure the sensations stay mild and reasonable throughout the pose. As you remain in the shape, the location or intensity of sensations may change and become too strong or too subtle. If the sensations become too intense, reposition the body or props, or take a break to rest the body completely. Conversely, the tissues may continue to relax and release, causing sensations to lessen. If so, you might feel prompted to shift a little deeper into the shape to ensure you're maintaining a mild level of sensation for the duration of the posture.

Years back, a student who was new to my class approached me wanting to share how relieved she was to learn that she was allowed to move and make adjustments while holding the postures. In her previous experiences, she had somehow misunderstood that in Yin Yoga, she was required to stay completely still. It was unfortunate that she'd had that experience in the past, as not making adjustments in a pose could lessen its effectiveness or even be dangerous and cause injury. As teachers, it's important we communicate clearly that stillness in Yin Yoga is relative. Students always have the permission and responsibility to make necessary adjustments based on the sensations they're experiencing and the wisdom of their own bodies.

By remaining attentive as the environment of feelings inside us constantly shifts, we practice listening carefully to the language of the body to make simple and well-timed adaptations. These small shifts allow us to receive the maximum benefit while also ensuring we don't exercise one part of the body at the expense of another.

Even when we feel relatively still on our mat, consider all of the ongoing movement inside the body. Our hearts beat on average sixty to ninety times each minute, pumping five to six quarts of blood. In that same sixty seconds, our eyes blink fifty times, forty-thousand skin cells shed, the kidneys clean twenty percent of our blood, and billions of electrical signals pass through our brains. That's just our physical tissues! Consider the Qi moving through us, the continual river of thoughts flowing, and emotions coming and going like waves. It's easy to understand how both yin stillness and yang movement are ever-present.

Although the postures are relatively simply shapes, the quiet stillness of Yin Yoga & Meditation is at times challenging. If you struggle with being still, whether on the mat or in life, know you're not alone. The ability to remain still with ease is a skill, and our busy lives don't always give us much opportunity to practice it. As we'll learn in the next practice principle, "Watch and Welcome What's Happening Inside You," honing our ability to be compassionate observers helps us get better and better at remaining still even as the waves of sensations, thoughts, and emotions rise and fall within us. With diligent, steady practice, we can increasingly inhabit a place of peace no matter where we are or what we're experiencing.

Practice Principle 4: Watch and Welcome What's Happening Inside You

The physical exercise and extended stillness we inhabit in Yin Yoga & Meditation combine to provide a special opportunity to observe our interior landscape in all of our layers of being. Our next practice principle, "Watch and Welcome What's Happening Inside You," invites us to stay curious and friendly toward what arises each moment, and to explore the options of doing and non-doing in response. The pause of each pose carves out a window of time to inquire: *What's actually happening inside me right now?* Watching our internal experience with care, we practice the skill of staying present to receive our experience with kindness, being a friendly host.

The noise and busyness of a day has the capacity to distract us from all that hums under our surface. Like a stone dropping into a river, the fourth practice principle helps us to train in letting the awareness drift downward past the hustle and bustle of the external world into an inner place of quiet calm. From this new vantage point, we can embody a relaxed and welcoming attention, aware of and touched by what's happening but not carried it away by it. Just as a stone lays still as the rushing water moves around it, we practice each posture undisturbed by the currents of sensations, thoughts, and emotions swirling around and through us. Receiving our experience with this equanimous awareness, we give ourselves the opportunity to feel before we follow any urge to immediately react.

Encountering the Three Marks of Existence

As we remain committed to watching the present time, we'll likely encounter the Three Marks of Existence. As you'll remember from the "Root Wisdom Traditions" section, Buddhism teaches these Three Marks are aspects common to everything we experience: *impermanence*, *imperfection*, and *interconnection*. Staying curious as we watch the changing internal landscape in body, mind, and heart, we might find these three characteristics appear in surprising ways.

The more we watch, the more we see impermanence. Everything within us is continuously transforming into something else. These ever-present shifts are a mirror of the natural world around us as landscapes, seasons, and the whole of the universe itself continues to transform. In Yin Yoga & Meditation, we have space to perceive our bodies as a field of ever-changing sensations arising and falling away. We observe thoughts continually shifting like clouds across a windy sky, and our feelings rising and subsiding like waves moving through an ever-flowing ocean of emotion. Our internal life-force energy, too, is perpetually shifting.

We'll also have the chance to encounter the second characteristic: imperfection. Maybe, for example, one day you're so happy to be sitting on your mat ready for practice, but you notice your shoulders feel a bit tight, or the room is too cold or too hot. Maybe your body is ready to release tension, but your mind keeps circling around a frustrating circumstance from earlier in the day. Observing and welcoming our experience with understanding and gentleness has the power to reduce our anxiety around imperfection. In Yin Yoga & Meditation, there's no perfect mental state to attain, no ideal body, and no perfect practice. When we notice an aspect of our body, a pose we're in, or our practice in general isn't one hundred percent perfect, we can smile to ourselves and remember that imperfection is our natural, beautiful state.

The third aspect, interconnection, is another profound teacher both on and off the mat. Careful watching in our practice, just as in life, shines a spotlight on the glowing lines of energy that connect all happenings and all things. Let's say, for example, when we first enter a pose, we sense a continuous line of physical tension that runs from the back of our head, through the neck, down along the torso, and into the abdomen. After holding this posture for a bit with a mild stimulation, we may sense this whole chain of tension beginning to unwind while we're consciously breathing and inviting the body to relax. As our physical tissues loosen, we might begin to notice our thought cycles loosening, too, and start to sense a bit more spaciousness flowing through the mind. A relieved mind helps to dissolve tensions in the heart, letting us remain restful in the constant flow of changing sensations, mental formations, and emotions.

Welcoming to Transform

There's a story in the Buddhist canon about the Buddha's nephew, Devadatta, who was overcome with jealousy of his uncle. In a plot to kill the Buddha, he riled up a cranky bull elephant named Nalagiri and set him loose into the place where the Buddha was walking with some monks. As Nalagiri stormed wildly toward them, everyone scattered except the Buddha, who turned with compassion toward the beast, determined to place only peace between them. The power of authentic lovingkindness was irresistible as the elephant came near and its fierceness began to subside. Within seconds, Nalagiri was kneeling at the Buddha's feet having his trunk stroked gently.

Inevitably, we will all sometimes encounter what feels like an agitated, stomping elephant where our mind should be, including when we're trying to sit peacefully on our practice mat. Instead of running from or fighting with ourselves, we might try experimenting with the Buddha's approach, defusing the moment by infusing it with the energy of lovingkindness. We might whisper to ourselves: *Oh, wild mind of mine, the door of my heart is open to you.*

With the deep work of the Yin Yoga exercise, vulnerable or difficult feelings potentially will arise alongside uncomfortable physical sensations. Very freeing or peaceful feelings will also happen in the practice, or you may feel a sense of deep comfort and release. Each emotion, no matter what it is, however painful or neutral or beautiful, has a good reason for being what it is. One of the greatest gifts of compassion we can give ourselves is a recognition that all of our feelings are perfectly natural and part of the human emotional landscape, even the challenging ones. On the mat, we practice accepting them with warmth just as they are and understand that, like a wave moving through an ocean, they will arise in us, manifest, and then go.

While in your postures, take some moments to look at the condition of your heart and see if you can offer a gracious invitation to whatever you find there and the space it needs to be exactly as it is. Maybe you're feeling tired or frustrated. It's OK. Maybe you're feeling peaceful and settled. It's OK. There's no need to rush into changing anything; it's all OK. Simply notice with friendliness. Unless painful physical sensations arise, Yin Yoga guides us to resist the temptation to reflexively react. In each moment, we have the choice to do...or not-do. When we choose to lovingly attend to what presents itself, letting it be what and how it is for as long as it is, we free ourselves from the impulse to judge, evaluate, or oppose. We release the weight of any expectations and let the freshness of our experience bless us.

Meditating Like a Mother

Watching with welcoming attention isn't always easy. Thich Nhat Hanh taught a technique to help us work skillfully with and transform challenging emotions when we encounter them. He calls this "meditating like a mother." We start by calling what we're feeling by its name and beginning to embrace it like a mother holds her baby. *Hello, my darling anxiety, I see you and know you are here. It's ok...I am here for you.*

Once we recognize the emotion, we're able to be present for it and take care of it, calming it with an abiding gentleness. Consider how when a baby cries, the mother doesn't shout at him or run screaming out the door waving her arms in the air. She stops what she's doing and goes to him, holds him tenderly, and soothes him. Should we encounter difficult feelings on the mat, we can do that, too. Embracing a painful emotion begins to soothe and change its energy as we hold it with a calm and loving attention, just like holding a child tenderly and comforting him with affection and sweetness begins to settle him. Even after just a minute or two of offering the strong emotion our comforting attention, it will lose some of its spark and strength, and we feel relief.

Because our emotions create physical responses in the body, encountering difficult emotions sometimes triggers physical tension. Using the breath to help ourselves stay present and at ease allows us to release places of holding as we find them. When we choose to not-do, we have a chance to feel what we encounter, find where it presents itself in the body, and use the breath to soften it. Staying with it, inquire: *What's happening now in my heart? Is there any space expanding? What happens if I'm willing to hold this feeling with tenderness instead of trying to push it away?*

We inhabit profound freedom when we recognize our ability to be there, really be there, for whatever we're experiencing. When I was living on the southern coast of Maine, one of my neighbors was a retired deep-sea diver. He was telling diving stories one afternoon and asked me if I knew the fastest way to make a shark go away. "Close your eyes!" he joked. Although we might sometimes feel tempted to close our eyes to what we're feeling to make it go away, when we acknowledge our experience and offer responsive energy of the heart to open in welcome, that inner alchemical process of healing begins. In that loving space, pain, fear, or confusion, whatever it is, starts to soften and transform. When we commit to watching and welcoming what arises within us, a world of possibility opens before us. The real miracle of this life is being alive and awake to what's happening right here, right now. Our time on the mat provides optimal conditions to continue cultivating the skill of compassionate observation that helps us stay present with kindness and courage no matter what a moment delivers.

Choosing Our Habits

As we learned in "The Mind Layer," our brains have the power of plasticity, the ability to change. Whatever we practice becomes stronger, so what we do and how we do it is an exercise in training and in choice. When the mind wanders and we call it home, what tone do we use? Coming back to presence is a cause for celebration and tenderness...*welcome home!*

Perhaps you're familiar with the Buddhist Lojong mind training slogans, a series of short instructional sayings traditionally used to train the mind in lovingkindness and compassion. I've kept them for years on a stand in my home, placed where I'm sure to pass by them each day. One slogan I've been working with is "Train Wholeheartedly." Over time, it's prompted all types of reflections: *What am I training in this moment? What is my approach? Is there anything distracting me or any unconscious habit energies dividing my attention right now?*

The same lines of inquiry are helpful in our practice, too. Are there any habitual approaches that prevent us from reaching all parts of who we are? Do we naturally tend certain aspects of ourselves while ignoring others? Are there any fresh approaches to try? Choosing what we do or not-do with regularity and selecting the habits we develop empowers us to adopt new and nourishing ways of responding. When we notice we're distracted on the mat, we can inquisitively say to ourselves, *Oh, I got distracted. Hmmm...what was that?* Whether we're investigating happenings in the physical body, our Qi channels, our mental formations, or waves of emotion passing through the heart, one key is staying curious, for curiosity and judgment cannot coexist.

Think of your attention like the sun on a balmy summer's day. As you watch, let the warm, gentle sunlight of your awareness shine on the inside and nurture the habit of welcoming your experience with friendliness, inviting the heart to open with ease to whatever you find.

Reducing Reactivity

Understanding and reducing our propensity toward reactivity is a primary theme of Pema Chödrön's teachings. She shares a Tibetan word for this tendency: *shenpa*. Shenpa is like a hook, snagging us into conflict, or the emotional charge that surges us into hastily doing something. We might experience it as the bristling sensation when someone cuts us off in traffic, we get criticized at work, or our child stomps his feet instead of cleaning his room like he promised he would. It's the tripwire trigger, the urge to get away, fight, or force something. Shenpa sweeps us right into reaction before we even realize it. This energy is like a wave cresting, and the earlier we catch it, the more effectively we're able to work with it. The watchful stillness we inhabit in this practice provides an excellent training ground to slow that wave before it crests and crashes.

On the mat, just like in life, we'll unavoidably find things we don't prefer, such as stiffness, boredom, a limiting injury, some uncomfortable conditions, or stormy internal weather. Yin Yoga & Meditation is a safe place to get good at working with conditions and situations that may or may not match our preferences. If we train ourselves to pause and not-do when the impulse to react is strong, we begin to break negative cycles and broaden our perspective. With this wider view, we're able to receive our experience with a more constant kindness and respond from a place of clear sight, intention, and wisdom.

There's a story about a mighty Samurai warrior who sought a wise old Zen Master to ask him about the nature of heaven and hell. The warrior approached him and knelt at his feet. "Great Master," he said, "please tell me about the nature of hell."

In response, the Master scowled and scoffed, saying, "Why would I tell such a miserable one as you about anything? You are not worth even a breath." The Master carried on insulting the warrior until the warrior grew so angry that he leapt to his feet, sword lifted and ready to strike. Just then, the Master raised his hand as though it was a mirror and said, "That, my son, is the nature of Hell." His words went deep into the warrior's heart, and the warrior fell to his knees in tears. "And that, my son," the Master continued, "is the nature of Heaven."

In his encounter with the Zen Master, the Samurai realized he'd become carried away by shenpa. Like the warrior, we may at times feel the wave of shenpa accompanying strong physical and emotional stimuli on the mat and in the rest of life, too: challenging situations, frustrations, fears, anxieties, and disappointments. Also like the warrior, we have the capacity to equip ourselves with the ability to pull back from these eruptions, come home to ourselves, and more peacefully inhabit this moment. We can consciously strengthen this skill every time we come to the mat. In training ourselves to watch and welcome what arises, we clear the pathway home to the steady mind and soft heart within us.

Practice Principle 5: Transition Like a Tortoise

Our next practice principle, "Transition Like a Tortoise," focuses on our approach to exiting the postures. More than just a series of individual poses, a Yin Yoga & Meditation session is a continuous journey and ongoing meditation. During this unhurried flow from one Now into the next, we have the chance to maintain a continuity of awareness and observation. Transitions are full of information. When we pay close attention to each moment, resisting judgments or distractions, we grow in understanding about the experience we're having and also about ourselves.

Transition Training

On any given day, we transition dozens of times. Whether from conversation to conversation, coming home from work, going to see friends, or tucking our kids into bed, we're almost always moving from one thing to the next. You might wish to take a few moments to reflect on the transitions that you experience in an average day, big or small. As you're reviewing the shifts you make, consider how you feel in those in-between times. Treating these shifts as things to get through can be tempting. Maybe we feel bored and distract ourselves or use the time to replay the past or rehearse for the future. Maybe we feel impatient: Let's get to the next thing, already. What about more significant life shifts like moving from one city to another, starting a relationship or changing jobs? Call to mind a big transition you've been through. How did you feel during that time? Did you feel vulnerable, excited, uncertain, anxious, or hopeful? All of the above?

Our Yin Yoga practice, like our days, is a series of shifts. Moments of transition might sometimes feel unsettling on the mat. Change isn't always easy. There in the in-between, however, we have a chance to collect our energies and notice where and how we are, and what we're experiencing. On the mat, we train in continuing to manage our attention even while we're moving from one position and into another, staying steady and present with whatever the moment holds. When approached mindfully, transitions become beautiful bridges, opportunities to relate to our next encounter with more presence and freshness.

No Need to Rush

How we move between postures is just as crucial to the safety and efficacy of our practice as time we spend in the poses themselves. Moving carefully into these moments of post-posture recovery gives our viscoelastic connective tissues a chance to safely revert to their more stable state. The area worked by the pose may feel a bit weak, stiff, creaky, brittle, or delicate. These sensations are common and expected as long as they're relatively mild. Sudden or forceful movements directly following a Yin Yoga posture or session could potentially injure the very tissues we're trying to support and interrupt the natural unfolding of the possible benefits. We don't want to undo the impactful work of the pose, so just like we ease consciously toward mild sensation while entering a pose, we ease away from that boundary with equal care as we emerge.

The yin way is mindful, relaxed, and slow, like a Sonoran Desert tortoise easing almost imperceptibly across the arid landscape. In the shift from the stillness of the pose into the movement of the transition, the mind has a tendency to run off somewhere else. As we slowly rise from a posture, our body may have something to say. In this short-lived pocket of space, we'll want to listen with care to the immediate aftereffects of the exercise. During these moments of stimulation release, do we notice any shift in sensations appearing in the areas just targeted or another part of the body? Perhaps there's a flush of fresh energy, a waning of sensations, or a feeling of release. Do we see any trends in the mind as we exit our pose?

Taoist practices encourage us to move like a river flowing effortlessly downstream, unhurried yet responsive, moving forward with both purpose and flexibility. When we embody the nature of water, we align with the most yin-like element within us and nourish our yin energies. Tension requires physical resources, so unconscious chronic tension consumes energy unnecessarily. Interrupting patterns of tension and reactive tendencies creates new pathways of openness and relaxed flow within us during our daily activities and interactions, which can be deeply refreshing and invigorating. Yin Yoga poses stimulate the flow of Qi through our internal energetic architecture. If we move too quickly or forcefully, the tissues can constrict and impede the little rivers of energy that deliver Qi throughout the body. Moving mindfully helps keep that flow open so we continue to benefit from it during the periods of rest.

Quick physical motions can also disrupt the mind, like a rock splashing suddenly through the surface of a calm lake. Though water is disturbed in an instant, the resulting waves ripple outward and take time to resettle. Offering ourselves the benefit of mindful transitions settles the spirit as we gather our attention into this brief yet information-rich time.

Our ever-present companion, the breath helps us facilitate a smooth and unified journey out of the pose. Before we rise out of a posture, taking a couple of moments to feel and follow a few mindful, slow breaths centers the awareness and prepares the body for a conscious change. Our attention spotlights where we are, enabling us to make a conscious transition to where we're heading.

Placing our awareness on the continuous stream of in-breaths and out-breaths steadies the mind. The always-changing nature of the breath serves as a source of inspiration for our transitions. We feel how the in-breath turns into a pause which then turns into the out-breath. The out-breath then becomes the pause from which the in-breath begins again. There's no rush; breath turns into pause and then breath again, one continuous whole.

Intentional transitions, whether arriving to the mat, leaving our practice, or moving between the poses, give us the chance to settle the attention into a place of presence and receptivity. Stitching our experience into a unified whole, mindful transitions threaded into our mat time cultivate our yin qualities and help keep our practice safe and full of opportunities for observation and insights.

Practice Principle 6: Rest Regularly to Recover and Reconnect

Our next practice principle is "Rest Regularly to Recover and Reconnect." Rest is as essential as preparation and practice, but it's not something we're often encouraged to do. Though adequate sleep is one of our most basic survival needs, in the rush of life we may find ourselves approaching it as if it were a suggestion. A 2014 survey by the U.S. Centers for Disease Control and Prevention found that a third of American adults suffer from insufficient sleep each night. Associated with high blood pressure, heart disease, stroke, obesity, diabetes, and mental distress, ongoing short duration sleep can have devastating health consequences. Taking time away from our yang activities to rest and renourish is critical for our long-term effectiveness, balance, and wellbeing.

Maybe you've encountered the story of a very strong woodcutter who was determined to do his best for his new employer. His boss gave him an ax and sent him off to work. The first day, the woodcutter brought in eighteen trees. "Congratulations," the new boss said, "keep up the great work!" Feeling motivated, the woodcutter worked harder the next day but could only bring in fifteen trees. On the third day, he exerted even more effort and inexplicably brought in just ten trees.

Disheartened and convinced he was losing his legendary strength, he went to the manager and apologized for performing so poorly. "Well, when was the last time you sharpened your ax?" his boss asked.

"My ax?" the woodcutter replied, "I had no time to sharpen it, I've been too busy cutting down trees!"

In his zeal to remain productive, the woodcutter had forgotten to sharpen and maintain the tool he was relying on to do his work. Though it often feels challenging to prioritize rest when there's so much to do, rest is essential for balance and an antidote to stress, necessary for self-healing both in life and in Yin Yoga & Meditation. Thankfully, rest is a skill we all have the ability to sharpen, and our mat is the perfect place to practice.

Resting for Safe Exercise and Tissue Recovery

Counterposes for recovery and an adequate restful Savasana at the end of a practice session are as critical to the safety and efficacy of our practice as the poses themselves. Just like a good night's sleep gives both body and mind a nourishing break to repair, incorporating periodic rest gives our connective tissues the chance to recover. Inadequate rest for the exercised tissues hinders their ability to rebuild, and the tissues may deteriorate over time. Maintaining a balance of stress and rest helps us to avoid over-stimulation, pain, and potential injury. Likewise, we need to offer our bodies enough time to recover by avoiding strenuous weight-bearing activities directly after Yin Yoga.

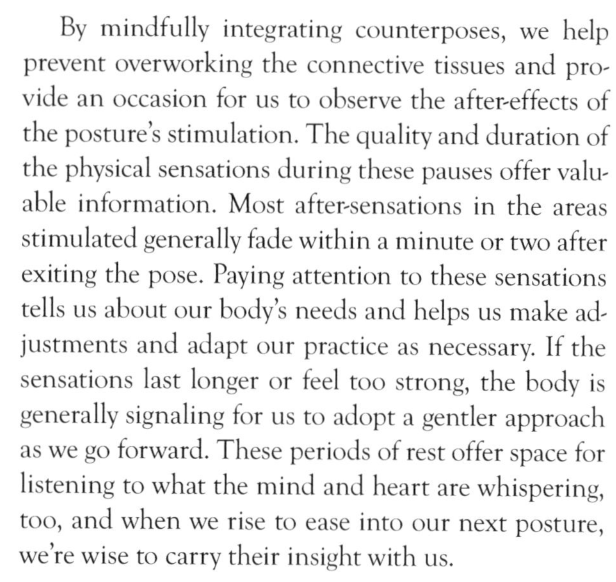

By mindfully integrating counterposes, we help prevent overworking the connective tissues and provide an occasion for us to observe the after-effects of the posture's stimulation. The quality and duration of the physical sensations during these pauses offer valuable information. Most after-sensations in the areas stimulated generally fade within a minute or two after exiting the pose. Paying attention to these sensations tells us about our body's needs and helps us make adjustments and adapt our practice as necessary. If the sensations last longer or feel too strong, the body is generally signaling for us to adopt a gentler approach as we go forward. These periods of rest offer space for listening to what the mind and heart are whispering, too, and when we rise to ease into our next posture, we're wise to carry their insight with us.

We have many recovery poses available to us, including prone, supine, seated, and even standing postures. Some of these poses are held in stillness, while others incorporate gentle, mindful movements synchronized with the breath to support the inner awareness. In the "Counterposes for Balance, Rest, and Recovery" section, I've detailed a variety of options for you to consider as well as specific suggestions for how to integrate them into your practice. Whether still or gently moving, counterposing provides the physical tissues a chance to restore and offers a period for relaxed observation of any rebound effects that may ripple through us.

We might, at first, be tempted to skip these periods, perhaps not being used to prioritizing rest. If counterposes or Savasana initially feel unfamiliar or a little challenging, know that the more we practice, the more natural these recovery poses will become. Give yourself and your students plenty of permission to rest regularly, offering reminders every so often during the session to listen to the body's signals and that it's OK to come out of the shape and counterpose whenever it feels right.

A Time to Notice

Counterposes also allow us to observe our inclinations and attitudes toward movement and stillness. Do we happen to notice a preference to move? Movement can sometimes be a conditioned tendency and a form of distraction or unconscious resistance, a way of scooting away from what we're feeling. Stay curious and attentive to locate what's true for you. As we shine the light of Mindfulness, we help illuminate any unhelpful habits keeping us from fully experiencing the present moment.

French composer Claude Debussy asserted that music resides in the space between the notes. In Yin Yoga & Meditation, rest is a place where the song of our practice plays. In the pause of the counterpose, we feel the release of the stimulation and watch with curiosity, allowing the reverberations of the pose to play themselves out without judgment. Rest is a chance to steep in the echoes of the pose and grow in awareness of how it worked inside you. *What effect did that pose create in me? What do I feel? Is there something being revealed? Has something shifted or transformed?* Perhaps we experience a sense of release of physical tension or maybe an energetic release. Opening the mind to the movements of energy, we train in sensing its subtle sensations, feeling as our awareness follows whatever arises.

A release of tension in the physical body may jostle thoughts and emotions ready for release. Yin Yoga works deeply with our body's tissues and touches areas where we may physically or energetically store emotional upsets and wounds, allowing what was hidden to rise. Like bubbles rising to the surface of a lake, old hurts and storylines may begin to wiggle loose to flow up and away. This is one reason it's important to continue to observe with kindness, breathe well, and invite the body to relax as much as possible during counterpose recovery. At times, we might also feel called to place our hand to our heartspace in comfort, gratitude, and acceptance.

When we incorporate conscious recovery into our time on the mat, we develop a beautiful dance between doing and being, experiencing the practice as a continuous whole rather than a series of stops and starts. Just like the breath is neither inbreath nor out-breath alone, stress and rest are one integrated pattern, each component supporting the work and value of the other. Experiencing first-hand the benefits of balancing stress with periods of rest, we find any mental resistance toward incorporating these pauses begins to shift. Instead of seeing periods of rest as something we squeeze in if we have a few extra minutes, the act of resting begins to feel as beneficial and natural as any other part of our practice.

Savasana – A Journey Home

At the end of our practice, a substantial rest in Savasana pose offers blessed space for integration and complements the release and rebalance that Yin Yoga & Meditation offers to all layers of our being. Savasana is an opportunity to experience poignant reconnection with our deepest consciousness. In a position of neutral sensation, which we'll explore in the Savasana Yin Asana Spotlight, we invite total relaxation to spread through the body, opening the door to a quiet, profound awareness. As we rest, we might experience the body as a field of ever-changing physical and energetic sensations. Thoughts and feelings make their slow way like birds through the clear sky of our minds. As we watch the changes moving through our internal landscape, we witness the temporary nature of our experiences, that law of nature assuring all things come and go, moving at an ever-changing pace past the steady awareness shining within us.

Empty yourself of everything.

Let the mind rest at peace.

The ten thousand things rise and fall while the Self watches their return.

They grow and flourish and then return to the source.

Returning to the source is stillness, which is the way of nature.

– *Tao Te Ching, (Gia-Fu Fen and Jane English translation)*

As we get better and better at being a stable, compassionate witness to these moment-to-moment changes, we strengthen our connection to our source and the fundamental serenity of our hearts. The allowing attention that helps us perceive without reaction has the power to peel back any layers of misperception and mistaken ideas that separate us from the truth of who we are and the meaningful part we play in this world.

Ultimately our Savasana rest invites us to journey further into silence and stillness, inhabiting the space of the heart. All of the attention relaxing into this place completely, letting everything else fall away, moving beyond images, sounds, and words, transcending the body...thoughts...the individual...time and space...transcending all, dwelling in boundless awareness, connected with all. Only stillness and a deep quiet remains there in the middle of the heart, a pathway to our enduring, transcendent center.

Planting Seeds of Realization

The combination of Yin Yoga, Mindfulness, and Yoga Nidra has a powerful and synergistic effect when blended within the practitioner's heart, and this remains true in our final relaxation time. The release of accumulated layers of tension prepares us to explore the yogic element of Sankalpa, a short mental statement of our deepest intention. Choosing to identify and incorporate Sankalpa into our practice can aid the release of unhelpful habits and self-limiting beliefs and help to reshape our life and create the days we desire.

When the Sankalpa is planted with confidence and love into the subconscious mind, we gain access to the vast forces of our spirit to support its realization in our lives. Connected to our most genuine intentions and guided by the compass of the heart, whole life transformation is possible. When we abide in our sacred nature, we recognize, trust, and celebrate the truth that the power of transformation lies within us.

If you're new to the practice of Sankalpa, there are many ways to discover yours and begin working with it. One simple way to start is to ask yourself: *What brings me joy and light? What brings freedom to my heart? If I was giving a gift to the world, what would be in my hands? What feels like my most natural way of being?* You might try the "Discover and Super-Charge Your Sankalpa with Visualization technique" (p. 252) as another way to uncover and empower your Sankalpa.

Unencumbered by tension, we're empowered to move ever inward to reconnect with our heart of hearts and water the seeds of our deepest intentions. This present time is the perfect time to steep in our most heartfelt wishes, knowing the life source flowing through us flows through and connects us to all things. It harnesses the pulsing power of the universe itself, which has brought us here with grace and gratitude to design the life we deserve and help others do the same.

Practice Principle 7: Continue to Cultivate

Whether in a pose, in our practice, or in daily life, we can continue cultivating the skills we're sharpening on the mat. Our final practice principle, "Continue to Cultivate," reminds us that the more regular our practice, the deeper the benefits we'll experience, and the more reliably the skills and qualities we hone on the mat will show up for us in our daily lives.

> Practice becomes firmly grounded by long constant efforts with great love.
>
> – *Yoga Sutra 1.14 (Swami Vivekananda translation)*

Time, Consistency, and Patient Persistence

We know remodeling our yin tissues takes time and consistency. Like brushing your teeth, it's not once and done. As one of my blessed students eloquently stated, Yin Yoga & Meditation is a "whole-self maintenance program," not a singular act. The postures help our yin tissues stay stronger and hydrated longer when practiced with regularity. Compassionately repatterning the mind, too, takes repetition and a continual dedication. We're wearing new grooves, letting unhelpful pathways grow over like a forgotten trail in the woods and tracing new and healthy patterns into our mental landscape. Daily life can have a way of undoing some of the work we do on the mat. Unexpected circumstances, setbacks, unintentional slights, harsh words, or just the sheer flurry of a day has the ability to upset the balance and calm we cultivate on the mat. We persist and persevere, trusting that these skills of kind observation, receptivity, and non-reactivity will strengthen over time. Practice becomes an ongoing process of restoring balance that gets easier and easier.

There's an old Chinese folktale about a wise man called to the Emperor's palace due to his reputation for easily getting along with everyone he met. His gift of relating to people was known far and wide across the lands, and he was deeply respected by all his kingdom for the remarkable harmony he was able to bring to every circumstance. Upon his arrival, the Emperor welcomed him with a lavish procession attended by the whole court. After the parade, the Emperor had a personal meeting with the sage to request that he write a ten thousand word document describing the method by which everyone in the empire could create peaceful and harmonious relationships. The man agreed and retreated to the far end of the palace to write.

Five days later, the wise man returned to the great hall with a heavy scroll. After his servants unrolled the paper onto a long table, the Emperor approached to begin reading what the man had written. Some moments later, the Emperor smiled and nodded his approval. The wise man had indeed written ten thousand words just as the Emperor had requested. His message, however, consisted of just one word written over and over again: patience.

Our practice will work its magic within us when we work diligently with intention, loving care, and patience. Along the way, we all will experience hindrances like restlessness, aversion, sleepiness, boredom, worry, and doubt regardless of how pure our intention or how high our enthusiasm. Let these feelings be heartening evidence of our shared human experience and inspiration to keep practicing.

We all have mental and emotional tendencies that may surface on the mat, and with them come opportunities to see these and other obstacles, not as distractions from the practice, but rather as the practice itself. They give us the chance to exercise the abilities we're honing. What happens if we offer a few sweet words when we notice our attention has wandered and welcome ourselves back home? When the temptation arises to judge or to doubt our ability to effect change, perhaps we're able to find some room for a breath in and a breath out and bring our attention into the space of the heart. Maybe we take the time to whisper to ourselves, *It's OK, I know you're doing your best. It's OK.*

As we know from building any skill, the effects aren't always immediately noticeable. Over time, things just start to flow a little more effortlessly. If ever the effects of your practice feel dim and you're not sure any of this is helping, you might think of it like splitting wood. You keep hitting the block of wood with an ax, and time after time, nothing happens. Then, on the fourth time, the wood breaks. There was nothing special about the first time, the second time, or the third time, but with each fall of the ax, the wood fibers weakened. We just keep hitting the wood with the ax, and eventually, the wood splits. It's the same on the mat. Our efforts, patience, and persistence make all the difference, and over time, we experience the benefits. All kinds of challenges and distractions arise, just as they do in the rest of life, but if we just keep walking the path, keep practicing, and keep showing up for ourselves, our diligent effort will pay off.

In our Yin Yoga postures, we continue cultivating the skills that we exercised when observing all of our practice principles. Arriving with freshness to each new moment, we can revisit our intentions as inspiration for our practice. As we meet and maintain mild sensation, we continue to cultivate a relaxed, compassionate awareness to welcome the guests of sensations, thoughts, and feelings with friendliness and curiosity. Transitioning mindfully and revisiting rest whenever appropriate, we assure the physical safety and efficacy of our time on the mat and nurture energetic and emotional balance.

While practicing present moment awareness in a pose, we'll at times get side-tracked. Once we notice our attention is not where we intended it to be, without any judgment, we notice what's getting in the way and invite ourselves back home to the present time. This process of honing the skill of starting over helps us cultivate a continuity of natural presence. When we notice we've gone off track, we just begin again. Almost right away we can feel what freedom and relief starting over brings.

Guiding the attention back to the breath and its sensations shifts our focus and grounds us, drawing us back to our direct experience of what's happening inside us. We may discover that challenges are opportunities disguised. Rather than fighting with distractions, what happens if we open to them as just another part of the practice instead? If we use objects of distraction to nurture the qualities we value, what once was a frustration transforms subtly and powerfully into a point of interest, inquiry, and insight. If a specific technique or approach isn't working, we begin again with another one. Instead of feeling like we've fallen short or done something wrong, we practice our starting-over skill: patience...persistence...patience.

Waking up this morning, I smile.

Twenty-four brand new hours are before me.

I vow to live fully in each moment...

– *Thich Nhat Hanh*

Like the sun every morning, we rise again. Was it yesterday cloudy? That's OK, we'll shine today. Like every breath in and every breath out, we can always begin again. We are always brand new.

Savoring

Savoring strengthens the neural pathways of appreciation and gratitude. The simple act of acknowledging your effort reinforces the good work you're doing in your practice and reaffirms your continued commitment. Acknowledge your effort and your successes, noticing the changes you experience in your physical body, your mind, and your heart. Regularly spend some moments reflecting on the fruit your practice bears in all areas of your life. You might find journaling after your practice sessions while your experience is fresh helps you savor the benefits of your time on the mat.

A brief sitting meditation or other extended, marked moment of pause at the end of the session is a rewarding way to savor the effects and reflect on the skills and gifts we've cultivated through our practice. These pauses serve as moments to set our intention and bring our experience with us into our day, benefiting ourselves and those around us. Inquire: *What worked well? What do I want to continue or change?* If you're leading others on the mat, encourage them to take just a few minutes before they rise to reflect silently on what their body, mind, and heart are sharing with them at that moment. Maybe you find that closing with a shared prayer, mantra, or chant is the perfect way to seal and honor the experience.

Newspaper columnist L. M. Boyd once told the story of a 6'6" boxer from LSU in the 1930s named Bigboy Blalock fighting a tough opponent from the Mississippi State Bulldogs. In the second round, Bigboy threw a roundhouse punch. The Bulldog stepped forward at just the right time, and his head caught the inside of Bigboy's elbow. Given the power of the punch, the man's head acted as a lever, and Bigboy's arm whipped around in a full circle, fist connecting squarely...on his own chin. He fell flat on his face for the count, and Mississippi State won the match. That day, Bigboy went down in history as the only fighter to knock himself out with a right punch to his own jaw. Likely, we all know how it is to get in our own way from time to time!

Similarly, when trying to keep a consistent practice, we'll encounter snags now and then. To make a commitment to our practice and stick with it, being realistic is important and also individual to each of us. What balance looks like for you might not be best for someone else, so you might inquire: *What does balance look like this week? Is there a time of the week that I'll be able to show up consistently? Would I benefit from blending some home sessions with group classes at a studio?* We can always make adjustments as the flow of our needs, responsibilities, and schedules change.

If you've been struggling to find time to get on the mat, see if you can identify what seems to be getting in the way. Maybe you've set an unreasonable expectation. If that's the case, start small, setting a practice length that's more workable for you right now. The benefits of Yin Yoga & Meditation rely more on consistency than the length of time, so if the day is too full for an entire session, no need to worry. Perhaps you set aside five minutes to do one pose, a sitting meditation, or another meditative technique of choice. A few mindful minutes of regular practice is much better than none at all. You might also consider if there's a mixture of shorter and longer Yin Yoga & Meditation sessions that will help you be consistent. Perhaps it's pairing a few fifteen-minute home sessions with a longer group session in a studio once a week. You might find that simply enjoying some quiet minutes on the patio following your in-breath and out-breath as you stare at the sky is the perfect way to collect a little more peace each day. Maybe you do a bit of walking meditation by the lake or along a forest trail. Tailoring your expectations and practice to work with your life circumstances is a way to gain momentum while staying gentle with yourself. Like anything worthwhile, Yin Yoga & Meditation will bring us the richest, longest-lasting benefits when practiced with diligence.

Recalling the value and purpose of our time on the mat is another way to continue to cultivate commitment. You might remember how you feel when you practice regularly and how that differs from how you feel when you don't. You could call to mind what benefits it brings you and, by extension, the people you love. Reflecting or establishing an immediate or longer-term Sankalpa can also reinvigorate another pathway for your continued practice. Perhaps post your Sankalpa near your mat, say it like a mantra, or make it a focus of your meditation.

The Gifts of the Practice Follow Us Wherever We Go

As we continue cultivating the skills and qualities that support present moment awareness on the mat, the more readily available they are to us off the mat, too. Compassionate attention, the conscious release of tensions, and slow, mindful breathing naturally show up for us when we need them, rising within us to meet the circumstances that find us. With patience, we transform stress into peace and reaction into spacious relaxation. Over time, the desire and ability to show up for our practice naturally expands, and perhaps five minutes turns into ten and one pose into three. Our body, mind, and heart don't need us to force anything. We can trust the instinctive evolution of the time on our mat to serve us.

The gifts of our practice begin to infuse our daily decisions and every interaction, allowing our awakenings on the mat to support our health, happiness, and the ways we contribute to the world. Happiness is a talent, skill, science, and art. The more we nurture the skills that build our ability to be happy, the happier we become and the happier we make others, building the networks of joy, connection, and contentment ever outward.

Our practice isn't something to attain, accomplish, or complete. It's a continuing journey, and it's our journey. The starting-over skill we're building helps us in all areas of life, not just on the yoga mat. We know that if we make a personal mistake, we can start fresh. If we take a wrong turn, we can turn around. If we make a choice that doesn't yield what we wanted, we have the ability make another and start on a different path. Every day gives us a chance to continue to cultivate the qualities and behaviors we want to nurture, whether in our practice, our relationships, our work, or in the fundamental direction we're pointed. This beautiful life we're living *is* the destination, and the richness of the trip we take is up to us.

Chapter 6

Jewels of Encouragement for our Practice

In this chapter, I'll be sharing some jewels of encouragement from the foundational root teachings of Buddhism, Taoism, and Yoga Nidra that have been invaluable teachers and companions for my practice, teaching, and daily life. A core element of the Mandala Map and intentionally interwoven throughout this book, these jewels of encouragement are offered here as suggested touchstones, guides for inquiry, and nourishment for the spirit as you journey inward. Each has the potential to shed light on our Yin Yoga & Meditation experience. These jewels are just a few of many from the sacred teachings, and I invite you to carry them with you as you continue your journey of self-discovery off the mat, too. Perhaps you'll uncover additional encouragements in your own practice and study that you'd like to incorporate as well.

Jewel ~ Resting in the Beauty of Our Imperfection

Maybe you've heard the story of the master who walked with his student to the river each day to gather water into two large pots. One of the pots had a sizeable crack in it, and by the time they reached home, half of its water was gone. Eventually, the student asked him why he continued to use a broken pot that wasted so much water. The master inquired, "Are you sure this pot is broken, my son? Pay closer attention to the path tomorrow."

The following day, the student again walked with his teacher toward the river, and looking around, he noticed that while one side of the path was just dirt, the other side was lush with many beautiful flowers blooming. The master paused and turned to his student, saying, "We mustn't be so quick to judge things around us to be broken or useless. You see, I planted seeds along the path and have used the cracked pot to water them each day as we traveled so the flowers would bloom and show their beauty to the world."

The student realized that instead of making the pot useless, the pot's imperfection created a brand-new use for it. I imagine we can probably all think of times when we held a predefined notion of how something should look or behave in order for it to be good, correct, or useful. This jewel of encouragement invites us to look in a different way. If we shed the notion of a specific value or use for the pot, we get to ask different questions, and look with our heads and hearts and not just our eyes: What else does this pot offer? What unique gifts and intrinsic value does it have just as it is? A cracked pot is indeed an unsatisfactory vessel for boiling water, but what a magnificent watering jug it can make!

We receive lots of messages in life about what perfection looks like, how everything should be – how we should look, the kinds of jobs we should have, the cars we should drive, the kinds of kids we should have, the sort of parents we should be – the list is endless. The images of this expected perfection flash unceasingly across our television screens and social media feeds. The inability of reality to live up to the golden filters of our culture places a real burden on us, especially in our youth.

A recent study by Thomas Curran and Andrew Hill looked at the mental health impact of perfectionism over the last several decades, analyzing studies and data sets of American, Canadian, and British college students' responses to the Multidimensional Perfectionism Scale.[1] Three types of perfectionism scores were analyzed between 1989 and 2016:

- Self-oriented perfectionism, imposing unreasonable standards on ourselves
- Other-oriented perfectionism, putting unreasonable standards on others
- Societal perfectionism, the perception of external expectations for perfection

Over these twenty-seven years, all three types increased by double digits, with the perceived external expectation for perfection metric jumping by thirty-three percent. These increases come at an enormous cost to our mental health and happiness, with correlating rises in depression, anxiety, loneliness, suicide ideation, eating disorders, and body dysmorphia.[2]

I'm sure nearly everyone has, at some point, felt the pressure of perceived expectations of perfection. Our bodies change as we age. Societal conditioning, and stories we've been told of how we don't measure up or how we're falling short in any number of ways, can make their false and harmful impressions on us. We might develop a condition or injury that introduces challenges or physical limitations we didn't used to have. Any of these experiences could make us feel less than whole.

I've experienced how hard it is to keep showing up and facing the day's reality while feeling broken in some way. When I was healing from my concussion, I couldn't rely on my brain to steer me toward answers to even simple questions, and I'd say words I didn't mean to say when the usual synapses didn't fire as planned. It's a vulnerable place to be, especially when you speak for a living. Relatively easy standing balance poses required significant modifications. My injury required me to renegotiate my relationship with my body, mind, and heart. Again and again, I trained in inviting myself back to the present moment, reminding myself of the healing potential of my practice when I allow it to be as it is and myself to be as I am.

In this process of reorienting myself with compassion, I was able to grow an acceptance of my situation. I found some new and creative ways to approach my mat time to strengthen my body and help it recover, and I learned to lessen the pressure on myself while teaching. I shared my experience openly with those around me and my students to inspire understanding that there was nothing to be embarrassed about or ashamed of – we all are where we are. In addition to restoring more balance to my body and spirit, I believe my injury helped me become a more empathetic teacher for my students. It renewed my sensitivity and deepened my understanding of the physical, energetic, and mental-emotional costs that self-perceived imperfections and unworthiness can inflict on the spirit.

Like the difficult times we're all faced with in life, our perfect imperfections arrive with an invitation for self-acceptance, growth, and an opportunity to look at things, and one another, a little differently.

When we change the way we look at things, the things we look at change.

– *Dr. Wayne Dyer*

Maybe you'd like to take a few minutes to reflect on your relationship with imperfection and notions of usefulness:

- Can you think of a recent time you encountered an object around your home that was "broken" or seemingly used up that you were able to put to use in a new way?
- Is there a quality or aspect of yourself that in one circumstance seemed less than ideal but when considered in light of a different situation turned out to be a real strength, or a unique gift you brought to the world around you?
- As you practice on your yoga mat, is there anything that feels imperfect? Sit with it for a few moments, looking more and more deeply into its nature. As you spend this heart-time with it, what beauty or other benefits do you see?

This touchstone of our practice encourages us to view ourselves with acceptance and embrace ourselves just as we are, beautiful and perfectly imperfect. As we look, we see imperfection is inherent in all things. Imperfection isn't disqualifying, it's the natural state of everything, including us. Understanding that im-

perfection is part of our shared humanity, we can find greater peace and give others permission to hold themselves with the same loving and accepting regard.

Jewel ~ Cultivating Balance and Energetic Harmony for Wholeness

If you've been blessed with the chance to stand where the ocean meets the land, you're familiar with the serene sequencing of each wave rolling in and pulling back into the sea. This ebb and flow is a manifestation of the innate balance in Mother Nature's wisdom. For every arrival, there is a departure, and for every sunset, a sunrise will come. Though life sometimes shifts us out of the flow, we remember that we are made of energy, and our natural state is balanced and harmonious. This inherent equilibrium is reflected in the ebb and flow of our breath and the flow of life-force through our internal energetic network and in the sea of Qi surrounding us.

When our yin qualities are undernourished, our yang side becomes dominant. This imbalance is felt inside us, and we can sense the lack of balance around us, too. We see the devastation in the natural world in a loss of rainforest, the lungs of the earth, and the loss of species on land, in the air, and in the sea. Overly yang consumption and striving has accelerated climate change, bringing coastal and inland flooding, fires, and extreme drought, all devastating to our human communities, too.

Imbalance in daily life tangles us up on the inside, tightening our tissues and stopping the smooth, balanced flow of energy through the body. Stressing our yin tissues compresses, twists, and tugs our Qi channels, knocking blockages loose and helping to ensure a more even, harmonious flow of energy throughout the body. Healthy, vibrant Qi serves each Organ pair, which, in turn, keeps our physical tissues well and supports our emotional and mental health. Balance in one layer of ourselves nurtures balance in all.

Balanced flow is like our home base, our resting state. We flow like a river streaming downhill, navigating around any obstacle with ease. One way to notice balance and flow is to feel for its opposite: Where is there resistance? Does anything feel out of sync right now? Where is there tension? When we forget that the nature of all things is to flow, to come and go, we can get caught in the trap of resistance.

> It is like a boat going to the ocean. Before it reaches the sea, it is dragged with much effort, but once it reaches the sea, it is propelled without effort by the wind. The distance it travels in the ocean in one day is further than it could be dragged by force even in a hundred years.
>
> – *The Avatamsaka Sutra (Thomas Cleary translation)*

Yin Yoga & Meditation is a microcosm of some of the ways we can seek and encourage balance. We bring stresses to our yin body, for example, to exercise and help restore our soft tissues, nourishing the strong and even flow of Qi within us, and consciously encouraging our body to relax and let go. The stress-and-rest rhythm in our practice reflects and reinforces the importance of the yin and yang complementary qualities, helping us avoid both harmful extremes. On the mat, we cultivate an attention that balances a focused yet relaxed and compassionate awareness as we stay attentive to our moment-to-moment experience. In each posture, we find the stayable stress that balances sensation with relaxation and stillness with mindful adjustments.

For me, finding balance is a life-long training and commitment. Each moment is an invitation to re-discover the center place among doing and non-doing, talking and listening, accomplishing and resting, offering and refilling. Sometimes, even when it's the best thing to do, the hardest thing to do is...nothing. Stopping isn't always easy, but with practice, we get better at recognizing what brings us balance. If we're working, is it possible to do it in a relaxed way? When we're picking up after our children or running errands for our elderly parents, perhaps we relax our shoulders, unclench our jaw, and breathe slowly and mindfully along the way. While at my desk, I regularly use the Plum Village meditation app on my phone. When the Mindfulness bell rings, I let my work go for a few moments and take three conscious, deep breaths. Sometimes I'll complement this with a body scan to intentionally release any tight muscles or a moment of gratitude or an inner smile. Offering ourselves even these little pieces of relief to rebalance makes a big difference in a day.

You might take a few minutes here to reflect quietly or write in your journal about the quality of balance in your practice and life:

- How would you characterize your days right now: balanced, unbalanced, or somewhere in between?
- Recall a couple of examples in your life when you adopted a more harmonious and balanced approach. What prompted you to realize that things were out of balance and something wasn't quite right? What decisions did you make, and what actions did you take to restore your centering energies? How did it feel to come back into balance?
- Does the meaning of balance shift for you based on your life circumstances or the season of life you're in?
- Is there an intention of balance you'd like to set for yourself for your next Yin Yoga session? How would this intention benefit you on the mat?

Finding and maintaining balance may be a moving target that's not always easy to hit, but balance within us, just like the natural equilibrium in the ecosystems around us, is innate to who we are and essential for our whole-self wellbeing. Using the Mindfulness skills we develop in Yin Yoga & Meditation, we continue to learn how to recognize what balance means for us in each moment and get increasingly adept at doing, or non-doing, whichever best helps us regain and maintain our center.

Jewel ~ Embracing Impermanence to Cherish Each Moment

A student once complained to Zen Master Shunryu Suzuki Roshi that although he'd been listening to his lectures for years, he found the Buddhist concepts too complicated and didn't understand them. He asked Master Roshi if he would please explain all the teachings in just one sentence. Everyone sitting in the room chuckled. Master Roshi did, too, then replied, "Sure - everything changes."

Remembering that things will not always be as they currently are has the potential to bring tremendous freedom and relief. Living on the Maine coastline, I was often at the water's edge, sitting for hours watching the endless stream of waves crashing ashore, wave after wave arising then spending itself against the rocky outcroppings, each a unique manifestation of the ocean – persistent, then gone.

We know that everything is of the nature to change: seas, seasons, cycles of growth-release-growth, thoughts, sensations, feelings...they all shift. We learn from watching the ocean what we learn from observing the external circumstances in our lives and the shifts in our internal weather: all is always changing. A wave in the north Atlantic will rise, fall, and be replaced by another wave, just as a thought or emotion will arise within us, manifest, and then fall away as another takes its place. Is there any use in rushing or resisting a wave? Is it possible to grab hold of its beauty and force it to stay?

Not one thing will remain precisely as it is this instant, neither in our practice nor the rest of life. Thich Nhat Hanh once said if there was one thing he could teach everyone, particularly young people, it would be that everything is impermanent. Whether physical, mental, or emotional, favorable, distressing, or neutral, all life circumstances will change. The impermanence of every happening invites us to treasure and relish all that is delightful and nourishing without attaching to it. Nothing is permanent, so we're encouraged to let the present goodness saturate our hearts, grateful for it while it lasts.

Similarly, even heavy or challenging times arrive with an invitation to meet them with compassion, tenderness, and courage, for they, too, cannot remain exactly as they are.

A leaf carried along the surface of a river doesn't attempt to stop the current, it lets go and takes the ride, allowing the river to move as it wishes. As we call on the allowing side of our yin nature, we too can relax and let go of expectations or ideas of how things should be. Nurturing an accepting attitude, we create an atmosphere of openness to the circumstances in our practice and life, and our response to them begins to flow with greater ease.

I have a dear friend who, years ago, lost his job unexpectedly. Rather than shutting down into a fearful or depressive reaction, he opened his heart with acceptance to the circumstance and took the opportunity to fulfill a long-held dream to pursue an extended, immersive Qigong training in Thailand. His courage and receptivity remains an inspiration and a shining example of how the changing nature of all situations can be a valuable ally. As American poet Henry Wadsworth Longfellow noted, the best thing you can do when it's raining is to let it.

The law of constant change is true on the mat as well, where all kinds of thoughts, sensations, and feelings will show up. Here's a breath mantra we can use on or off the mat to help welcome the natural flow of our ever-changing present moments:

Breath like an ocean full of waves,

Breath streaming in...breath streaming out.

Body like an ocean full of waves,

Sensations arriving...sensations diminishing.

Mind like an ocean full of waves,

Thoughts manifesting...thoughts disappearing.

Heart like an ocean full of waves,

Feelings arising...feelings subsiding.

We know we can't stop waves in the ocean which rise and fall, so too, our inner landscape rises and falls, comes and goes, flows. In Yin Yoga & Meditation, we can practice allowing the fluidity of sensations, breath, or moods to come, feel them fully, and then let them go. Cultivating this yin quality of allowing, we build a foundation for acceptance and natural release.

Though not always easy in the moment, change is a wise and beautiful teacher when we give ourselves space and permission to learn from it. Accepting impermanence in our practice, in ourselves, and in the world opens the door to living with greater gratitude, ease, and purpose no matter which circumstances arrive.

Jewel ~ Releasing Tensions for Real Relief

One of Thich Nhat Hanh's most persistent and inspiring encouragements was that we must learn to release the tensions. I'm guessing we've all felt how tensions can accumulate in any layer of ourselves. If left untended, they can fatigue the body, cloud the mind, stiffen the heart, and stifle the spirit.

We often carry these tensions unconsciously, unaware of their weight and the ways they intermingle within us. The many layers of who we are constantly communicate with one another, and that continuous dialogue also includes the transmission of tensions. Just as a troubling emotion within us could manifest as a harsh word toward someone we love, tension impacting the body also touches the mind. What hinders the heart impedes the little rivers of Qi streaming inside. The consistent communication between the layers within us also means each is a potential pathway for relief.

To interrupt the stress-tension cycle, we need to skillfully intervene again and again as we retrain our central nervous system to respond appropriately. This activity is mutually reciprocal; the more we're able to relax and enjoy its benefits, the more our spirit's wisdom invites us to do just that. In Yin Yoga & Meditation, we feel these effects as we bring our awareness back to the present moment with kindness, again and again, as many times as it takes, inviting our body to settle and our muscles to unwind and let go.

In our practice, we have the time and opportunity to explore how tension release in one part of our being is able to bring real relief in the others. We might, for example, focus on quieting the mental landscape through a directed breathing exercise. Concentrating the attention on the in-breath and out-breath naturally settles the physical body, so relaxing the mind invites the physical body to follow. Release in the physical body supports a free flow of Qi through the channels tracing through the tissues. Because our energetic Organ network influences our emotions, harmonizing our inner energies has a rebalancing effect on how we feel. Each aspect of who we are therefore becomes a potential pathway of release for all the others. This is empowering because no matter which layer of being we engage with, we're able to use it to access and bring ease to the rest. We can choose to put this same jewel of encouragement to work for us in daily life, too, using the miracle of our interconnection to infuse relaxation and harmony into any circumstance.

Jewel ~ Nurturing Interconnection through Lovingkindness

Yin Yoga & Meditation invites us to consider that we are not just in the universe but that the universe is in us, too, unbounded by time and place and space, no past or future, no here, no there...no separation. Consider that at our core, the heart of the universe, is endless peace, undisturbed harmony, and unconditional love. In this landscape of interconnection is our most profound healing, where all things are in all things, where you, me, and all that is remains linked.

Intrinsically linked to everyone and everything, each of us is not an island in an ocean but the ocean itself. None of us can *be* alone – this is the root of Thich Nhat Hanh's teaching of interbeing. We may feel alone in the rush of a day or the crush of a tough or lonely period, but the boundaries between what is you and what is me are more porous than they may at first appear. Our energies, like the warm glow of the sun, travel outward and outward, connecting us with all that is. Every word we speak makes a wave, a ripple in the sea of energy. Each of us relies on one another, exists because of one another, and gives life and love and inspiration to one another. Even the simple act of sharing a warm smile with someone we pass on the street demonstrates how the energy of welcome travels as their face lights up and sends a smile back.

If you'd like, sense for a few moments how your energies stream ever outward. Let your breath be natural as you reflect on one positive thing that's happened in your life or one loving thing you've done and how it has flowed beyond you into the world. Perhaps you recall a seemingly small thing...a dollar given, food delivered, water conserved, a hug offered, words of encouragement extended, or an opportunity provided for you or someone else to grow or shine. See and feel it clearly, letting the details of the circumstance sharpen in your mind and the emotions of the experience manifest within you. Now, trace with your mind the ways it has impacted you or others over the days or years. What other acts, words, or decisions has it sparked? Stretch your mind as far as possible and imagine the many ways it has touched your family, friends, friends of friends, colleagues, your neighborhood, others across the world, the animals with whom we share the earth, or the earth itself. Everything that happens has an infinite effect, in some way touching everything else. Let this intricate, inspiring web of life connections fill your mind and heart.

jewel

So Hum is a traditional breath meditation that reinforces the interconnected nature of all things. So Hum is the song the breath sings. On the inhale, we hear So...on the exhale, we hear Hum.

You might try this mantra, listening to the sounds of So Hum as you breathe:

Breathing in,
So.
Breathing out,
Hum.
So...I am.
Hum...that.

I am...that, I am connected within the whole of the universe, all happiness and happenings intertwined. The more we open our hearts, the more others are encouraged to open their hearts, too. Like laughter, compassionate awareness and generosity of spirit are contagious. Each act of goodness sews itself to another to create a kind and loving fabric that holds all of us together. When we take specific actions, like the simple act of coming to our mats, we support our own wellbeing. That act supports and nourishes everyone and everything we come into contact with. Honoring the interconnected nature of all things reduces suffering and grows peace within all of us. As long as we live, as long as we breathe, we enjoy and spread the song of our breath, So Hum, the song of interbeing.

CHAPTER 7

THE YIN AND YANG WINGS OF NATURAL PRESENCE

In the quiet stillness of Yin Yoga & Meditation, we exercise the physical body while also exploring the inner landscapes of the whole of who we are. To support safe physical exercise, we provide ourselves and our students with a variety of posture instructions, including technical cues such as pose contraindications, modifications, focus areas, and the use of props. Similarly, we can offer meditative inquiry cueing and mindful guidance to aid skillful navigation of the vast territories of the mind, energetic architecture, and heart.

In the "Watch and Welcome What's Happening Inside You" practice principle, we discussed ways to anchor our attention and receive our experiences with friendly caring. A key part of our Mandala Map, present moment awareness is often spoken of as a bird with two wings, perception that is simultaneously clear-sighted and compassionately responsive. You might think of these two wings as the yang and yin of natural presence, joining the *what* of our perception with the *how* of our reception.

Awareness Anchors

The act of anchoring the awareness is the more active yang-like wing, helping us stay attentive to what we're experiencing. With this wing, we grow our natural ability to concentrate our sustained awareness on internal arisings, the *what* of our experience. Anchor words such as aware of, greet, recognize, notice, watch, and observe, among others, help us to place and hold the awareness steady on the Now.

The yin-like wing of presence is the essence with which we receive our moment-to-moment happenings. This wing imbues the tone and manner of our attention, the *how* we attend to our experience. Our breath, curiosity, spaciousness, smile, gratitude, kindness and compassion, as well as insights from the natural world are some of our most steady and trustworthy internal guardians. Like shining a light along a trail leading into a beautiful forest full of wonder and possibility, we call on these inner resources to help illuminate the journey we make into our practice and ourselves. Our yin qualities include our natural ability to sense, feel, allow, accept, let go, yield, and not-do. They function like a softened golden filter added to the spotlight of our mindful attention, keeping it patient, nurturing, and free of judgment.

Just as a one-winged bird will have difficulty getting off the ground, both of these wings are necessary for our practice of presence to soar. If, for example, we only offer diligent attention and investigation without a kind approach, we could fall captive to our inner critic delivering harsh judgment, commentary, and complaints. On the other hand, if we're unaware of what's happening, how can we be open to receive and respond wisely? Like the bird aiming itself toward the sky, we need both wings to fly.

Receiving our Experience

The yin and yang wings of natural presence work collaboratively to steady and nurture our innate capacity to swing the door of the heart open to the present moment and treat each arrival warmly, whether it's a sensation, thought, feeling, or circumstance, even when challenging. In positive circumstances, they ensure we're fully aware of and appreciative of these moments of life, present to savor and celebrate them with a heart of appreciation and joy.

Working as one, these two wings encourage compassionate observation and provide a mutually supportive refuge for further developing a loving and accepting attention. From their sanctuary, we can wake our minds and hearts out of conditioned habits and reactions so that genuine presence, natural wisdom, and true compassion guide us in a pose, our practice, and in our life.

Chapter 8

Yin Guardians, Trusted Companions

In this section, we'll take a deeper dive into the yin guardians that have accompanied our travels through the Mandala Map and serve as trusted companions in our practice. You'll also find some meditative inquiry for your personal reflections on what the guardians illuminate inside you and how you might call on their energies to support you on the mat.

Guardian ~ The Breath

Our Personal Zen Master

The breath is like our personal Zen Master, always with us, full of wisdom, and willing to teach us. Although working skillfully with the breath may not have been a focus of our coursework in school, we can grow in our understanding of this ever-present yin guardian and strengthen our ability to put it to use. How we feel, what we think, and our circumstances in life all change, but one thing stays true: the breath is an effective and accessible tool that helps us calm and heal the body, settle and soothe the mind, and reconnect our awareness with the peace that lives within us. Learning to listen to and use the breath to support our health and happiness is a skill we can improve to serve us on the Yin Yoga mat and through the day.

What's the secret to life? Just keep breathing!

– *George Burns*

In the general "rule of threes" survival guidelines, we are able to survive three weeks without food, three days without water, three hours in a harsh environment, and just three minutes without air. Our breath is central to every physical activity we do, affecting our digestive system, heart function, cellular growth, and muscle tone. The quality of our breathing directly affects the health of our physical body, and in turn, the quality of our wellbeing. The better we breathe, the better we live.

We breathe the world, and the world breathes us. The earth exhales oxygen for us to inhale. We exhale the carbon dioxide the earth inhales. Our lives and this earth co-exist as one sustained breath cycle. During an average lifetime, a person shares their breath with the universe half a billion times. What an extraordinary collection of opportunities we have every single day to reconnect with our body, mind, heart, and one another. As we breathe with awareness, we're reminded that we belong to each other, the exchange of each breath evidence of our harmonious union.

Breath is life, so when we deepen the breath, we expand and enhance the vibrancy of our life-force energy. When we improve the way we breathe, we build our internal Qi stores and feel better in every way. The breath is a primary tool we have, not just for accumulating and replenishing our energy, but also for circulating Qi to help keep the network of energy within us balanced and flowing well, supporting us physically, mentally, and emotionally.

Reveals and Transforms How We Feel

In the breath, we have a sage advisor and constant companion who knows us intimately and is constantly communicating information about how we are. There's a marvelous symbiotic relationship between our breath, body, mind, and heart. Like a mirror, the breath continually reflects the experience of our physical body in each moment and reveals what mental and emotional patterns may be playing out within us.

As we learned in the "Move Mindfully to Mild Sensation" practice principle, a labored breath likely indicates we've pushed the body further into a posture than it's ready to go. Similarly, if we feel anxious or upset, we tend to experience shallow, rapid breathing. At times when we're feeling peaceful and content, perhaps taking a relaxing stroll with a loved one, our breath will be easy and full. Because the breath changes as our experiences change, observing the nature of the breath provides information about what we're doing and how we're feeling.

If we transform the way we breathe, the way we feel transforms too. Imbalanced, rapid chest breathing that only engages the top of the lungs induces the stress response, while relaxed whole-body breathing induces the relaxation response, releasing physical and mental tensions. Using the insight we receive from the breath, we're empowered to respond based on what we learn, whether on the mat or during our day.

Breathing well not only nourishes the physical tissues of our body but also helps settle the nervous system, allowing us to stay more attentive and present. If the body is tense, the breath can relieve it. If the body is tired, the breath can energize it. If the mind is unmoored, the breath can anchor it. If the mind is dull, the breath can enliven it. Each time we stay present for, and breathe with, discomfort or challenge, we teach our central nervous system that the breath can comfort it. Using the breath in this way increases our tolerance for emotional and physical triggers by growing our ability to relax, even in the face of difficulty.

Finding Freedom in Letting Go

Constantly changing, the breath is a living demonstration of impermanence. It consistently reminds us of the temporary nature of all things. Every thought, sensation, feeling, and experience arises, exists, and then subsides. Whether pleasant, unpleasant, or neutral, all will change. Staying attentive to the breath helps us stay attentive to the whole of our experience, as it is, for as long as it is.

Wherever we are and whatever's happening, we have the ability look to the breath, our personal Zen Master, to remind us in each moment how much freedom and possibility lie in the act of letting go. If we refused to surrender the in-breath, we wouldn't be able to exhale toxins from our body and make room for new air. If we refused to let go of the out-breath, we couldn't bring in fresh oxygen to nourish our cells. A willingness to let go makes our very life possible.

In your practice, you may find yourself holding onto something too tightly, whether an interaction earlier in the day, a nagging anxious thought, or a preconceived notion of what a particular pose was going to feel like. If so, practice acknowledging it with kindness, then bring your awareness to the breath. Breathe in fully and feel your body relaxing deeply into each out-breath. Acknowledge how the in-breath nourishes, and how the out-breath supports release. Steep in the sense of liberation that comes from letting each breath go in its time. With each out-breath, what if you were to imagine whatever it is you were holding onto begin to loosen and let go, like a bird nimbly rising from a branch into the sky?

Holding tightly onto one thing deprives us of something else. Just as denying ourselves a deep inhale prevents maximum nourishment, denying ourselves varying experiences causes us to miss out on the freshness of inspiring new possibilities. Perhaps you've experienced the upset of losing something you would have preferred to keep. You might inquire, did you also find any unexpected joys arising in the space that loss left behind? If our hands are full, how do we receive, whether a new opportunity, a different perspective, or a gift of grace? The act of letting go isn't without challenge, but the more we practice it, the more easily it will come. We can take inspiration from the good work the breath does as it lets go over and over, filling and emptying, filling and emptying, and in the process, sustaining our life.

You have an appointment with life, an appointment that is in the here and now.

– *Thich Nhat Hanh*

The breath has just one destination. Like climbing into a taxicab, the breath is a vehicle that will always drive us home to our body and to the present time. We experience this in our Yin Yoga & Meditation practice by following the in-breath and out-breath as it flows. Do this anywhere, anytime for a few moments, enjoying your breath's normal flow and then ask yourself: *Where am I?* The answer will be, always, *here*. Unchained from the past, freed from the worries of the future, the breath lives only right here in this moment. What a beautiful gift this breath gives, reliably bringing you to the here and now.

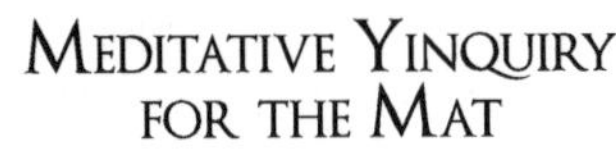

Meditative Yinquiry for the Mat

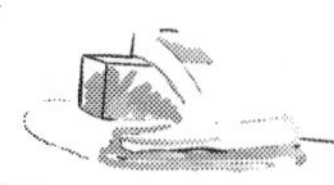

Whenever we're on our mat, our breath will give us information about our experience. As you steep in your postures, inquire: *How would I describe my breath right now? How is it flowing? Is this telling me something about the state of my body in this moment, or the state of my mind and heart? Is there anything I want to change based on what's being shared?*

Guardian ~ Kindness and Compassion

Safeguards of the Spirit

A practice of nurturing our loving and allowing attention, Yin Yoga & Meditation is an opportunity to train the mind in both self-awareness and kindness. When we treat ourselves with gentleness and understanding, we affirm that we are deserving of love. Sometimes without even realizing it, we're battling our body, arguing with our mind, or fighting with reality in some way. Showing up tenderly for ourselves and what we're experiencing is a fundamental, and in many ways revolutionary, act of kindness that extends far beyond ourselves.

There's a story of an elderly monk who fled Tibet after being in prison for an extended time. Arriving in India, he had the opportunity to meet with the Dalai Lama, who asked him to recount the hardships he'd endured while imprisoned. As he described the hunger and loneliness he'd lived with and the torture he'd suffered, the Dalai Lama asked him if at any point he felt his life was in danger. "In truth," the old monk answered, "the only time I felt at risk was when I felt in danger of losing compassion for my jailers." The monk was saying that compassion acts as a safeguard for the spirit.

On the mat, we build our ability to consistently respond with kindness. We know practicing will help us get better at playing the piano. The same is true with emotional responses arising in our brain. As you remember, our brains remodel themselves to reinforce commonly used pathways, so practicing kindness as an emotional response builds our brain's capacity to regularly prioritize compassion regardless of circumstance. What we practice grows stronger.

Kindness Transforms Us

When we connect, there is compassion. What if we encounter each other with well-wishing rather than judgment? This could change the world.

– *Norman Blair*

A 2018 University of Oxford study demonstrated that repeating acts of kindness increases our happiness levels.[1] In this experiment, one group of participants was asked to perform an act of kindness toward themselves, someone they knew, or a stranger every day for one week. At the end of the study, researchers found that those who had consistently demonstrated kindness each day reported feeling happier, regardless of who the recipient of their kindness was. The same study also found that even just observing acts of kindness performed by others boosted happiness in the observer as much as it did if they were performing the kindness themself. Whether offering kindness or simply watching it, kindness benefits our spirits.

In addition to the physiological benefit of raising levels of feel-good hormones like oxytocin and dopamine, the presence of kindness also prompts the production of a neurotransmitter called serotonin that helps to regulate our mood. The neurotransmitters generated when we extend or witness kindness keep us feeling uplifted, connected, and centered. Physically, the experience of kindness may also improve circulation, reduce blood pressure, and improve temperature and weight control. Kindness is a protector, inside and out.

Perhaps you've heard the ancient Indian tale of a small parrot who was enduring a terrible storm raging in the forest. At the height of the storm, lightning struck a dead tree, causing it to burst into flames. The frightened little parrot watched as the fire spread quickly and soon endangered all the animals who lived there. The parrot flew wildly about to warn the animals, but the raging fire had many of them trapped. Desperate to help her friends, the parrot darted to the river, dipped into the water, then circled back over the fire, shaking her wings to release the drops of water. The tiny droplets tumbled down into the blaze and vanished with barely a hiss. Again and again, the relentless parrot returned from the river, each time shaking drops of water from her charred feathers onto the mounting flames.

Though sincere, her small efforts were simply no match for such a massive fire. The divine eagle Garuda, the fierce God of Protection, noticed the flurried activity and flew down to the tiny bird. "Little parrot," he asked, "what do you think you're doing? This fire is much too large for you. Save yourself." The exhausted parrot turned to him sadly and said, "Lord Garuda, though I'm small, I'm just trying to do what I can." The little parrot's courage and compassion instantly touched Garuda's heart. Large tears began to flow down his face, falling onto the burning forest in massive streams. More and more tears poured from his eyes onto the fire, eventually extinguishing every last flame and saving the animals from danger.

What a sweet reminder of how acts of compassion, however small, make a difference and create change in ourselves, in others, and in the world. Kindness is one of the most potent energies we bring onto our practice mat as well as into the rest of our lives. I think of it as a guardian angel able to enter any circumstance, even the deepest suffering, and begin to calm and transform it. Kindness changes our emotional and physical terrain, what we see and how we feel, and these changes can't help but ripple out to those around us.

Every Kindness Matters

No act of kindness, no matter how small, is ever wasted.

– *Aesop*

Each of us has the capacity to create and amplify the energy of kindness in the world and choose to make kindness, which is to say the transformation of suffering, a priority. Belgian artist Francis Alÿs once created a piece called "Faith Moves Mountains." This community work of art took place in Lima, Peru to bring awareness to the many poverty-stricken political and economic refugees there. Five hundred volunteers stood at the bottom of a sand dune holding shovels. As the land art effort began, Alÿs synchronized their movements so that they moved the dune forward together, taking scoop after scoop at precisely the same time. Over a few hours, they succeeded in moving the sand mountain four inches forward! Working together, the refugees achieved in less than a day what would have taken the wind years to do.

"Faith Moves Mountains" is an inspiring demonstration that together, we're able to accomplish anything, even things that feel impossible. Connected to everyone and everything, every time we invite kindness to flow through us, we change ourselves, and thereby change the world. Every smile, every positive thought, every step we take in the direction of happiness and peace, every act of generosity, every time we say yes to trying, yes to life, and yes to caring and to love – every single one matters. Each of these kindnesses has the ability to move mountains, one shovel at a time.

Meditative Yinquiry for the Mat

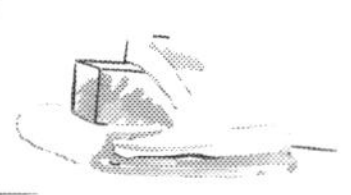

Yin Yoga & Meditation is a practice of bearing witness to the heart. By strengthening the quality of loving, allowing attention, we strengthen our commitment to be good company for ourselves however it is we're feeling. Consider: What does being good company for yourself mean right now? What kindness might you offer your body or your experience in this moment?

Guardian ~ The Shining Light of Curiosity

The wisdom teachings present curiosity as one of the most valuable approaches we can develop. The energy of this precious yin guardian is central to our mindful practice, helping us listen and learn and keeping us engaged and present. When we shine the light of curiosity on our experience, the shadows of doubt, self-judgment, and anxiety begin to diminish as interested inquiry takes their place.

Before yoga class one evening, a student shared a personal story with me about the unsettling experience she'd recently had when a small moth crawled into her ear. No matter how hard she shook her head, the moth wouldn't come back out, so she called 911, and they took her by ambulance to the emergency room. She said it was such an uncomfortable feeling, and the poor little moth must have been scared and confused too! It fluttered around inside her ear canal for more than three hours before the ER nurse extracted it. The student was shocked when the resident doctor mentioned this same thing had happened to her once, too. Instead of calling 911, she paused and remembered that moths are drawn to light. Curious if the same would be true for the moth in her ear, she went to a small room in her house, turned off the lights, and clicked on a flashlight. Sure enough, it wasn't long before the moth climbed right out of her ear and fluttered around the beam of light.

This story has stuck with me through the years as a compelling reminder about the power of letting things be long enough to get curious about them and how surprising insights often arise when we access our natural ability to be inquisitive. Like the resident doctor who wondered what the moth in her ear would do if she sat still in the dark and switched on a flashlight, in Yin Yoga & Meditation, we're invited to settle the body into stillness and shine the light of our curious attention inward.

An Allowing Attention

We can train in allowing ourselves to become fascinated by the interplay of our energy, emotions, mental habits, and physical tissues, even in those times it might not be comfortable. You might try this now. Stop here where you are and ask yourself: *What's happening inside me right now?* Notice what you find. Now, ask the same question again, but this time lead your inquiry with the relaxing and sustaining sound of *hmmmm*. Like this: *Hmmm...What is happening inside me right now? Hmmmm, what are these thoughts dancing around inside my mind? Hmmmm, how does my body feel?*

As you listen for your spirit's response, sense how adding this simple sound evokes a renewed sense of curiosity and wonder. Curiosity, like a good friend, invites us to look at what's happening with fresh interest, so we're less likely to become side-tracked by self-judgment or other unhelpful distractions. When we set the intention to inquire with an accepting tone, we're training our mind to focus more on opening to the moment rather than judging or ignoring whatever the moment holds.

Said another way, curiosity gives rise to an allowing quality of attention, slowing down our reaction timeframe to help us lean a little more into our direct experience. Leaning in longer lets our awareness linger in the nature of what's happening and open to new ways of receiving, like peering into a dark room requires time for our eyes to adjust. Sometimes a curious attitude and a soft tone are all it takes to illuminate more creative and compassionate responses. For example, while surveying the body for physical sensations in a posture, a steady, inquiring attention on our experience of the exercise allows us to make real-time mindful adjustments throughout the practice as our body requests.

Remaining inquisitive about the variety of thoughts, sensations, and emotions we encounter on the mat, we're able to work in alignment with our needs in the spirit of caring self-discovery. This commitment to curiosity extends off the mat, too, helping us hold ourselves and one another in the same gentle, welcoming light.

Meditative Yinquiry for the Mat

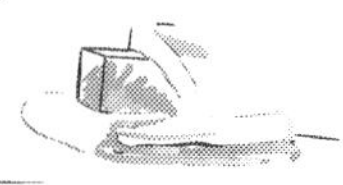

Shining the light of curiosity on whatever it is we're experiencing in our Yin Yoga & Meditation practice offers a pathway to stay present for ourselves on the mat. Embody the wonder of a child as you inquire: *Hmmm...what's here in this moment?* There's no need to evaluate or judge what you learn, just welcome it as an opportunity to grow in awareness, opening your heart to any insights that may arrive.

Guardian ~ Spaciousness

We are like the sky, with thoughts and feelings like birds flying through us. As the pace of life grows faster and faster, at times we find ourselves getting caught in reaction more easily. There is a pause available to us, a place that may become obscured but never erased. In that pause, we hear this yin guardian whispering, "You're as spacious and vast as the infinite sky."

Looking down at our body, we seem pretty solid, but as the New Zealand-born British physicist Ernest Rutherford pointed out, matter is mostly empty space. An atom is 99.9999999% empty space, to be precise. That's a whole lot of no-thing! To visualize this, imagine taking away all the empty space from the atoms making up your body. The condensed subatomic solids would be smaller than a granule of salt. That's how spacious we really are.

As we train in non-reactivity on the mat, Yin Yoga & Meditation allows us to inhabit our natural spaciousness and fully arrive into the present time. When we create space inside us, we have a place to go, a shelter from immediate drama, and are better able to step aside to see and feel clearly. We become a place of peace not just for ourselves but for others, too. What a beautiful gift to offer. Thich Nhat Hanh offered this example when telling of the many people leaving Vietnam in small boats during the 1970s. Often when the boats encountered storms and turbulent seas, people would panic, and the boats could sink. "But if even one person aboard can remain calm," he said, "knowing what to do and what not to do, he or she can help the boat survive. His or her expression communicates clarity and calmness, and people have trust in that person. One such person can save the lives of many."

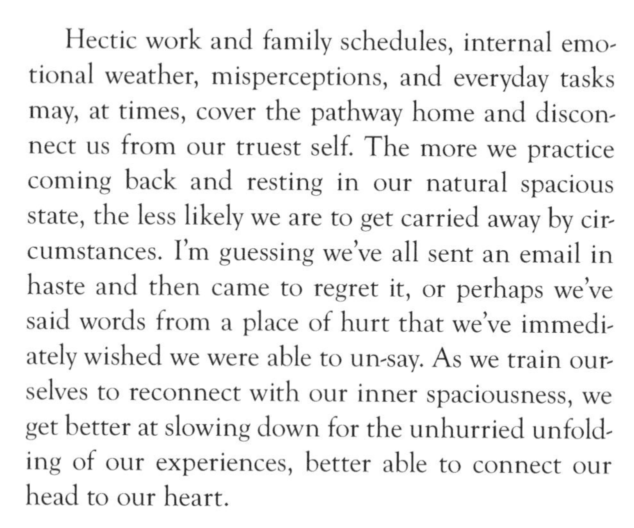

Hectic work and family schedules, internal emotional weather, misperceptions, and everyday tasks may, at times, cover the pathway home and disconnect us from our truest self. The more we practice coming back and resting in our natural spacious state, the less likely we are to get carried away by circumstances. I'm guessing we've all sent an email in haste and then came to regret it, or perhaps we've said words from a place of hurt that we've immediately wished we were able to un-say. As we train ourselves to reconnect with our inner spaciousness, we get better at slowing down for the unhurried unfolding of our experiences, better able to connect our head to our heart.

We can learn to notice the beginnings of an emotion as it starts to take shape and how it presents itself in our physical body. Aware of the mind-body connection, if we notice a knot forming in our stomach, for example, or that our breath is becoming a bit shallow, we recognize that these physical sensations could be signaling anxiousness or worry: *Ah, some tightness in my belly. It feels like I'm starting to worry about something.* From there, we can begin to inquire a little further to see what's there. In riding backward on the emotion's wave, we offer our spacious and loving attention to what is happening so that we have the feeling instead of the feeling having us.

Lowering the Temperature

Nepalese Buddhist teacher Tsoknyi Rinpoche often tells a touching tale of renewing his bodhisattva vow at the Buddhist shrine in Bodhgaya, India. Repeating the vow as he walked around the Bodhi tree under which the Buddha attained enlightenment, he felt something tap his head. Looking down, Tsoknyi was thrilled to see it was a treasured Bodhi leaf that had fallen. No one is to remove any leaves from the tree, but if one falls freely, it's fair game. He wasn't the only one who saw this coveted leaf drop, and soon others began to crowd around him. In an instant, he grabbed the leaf from the ground before anyone else could get to it...it did hit his head after all in this most sacred of times. Almost immediately, he felt ashamed. He'd been renewing a vow to end the suffering of all beings under this ancient and blessed tree, and no sooner than his prayer had finished, he had selfishly taken the leaf for himself. He chided himself inwardly, thinking, *I can't even give my fellow beings a little leaf!*

Overcome with guilt, Tsoknyi decided to crush the leaf in dismay. In that moment, a quiet voice from all of his years of practice rose inside him and intervened, saying, *Keep it. Let this leaf serve as a compassionate reminder that although our intentions may be sincere, we all become caught in human conditioning sometimes.*

Tsoknyi's story is an encouraging testimony that we never need to feel ashamed of being human. Each of us will make mistakes, act impulsively, or do things we wish we hadn't. Stepping back from the impulse to reactively judge or berate ourselves in those moments, we can take a moment to recalibrate ourselves to the principles and beliefs that guide us and be inspired to act in better alignment with them next time. Like the air conditioning coming to help a room's atmosphere transform from hot to cool, training ourselves to inhabit that internal space before reflexively acting helps lower our internal temperature and give calm and insight a chance to rise.

The Mindful Quarter Second

Our biology contains a built-in opportunity to help us inhabit our innate spaciousness. A scientifically proven, automated pause is wired into our nervous system. In the 1970s, neurosurgeon and researcher Benjamin Libet laid out the specific brain mechanics of this quarter-second pause. Libet led fascinating experiments related to this "readiness potential," the electrical change that happens in the brain which precedes voluntary acts. He found that the electrical change occurs before becoming aware of the intention to act and that the intention to act precedes taking action by about a quarter of a second. He explained these results by positing that the brain likely "bubbles up" a proposed action, and our consciousness then has about a quarter of a second to decide what we will do.

Author Tara Bennett-Goleman termed this built-in pause the "magical quarter second" in her book *Mind Whispering: A New Map to Freedom from Self-Defeating Emotional Habits*. Another way to think of it is as "the mindful quarter second" because it guarantees we have as many options as we do thoughts in our mind. The magical, mindful quarter second means that between every intention and action exists space for conscious consideration and choosing a wise, skillful response. Although reactions may feel instantaneous, as we see, the science says otherwise. We're never as stuck as we might at first think.

The mindful attention we develop in the Yin Yoga & Meditation practice helps us slow down to find that pause, stilling the body, turning our attention inward, and allowing the awareness to abide in the natural spaciousness always available within us. With training, we free ourselves from unconscious, habitual impulses and find the other side of reactivity, offering whatever is happening a steadier and more insightful reception.

Meditative Yinquiry for the Mat

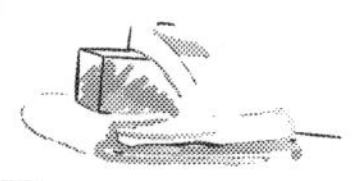

The Yin Yoga & Meditation practice invites us to inhabit our natural spaciousness. How could you find and expand your magic and mindful quarter seconds on the mat? What possibilities open to you as you do?

Guardian ~ The Alchemy of a Smile

Our innate ability to transform is a central premise in Taoist energy practices. Many techniques use something very ordinary to catalyze this extraordinary inner alchemy: our smile. This joyful yin guardian speaks an uncomplicated and inclusive language that moves past the intellect and the ego to speak right to the heart. Buddhism encourages warmth and compassion toward all. The Indian Yogic tradition instructs that friendliness is a measure of the success of our practice. Taoism teaches that a smile is one of the best medicines to give or receive. No matter who you are, where you're from, or what wisdom tradition you follow, everyone senses that a heartfelt smile communicates warmth, safety, and welcome.

The Smiling Circuit in the Brain

We don't need science to tell us a smile is capable of transforming circumstances, but there are plenty of studies to back the many benefits smiling brings. Early in the twentieth century, French Physiologist Dr. Israel Waynbaum theorized that facial expressions affected blood flow to the brain and triggered the release of specific brain transmitters. Modern research supports the tangible effects both smiling and frowning have on our biochemistry. Smiling activates the reward center of the brain, releasing happy hormones like endorphins and dopamine, while reducing stress-related cortisol. It also produces killer T-cells to boost the immune system and other signals to relax the muscles, improve breathing, reduce pain, and accelerate healing. Because these neurotransmitters are tied to the smile-activated muscles in the face, even forced smiles offer these benefits! In 2015, a team of researchers from universities in Switzerland and Germany published a study demonstrating that injecting Botox into muscles linked to sadness or upset alleviates feelings of depression. Preventing the face from creating sad expressions alleviated feelings of sadness.[2]

The next time you're feeling a little low, try enlisting your smile to uplift your mood. Simply take three slow, deep breaths, look up, and smile from ear to ear. Give yourself this smile boost anywhere, anytime and enjoy its immediate effects. Here's more good news: smiling is self-sustaining. A happy brain encourages us to smile and smiling encourages the brain to be happy. The more we smile, the more we want to smile, and the more we help those around us smile.

> Sometimes your joy is the source of your smile, but sometimes your smile can be the source of your joy.
>
> - Thich Nhat Hanh

guardian

There's an ancient Taoist story of a student readying to leave his teacher for the mountains, never to return. As they stood together in the courtyard, the old Taoist master signaled to him to come close. The student leaned in, anticipating his revered teacher would impart one last transcendent wisdom teaching. "Smile," the master whispered into his ear. The elevating energy of the simple smile is transformative, an open secret to health and happiness.

Shining the Sunlight of the Inner Smile

Taoism teaches that negative emotions may, over time, settle into our Organ Systems, those energetic centers within the body that oversee our physical, mental, and emotional functions. When negative emotions take up residence there, they can cause disruptions in all aspects of ourselves such as physical illness, emotional upsets, and energetic disharmonies. The Inner Smile is a foundational Taoist meditation technique used to heal and balance emotions. In it, we send a warm smile all through the body to initiate an alchemical process that helps to break this unhealthy cycle by transforming difficult or disruptive emotions into positive energy. In the "Inner Smile and Energetic Self-Love" technique (p. 262), we explore how to use this meditation exercise to infuse the body with the loving energy of our smile and convert negative emotions into compassionate, healing energy.

I had the good fortune to enjoy a delightful and profound inner smile meditation led by Sister Chan Khong in which we sent lovingkindness and appreciation to all parts of the body. Held in the expansive Great Togetherness Meditation Hall of Blue Cliff Monastery, the experience was so poignant and enveloped us all with grace and care. When done with sincerity, using the energy of the smile to offer all these aspects of ourselves authentic love and gratitude can be blissfully transformative.

Shining the sunlight of inner smile energy inside you is like soaking yourself in loving acceptance. As natural as a baby's bright grin, the inner smile invites our surrendering side to rise within us and welcome everything, expecting nothing. Offering this warmth to each part of ourselves melts walls of separation inside and around us. In this practice, we train our ability to truly open to our body, mind, and spirit, to be our own best friend without preconditions. We can relax more with who we are, where we are, as we are.

Our inner smile invites us to look at even the most hidden parts of ourselves with a certain softness, a tender and loving gaze that says: *I see you, I welcome you, and I love you.* Unbounded by stipulations and demands, this self-love and acceptance naturally extend outward to those we encounter.

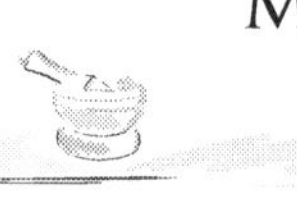

Meditative Yinquiry for the Mat

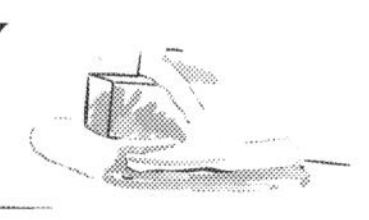

Are there any aspects of your Yin Yoga & Meditation experience that would benefit from the shine of your inner smile? Train your loving smile on them for a few moments, allowing its warmth to soften any edges of judgment or resistance. Notice - are there any shifts that you sense?

Guardian ~ The Natural World

Mirror and Healer

Have you experienced a moment of complete peace and a sense of sacred oneness when out in nature? Maybe you were poised atop a mountain, dipping your toes in a river, standing under a giant sequoia, or gazing up at the milky way galaxy, the moon, or the light of a fallen star finally making it to earth? Moments of grandeur and awe-inspiring feelings of interconnectedness don't require a trip to a far-off place. Even simple moments can be sacred, as when a glint of sunset dances atop a wave or you spy a lotus opening in morning's first light. Even just the fragrance of the forest as you pad over pine needles on a path casts a spell on the spirit.

Taoism teaches that we are happiest and healthiest when we live in close alignment with the ways of the earth, harmonizing ourselves with the natural energies all around us. When yang energy dominates our days, we may forget to take time to unplug, unwind, and reconnect to the magical web of life. This yin guardian, the natural world, beckons us to remember.

Nature Nurtures

We are of the earth, a part of everything that also is a part of us. One connected whole, we move through life on this planet impacting and impacted by every other thing: earth, sun, rain...plants, animals, insects... friends, family, neighbors, and the larger human family of which we all are part. Countless galaxies spin alongside our own in the boundless and unknowable expanse of space. Steeping in the inevitable sense of awe that arises, we can't help but be humbled by the world's majestic beauty and creative intelligence, honored to be alive and breathing on this earth. These precious moments of gratitude are rejuvenating for the body and restorative for the soul.

Is there a hill near you that offers a wide-open view of the sky? Perhaps climb it early one morning or at sunset time. Stand looking toward where the sky meets the land with your shoulders relaxed and your breath full and deep. As you breathe in, look down toward the earth, feeling rooted and stable. Breathing out, let your gaze rise high into the sky, letting yourself dissolve into its vastness and majesty. Breathe in and out in this way for a few moments, grounding, then expanding into all that is, allowing the infinite space to infuse every part of yourself... the universe itself embodied in you.

As far back as I remember, I've always felt incredibly alive, content, and whole when immersed in nature. Spending time outdoors under the sky has been a steady source of rejuvenation and restoration throughout my life. I grew up near Lake Ontario in upstate New York and enjoyed the beauty of four seasons. My love of different landscapes inspired me to live in and travel areas as diverse as the Meseta of Spain, the mountains and glaciers of Southern Chile, the forests and meandering rivers feeding Lake Superior, and the rocky coast of Maine. Living now in the Sonoran Desert of southern Arizona under spacious skies, I'm enchanted by the southwestern landscape dotted by majestic saguaros and ringed around on all sides by mountains: the Tortolita, Silverbell, Tucson, Santa Rita, Rincon, and Santa Catalina ranges. In just a few moments, I find the jeweled blue skies and breathtaking vistas transform my perspective and help me attune to the wisdom of mother earth.

Mother nature has always sustained our human family physically and spiritually. Indigenous peoples worldwide have lived in respectful relationship with the earth that fed their community, creativity, music, and medicine. In the last few decades, modern technology has infused nearly every aspect of life. In addition to the new ways of learning and connecting it brings, our always-on array of devices have the capacity to distance us from nurturing an intimate connection with the universe around us.

In his book *Last Child in the Woods,* author and journalist Richard Louv coined the term "nature-deficit disorder" to describe, as he writes, "the human costs of alienation from nature." More emotional and spiritual diagnosis than medical determination, he asserts this relatively recent state of detachment from nature has spurred a growing collection of scientific evidence pointing to higher rates of attentional challenges, emotional illnesses, obesity, and an overall lessening of stewardship and care for the earth. The infiltration of electronic technology into almost every aspect of our lives and expanding reliance on artificial intelligence has increasingly alienated human beings of all ages from the nurturing and healing possible in nature. "The more high-tech our lives become," he says, "the more nature we need. It's an equation."

Have you heard of the study done by Brighton and Sussex Medical school on the effects that natural soundscapes have on people experiencing high levels of stress?[3] Researchers found that just five minutes spent listening to nature sounds like babbling brooks and birdsong promoted heightened external awareness, faster reaction times, and decreased heart rates in participants who reported high stress levels. These sounds were associated with reducing the body's fight-flight response and increasing the parasympathetic response, helping people feel more present and relaxed. Fascinatingly, even artificial versions from a sound machine or mobile app produced these results. In addition, the study found that the more stressed a participant was, the more benefit they received from listening to the songs of mother earth.

The rhythms of nature invite and encourage contemplation and connection. When we live in harmony with the natural world and take time to savor its elegance, efficiency, and splendor, we find it's full of inspirations, signs, and messages. When first moving to the Tucson area, we noticed on our hikes that young saguaro cacti were often cuddled near palo verde and mesquite trees. With a little research, we discovered why. Called nurse plants, these trees provide shelter and support, nourishing the soil and protecting the growing cactus from the bright desert sun. What a rich metaphor for all the ways we nurture and are nurtured by one another. As we spend more time outdoors, our appreciation increases for all the ways the earth makes life possible for us and we become more inclined to be better stewards of the planet that holds us so tenderly by her side.

We can benefit from inquiring: What is there to learn when we look into nature's mirror? What wisdom do we find by immersing ourselves in and embodying the seasons and other natural cycles? The natural world is our safe keeper, mirror, and healer, ever-present and inviting us to integrate its wisdom into our life and continued practice.

MEDITATIVE YINQUIRY FOR THE MAT

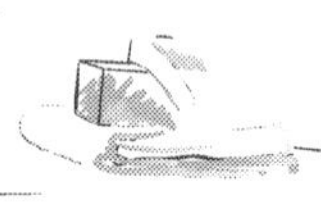

In our practice, we can experiment with emulating nature's ways to help rebalance our internal energies. Consider – are there times in your practice when you would benefit from rooting down like a tree, flowing like a river, or setting yourself free in the spacious sky of the mind?

GUARDIAN ~ THE HEART OF GRATITUDE

If the only prayer you ever say in your entire life is 'thank you,' it will be enough.

– *Meister Eckhart*

Each of us carries a heart of gratitude within, and the inward-turning nature of Yin Yoga & Meditation creates an optimal environment to stay connected with this treasured yin guardian. Consciously welcoming the energy of gratitude into our practice and present moment attention helps us recognize the good gifts each moment can bring.

We know in our hearts that feeling grateful feels good. Gratitude is an authentic expression of who we are: welcoming, connected, and loving. Rather than seeing something as less than or focusing on what's missing, gratitude helps us see more and more of the abundance that surrounds us. Research supports that when we practice gratitude, we feel better, are more satisfied with our relationships, and are more capable of coping with life's difficulties. We're also more likely to both seek and offer support when its needed, and are better able to learn from our experiences.

Flipping the Joy Switch

Experiencing gratitude generates more gratitude, kickstarting a virtuous cycle. Maybe you've heard gratitude referred to as the joy switch? Consciously calling to mind things we're grateful for prompts feelings of joy within us and is able to instantly transform our outlook. Just thinking the words "I am grateful for..." shifts our frame of mind by shifting our attention to what is right about this moment. The brain demonstrates what's called confirmation bias, meaning it looks for evidence of what it believes to be true. We're able to use this knowledge to our advantage by actively articulating and appreciating things we're grateful for, knowing the brain will respond and continue to locate more and more reasons to be thankful. Think of the energy of gratitude as a champion yin guardian for seeing the good.

Gratitude Changes the Brain

In addition to transforming the landscape of the heart, practicing gratitude rewires the brain. As we've discussed, science tells us that the more often a particular thought occurs, the more likely that thought is to recur in the future. That means we have the ability to actively, consciously rewire our brain to be more and more grateful. Connecting with the heart of gratitude is an act of compassionate repatterning, allowing the best of who we are to shine.

Psychologists Michael McCollough and Robert Emmons conducted an experiment in which a few hundred participants were asked to journal on a daily basis.[4] They split the participants into three groups, each of which would maintain a daily journal. Group one was asked to journal about what occurred that day without any other specific instructions. Group two was asked to document everything negative that happened that day. Group three was asked to write down things from the day they were grateful for.

At the end of two weeks of daily documenting the things they were grateful for, group three reported higher levels of optimism, enthusiasm, and energy than the other groups. The gratitude group was also less likely to experience stress or depression and more likely to help others, exercise regularly, and achieve the goals they set for themselves.

Practicing gratitude changes the chemistry of the brain and broadens our vision and ability to experience the circumstances of our lives with a refreshed viewpoint. In Dr. Emmons' book, *Thanks! How the New Science of Gratitude Can Make You Happier*, he explains that just as our body has a weight set point that feels natural, we have a kind of happiness set point as well. This happiness set point is the emotional plane we return to after big emotional highs and lows. Dr. Emmons suggests that regularly practicing gratitude is capable of shifting our happiness set point by twenty five percent, improving our happiness baseline and resiliency in the face of life's setbacks. Being grateful doesn't mean we have to ignore difficulties or pretend that everything about our life is perfect, but rather, the energy of gratitude serves as a lens that brings our blessings into clearer focus.

Be Grateful to Everyone

Inviting and hosting gratefulness is easy when great things are happening, but if you find it more difficult to call on gratitude when times are tough, you're not alone. As we've touched on, we're hard-wired to chase pleasure and avoid pain, but appreciation is an invaluable companion in unpleasant experiences, able to reshape our mindset and reorient our hearts toward grace.

I've mentioned how helpful I find the Lojong slogans, and one that is especially affecting for me is "Be grateful to everyone." A more literal translation is "Contemplate the great kindness of everyone." The idea is that everyone and everything around us is of fundamental benefit to us in some way. This slogan invites us to reconsider our ideas of what is valuable and what is not. This could certainly feel like a tall order at times, but as we train our perception to accept the possibility that *all* has the potential to be helpful, we open our hearts and minds in new and freeing ways.

Have you ever noticed how much a photo or painting's frame changes where our focus lands? By reframing our perspective, we transform our ability to engage with the circumstances of our lives in positive ways. Whatever it is that's happening, where will we draw the frame? What will we put in focus? Tough situations often open our hearts more than perfect circumstances. They cause us to grow, blossom, dig deep, and connect with our inner resources and those who love us. Shifting our viewpoint allows us to offer more compassion for ourselves and others, be happier, and provide support for those around us in need.

Many years ago, I had a business partnership that fell apart. Despite our company's success, the other party simply walked away from their commitment. In the months prior, I'd noticed customers kept mentioning yoga and how wonderful it was for relaxation and strengthening, shared they were teachers, or asked me if I practiced. It must have been a signal from the universe, because in the days after my business partnership ended, I remembered all those conversations and wandered into a yoga class hoping for some stress relief. I took that step onto a rented yoga mat and my life changed forever. Within a month, I'd enrolled in my first 200-hour yoga teacher training program. Though I was still moving through a difficult life shift, with the support of my fellow trainees and the healing power of the Yoga practice,

I was able to start looking at the circumstance with a greater degree of acceptance and curiosity. I was grateful for the people who encouraged me to try yoga, grateful for the newly found free time allowing me to participate in the program, and grateful for the wisdom and guidance of my first teacher, Amy Figoli. Within a year, the coming apart of one of my life passions ended up clearing the way for another, much more fulfilling path. My journey into yoga and the wisdom traditions of this practice has remained one of the most beautiful gifts of my life.

The idea of being grateful to everyone challenges the notion of what we might call obstacles. It asks us to inquire: *What if that difficulty isn't in the way but that it is the way?* We can reframe the problems we meet, large or small, as opportunities for growth and insight, and as sources of awakening and freedom. Our willingness to be grateful, whether the experience is pleasant or painful, overturns the idea that the trajectory of our life journey is somehow separate from the circumstances we encounter.

Pema Chödrön jokes that her meditation practice would be perfect if it weren't for her mind. We've probably all gotten stuck, at some point, in the idea that problems are somehow exceptions, that real life is a seamless stream of perfect occurrences, and difficulties are foreign objects that get tossed in our way. Being grateful to everyone asks us to remember that without problems, we wouldn't have anything to work with. If everything went perfectly, we wouldn't have the same chances to develop our patience, exercise our ingenuity and resiliency to overcome challenges, and continue to evolve into our best selves. When we invite an accepting attitude, we approach our difficulties from a new angle. Problems become like compost to work with to make the beautiful flowers in our heart garden grow. If, in our practice, we find our mind refuses to cooperate and stay in the present moment, running perpetually into the past or future, we have the chance to watch these movements of mind not as obstructions but invitations for appreciation and insight. *Wow, look at my brain go! I'm so grateful I have a mind that's so nimble and inquisitive!*

There's a story of a man named Bob who shared a hospital room with an older gentleman named Mr. Williams. Both men were quite ill, and as time passed, they struck up a friendship and spent many hours talking. Bob rested in the bed near the door, and due to his condition, was required to remain flat on his back. From the other bed, Mr. Williams often described the scenes outside in extensive detail for his friend: couples strolling by, the city skyline glistening in the sunshine, children playing along the sidewalks, and one day, even a passing parade. Forced to lie supine and stare at the white ceiling, Bob cherished every word.

One night, Mr. Williams passed away peacefully in his sleep. A few days later, Bob wondered if it would be possible to move to the bed by the window so that when he was able to sit upright again, he could enjoy the scenes his friend had so often described. Lifting himself slightly to turn toward that side of the room, he was shocked to find himself facing a blank wall. Bewildered, he called the nurse in and told her all his friend had shared. "Mr. Williams was blind," the nurse replied, "he couldn't even see the wall. He must have wanted to lift your spirits."

Mr. Williams had a heartening point of view and a vision well beyond eyesight. His window to the world was one of optimism and gratitude. When we choose gratitude, we make a decision to receive and respond from a different vantage point. Instead of being derailed by difficulties we meet on our path, we more consistently recognize and appreciate them as part of the path itself, as helpers and teachers that open the door of support to the benevolent universe in which we reside.

Meditative Yinquiry for the Mat

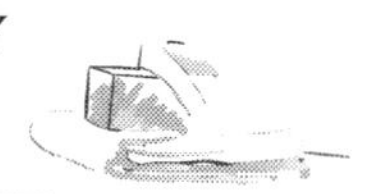

In our Yin Yoga & Meditation practice, we'll likely have encounters with something challenging or uncomfortable. What happens if you approach these moments as opportunities to invite the yin guardian of gratitude to help frame your perspective?

CHAPTER 9

ASANA YINPRESSIONS: PATTERNS AND POTENTIALS

Physical Safety and Efficacy on the Yin Yoga Mat

The practice principles of Yin Yoga & Meditation function as the framework for a continued safe and effective practice. We enter, experience, and exit the Yin asana with care and attention, understanding that rushing or forcing could cause injury and also obstruct the opportunity to nourish rebalancing yin qualities. The practice principles we've discussed offer a safe and effective pathway through each posture, encouraging us to stay attentive and kind, offering a willing ear to whatever the body may be telling us:

- Arrive to the Mat
- Move Mindfully to Mild Sensation
- Relax and Remain in Relative Stillness
- Watch and Welcome What's Happening Inside You
- Transition Like a Tortoise
- Rest Regularly to Recover and Reconnect
- Continue to Cultivate

Listening well allows us to respond compassionately to our experience in every pose and sense the ways the shape reverberates within us in the following hours and days. Continued watching of our experience helps us understand how our tissues received the exercise and if there's anything we need to consider changing.

In our postures, we're free from the external pressure of expectation; no single perfect expression of a pose exists to strive toward, no one ideal shape. There could be as many versions of a posture as there are practitioners. Low to the ground and slow, this practice allows us to find the phase of pose that's right for us each time we come to the mat. Because our collection of props, including the wall, supports a large number of variations, these shapes are available to many diverse bodies and individual needs. As you'll see in the Yin Asana Spotlights, if versions of one posture aren't working, there are often several substitute poses to consider which focus on similar areas of the body.

Safety Precautions and Considerations

As with any exercise, consult with your physician before beginning a Yin Yoga practice. As you read through these pages, please know the included collection of safety considerations isn't intended to be all-encompassing. There are valuable resources available that detail near-exhaustive contraindications related to yoga practice in general. One of the most comprehensive storehouses of yoga safety information is *Yoga Injury Prevention (YIP)*. YIP was created by Dr. Loren Fishman, a yogi, medical doctor, and author of multiple books, together with Victor Oppenheimer, Taliesin Oppenheimer, and Carrie Owerko.[1]

A top priority and responsibility for us as teachers and practitioners is to stay as well-informed as possible of precautions, safety concerns, and helpful modifications and substitutes. Of course, recounting every single medical issue, concern, or disorder as it relates to each pose every time we practice or teach a Yin Yoga class isn't practical. While ultimately each practitioner is responsible for the safety and efficacy of their own practice, my intention here is to highlight some primary contraindications and offer supportive considerations as you explore your own practice. If you teach, learning these will allow you to do all you can to help your students do the same.

Our bodies are unique with needs that are always changing, so we will each experience the poses somewhat differently. No teacher, however skilled and knowledgeable, is able to see what we're feeling on the inside. The external shapes we make offer some visual cues, but the sensations they produce are for each practitioner to feel and interpret. As we've discussed, props are important tools to consider in our practice, and specific suggestions for their use are included throughout this section and the upcoming Yin Asana Spotlights.

As teachers, we offer guidance and tools to empower students as they inquire internally to discern what they're sensing and keep the sensations appropriate. Here are just a few baseline ways we can support a physically safe and effective practice:

- Stay informed of and communicate specific contraindications and other safety considerations for the range of postures we're teaching.
- Allow the basic practice principles to guide the experience on the mat.
- Indicate modifications and variations as alternatives to postures.
- Make ourselves accessible for students to share their health concerns with us before and after practice time.
- Require students to consult their physician regarding any injuries, illnesses, or surgeries before beginning or resuming their practice.

One fundamental safety and efficacy guideline is that the parts of the body stimulated in the pose are also the primary areas of both potential benefit and precaution. Therefore, the sensations we feel in the physical areas of focus serve as one good starting point for our compassionate attention and provide some helpful guidance for choosing poses that align with the body's needs.

To help you practice safely as you consider your body's changing needs, you'll find a list of potential areas of sensation, as well as additional watch-outs, for each of the Yinpressions that follow. By staying watchful of the sensations that arise within a pose's focus area and throughout the body both during and after the posture, we're able to gauge what level of stimulation, if any, is advisable.

Our bodies require balanced stresses to remain healthy, but injuries or sensitivities shift what balanced and appropriate mean at any point in time. We'll want to ascertain if and when it's wise to exercise sensitive areas. Sometimes the area is just too tender and is best left alone while healing, in which case we opt for a posture that targets a different area of the body. If your healthcare team has agreed you're able to start or return to practice following an injury or illness, gentle work in that area could feel welcome. In these situations, you'll want to maintain softer sensations and shorter hold times. As we'll see, there are many alternate positions and prop options to help find accommodations and make modifications to either avoid or bring benefit to these more sensitive tissues while not over-stressing or aggravating them, as appropriate.

Students with bone conditions such as osteoarthritis, osteopenia, and osteoporosis will want to consult their healthcare team to check if the practice is advised for them, and if so, they should obtain guidance on pose selection and what level of sensation is appropriate.

Because Yin Yoga postures do not inherently require the practitioner to extend to their furthest possible expression of a pose, hypermobility is not a blanket disqualification if the practitioner's healthcare providers have indicated the practice may be helpful. Hypermobile practitioners are encouraged to do things that help create stability in postures, such as lightly and/or intermittently engaging the muscles broadly surrounding the pose's focus area. Incorporating stability and muscle-strengthening exercises into self-care routines also promotes balance.

For those living with Ehlers Danlos Syndrome, a group of connective tissue disorders characterized by joint hypermobility and hyper-flexibility of the connective tissues, Yin Yoga is contraindicated, and their physician's advice should be followed.

Because the stresses of the practice do cause a state change within our connective tissues to a more viscous state resulting in variable, temporary fragility, care should be taken to avoid vigorous yang-like weight-bearing exercise and activity directly after a pose or practice and until your tissues have recovered, which varies by individual bodies and circumstances.

Practicing During Pregnancy

Pregnant practitioners will want to work with their healthcare team to determine the best approach to their practice. Following medical guidance and staying attentive to the needs of the body, Yin Yoga & Meditation can make a lovely companion during pregnancy to settle the mind, create space in the body, and bring real relief while working mindfully with the breath to rest and restore.

There are special pre-natal considerations which apply, so pregnant practitioners are encouraged to continue to trust their inner wisdom and listen closely to their body and respond to its changing needs. For example, connective tissues soften and become more flexible during pregnancy due to the release of the hormone relaxin, which makes it potentially easier to over-stress the soft tissues and strain joints without realizing it. For this reason, students will want to consider softer boundaries and stay within the range of motion they had before becoming pregnant, especially when abducting the legs in postures (see "Yinpression: Hip-Leg Work"). Shortening the length of time each pose is held is another option, staying for one to three minutes instead of five to six minutes. Compressing the belly should be avoided, such as closed twists, so we'll be looking at other options available to explore. There are several factors to consider related to inversions which may or may not make them advisable for practice during pregnancy, such as prior practice of inversions and how far along the pregnancy is, therefore practitioners should discuss the best approach with their physician. The many variations and modifications available in Yin Yoga can serve to keep the practice accessible and supportive throughout pregnancy.

Yinpressions

Yinpressions are the component positions that form the basic building blocks of the Yin Yoga poses. By breaking the poses down into Yinpressions, we develop a fundamental understanding of the poses and numerous options available within them. Yinpressions can be used to explore a wide range of adaptations and modifications to ensure the postures are safe and accessible and meet our individual needs. This element of the Mandala Map encourages us to identify patterns within and between postures so we can create practice sessions that best serve our whole selves each time we come to the mat. Yinpressions encourage us to reflect on the positioning needed to reach different areas of the body, including exercising the joints in all their directions of movement. In addition to the physical benefits of the practice, Yinpressions also invite us to consider the mental, emotional, and energetic aspects of the shapes to further personalize the intention and tone of a session.

Rather than a complete exposition of all the anatomical layouts and functions of the body, the Yinpressions offered here are one way of thinking about the patterns and potentials of the Yin Yoga postures to bring us the fullest benefits in our practice. You may discover additional Yinpressions as you continue your personal practice. I've found them to be a valuable teacher in helping to grow in body awareness in each posture, and I hope you will too.

Yinpression: Seated Forward Bend

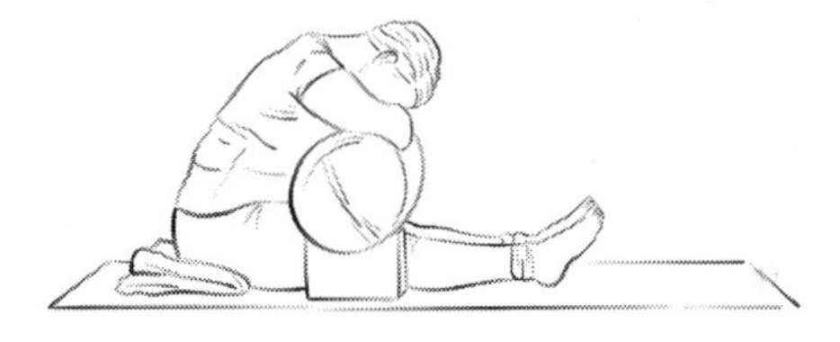

Bending the upper body closer to the front of hips/thighs; rounding forward, flexing the spine

asana

The natural inward-turning nature of forward bending calls us home to ourselves, redirecting our attention inward to the ever-shifting landscape of sensations, emotions, and thoughts flowing within us. Forward bends offer the opportunity for us to strengthen the yin qualities of quiet observation and listening compassionately to the needs of our body. Folding forward typically feels especially rebalancing after poses in which we twist or work into the hips and legs. Seated postures provide the foundation for many of our forward bends in Yin Yoga, whether the legs are crossed, straight, twined, or angled.

Potential Areas of Sensation

- Whole back line of the body
- Muscles and fascia of the back, specifically the lumbar spine and lower thoracic area, including the *thoracolumbar fascia* (TLF), that large connective tissue surrounding the intrinsic muscles of the back
- Spinal column, including the deep spinal muscles and *erector spinae* attached to the vertebrae which help keep us upright
- Organs in the abdomen: compression, which may aid digestion

Remember: The potential areas of sensation are primary areas of benefit and precaution. In the case of injury/special conditions in these areas, consult your healthcare team and/or avoid.

Additional Safety Watch-Outs (!)

Low back issues, including discs/sciatica, consider:

- Keeping a straighter spine and/or adding height under your seat

Tight hips/hamstrings or tender knees, consider:

- Increasing bend of the knees and/or placing a rolled blanket or bolster underneath knees or hamstrings for support
- Building height by adding prop(s) under your seat
- Adjusting the leg angles slightly, perhaps moving the legs further from or closer to the body or each other

Basic Guidance

To explore the Seated Forward Bend Yinpression while in seated poses:

1. Sit onto your mat on top of a single-folded blanket and extend both legs straight in front of you.
2. In preparation for forward bending, we need to begin with a mild anterior tilt of the pelvis to avoid slumping and potentially injurious loading of the low back.
3. Notice the orientation of your pelvis. Is it in a neutral, anterior, or posterior tilt? If a general refresher on these three pelvic orientations would be helpful, see "Acquainting with the Orientations of the Pelvis" (p. 67).
4. If your pelvis is in a slight anterior tilted position, proceed to step seven. Should the hips be tilted too far forward, try removing the blanket from underneath you so the pelvis is only slightly tilted, then proceed to step seven.
5. If your pelvis is in a posterior tilt with a flattened or rounded lumbar spine, elevate the hips more by placing an additional blanket, blocks, or a bolster under your seat to assist it into its neutral position, so it's tilted neither forward nor backward.
6. From the neutral pelvis position, gently tip the hips forward a bit to establish a slight anterior tilt. If this feels strained or requires too much effort, further elevate the hips with another prop underneath your seat until you're able to easefully bring the hips into this position.
7. Choose to keep your legs straight to explore the forward bend of Caterpillar pose or adjust your leg positioning according to the instructions of the specific posture you're doing.
8. Use a full inhale to lengthen the spinal column a touch more, then a complete exhale to root your sit-bones into the earth.
9. If you'll be folding over just one leg, rotate the upper body to face that leg. Otherwise, keep your upper body facing forward.
10. Once again, take a slow and long inhale. As you exhale, keep the length of your spine and the weight in the sit-bones as you begin to hinge slowly forward at the hips, lowering your upper body over the leg(s). Continue to root the sit-bones back and down onto your mat as you fold to help prevent additional unwanted pressure from moving into the knees.
11. If knees begin to object or hamstrings are too tight, depending on your leg position, adjust the bend of the knees and place a rolled blanket or bolster underneath them for support. You might try adding height under your seat with an additional prop. You could also adjust the leg angles slightly. If these changes don't

moderate the sensations, there's a good chance you've folded too far forward and should come up and out a bit.

12. Once you find a mild level of sensation in the forward bend, decide if you'll keep a longer, more neutral spine or if you'll intentionally allow your spine to flex more. Keep in mind that maintaining a more neutral spine is most often the best approach for students experiencing sciatica related to a herniated disc or other upper and lower back issues. Rounding through the back puts pressure on the front intervertebral discs and may exacerbate a disc issue and create additional painful pressure on the area of the spinal cord behind it.
13. If appropriate, rounding the upper body more in the forward bend offers a decompression for the length of the spine, spotlighting and opening the muscles and fascia through the back. Conversely, a longer, more neutral spine tends to create a deeper stretch through the backs of legs.
14. Check in with the level of sensation you're feeling through the spine, hips, and legs. Watch for localized, sharp, shooting, stinging, or other pain signals to determine the appropriate depth of fold for you.
15. If you're folding over just one leg and encounter painful compression in the hip or groin area, play with the upper body's orientation to the thigh. Moving your upper body to the inside or outside of the leg a bit may help free up this area and relieve the compression. You could also slightly adjust the leg position. If these adjustments aren't enough, be sure to ease out of the forward bend until the painful sensation disappears.
16. If the upper body is dangling in space rather than resting directly onto your legs and this feels OK, feel free to remain there. Otherwise, support the weight of your upper body with a bolster, blocks, or blankets. There are many creative prop options such as stacked blocks, a bolster angled vertically toward or away from the body, or a bridged bolster. To build your bolster bridge over your leg(s), rest the bolster across the tops of the legs and place a block under each end to support it. You could also consider using a chair or bench to bring the floor up to you if additional height is needed. Simply place a folded blanket across the seat and rest the forehead atop folded hands. Select whichever option allows you to relax into the shape and keep sensations mild.
17. Take caution with neck sensitivities. If you prefer to maintain the neck in a more neutral position, stack props to support the head so the neck is in line with the rest of the spine. Alternately, you could rest your bent elbows onto the props and let the chin fall into your palms. If the neck permits, allow the chin to drop toward the chest. This is neck flexion. Because our spine is one continuous chain, adding neck flexion can also cascade through the spine's length, increasing sensations anywhere along the vertebral column. Tap into this relationship to dampen or deepen the effects of the forward bend as needed.
18. If any ricochet sensations through the body become too great, explore some adjustments. You could, for example, lift up and out of the fold slightly, add additional support under the upper body or legs, decrease the degree of flexion of the neck, or prop the head to support its weight and angles.
19. To ease out of the forward bend, move yourself slowly upright with hands pressing onto the earth.

General Hold Time

- Average of three to five minutes, perhaps lingering longer as your practice continues to evolve, while newer practitioners might begin with one to three minutes and lengthen

Yinpression: Hip-Leg Work

We move the hips in six ways: flexion, extension, internal rotation, external rotation, abduction, and adduction.

With the large number of Qi channels charting through the legs and pelvis, Yin Yoga & Meditation offers abundant opportunity to clear stagnant energy and harmonize our energetic architecture. The hip areas are also common places of physical tension, given the large amount of time so many of us are required to spend sitting. Tensions here limit our freedom of movement and can impact daily activities as we age, so exercising these important joint tissues brings long-lasting benefits. The hips can carry our emotional tensions as well. Gently bringing physical opening to these areas with loving attention paves the way for stored emotions to loosen and freely follow their natural course.

Potential Areas of Sensation

- Hip joints
- Glute/IT band area of the buttocks, outer hip, and lateral thigh: Includes the gluteal muscles *gluteus maximus, gluteus medius, gluteus minimus*, and the *tensor fasciae latae* (TFL) as well as the *Iliotibial* (IT) *band*. The IT band is a fascial tissue that runs along the outer hip and thigh and inserts into the tibia. Often an area of tension, the IT band stabilizes the knee and helps it flex (bend) and extend (straighten). Also encompasses the six hip external rotator muscles which lie deep inside the pelvis and beneath the buttocks. This muscle group includes the *piriformis*, which can be a source of pain if it becomes too tight or spasms and begins to pinch the sciatic nerve, so we want to keep the *piriformis* hydrated, supple, and strong.
- Front of hip/thigh tissues: Includes the four quadricep muscles and several hip flexors, such as the *Iliopsoas*, which is a blending of the *psoas* and *iliacus* muscles. This essential core muscle group connects the torso to the legs and helps raise the thigh by flexing the hip while also acting as a critical spine and pelvis stabilizer.
- Back of leg tissues: Includes the hamstrings at the back of thigh and the calf muscles
- Inner-leg tissues: The entire inseam of the leg with particular emphasis on the inner thigh and groin areas. Includes the hip adductor muscles that fan primarily through the medial thigh from the pelvis to the thighbone. One adductor also reaches all the way into the top of the shin. The inner thigh adductors are hip-stabilizing muscles that help bring the legs together when they contract.

Remember: The potential areas of sensation are primary areas of benefit and precaution. In the case of injury/special conditions in these areas, consult your healthcare team and/or avoid.

Additional Safety Watch-Outs (!)

Tight hips/hamstrings or tender knees, consider:

- Increasing bend of the knees and/or placing a rolled blanket or bolster underneath knees or hamstrings for support
- Building height by adding prop/s under your seat
- Adjusting the leg angles slightly, perhaps moving the legs further from or closer to the body or each other

Basic Guidance

Here we'll briefly experience the six basic hip joint movements as a simple introduction or refresher.

To explore the Hip-Leg Work Yinpression while comfortably seated:

1. Sit on your mat on top of a single-folded blanket and extend both legs in front of you. In this seated position, you are already in hip flexion.
2. To move into deeper hip flexion, put soles of feet on the mat, then slide feet a little closer to your seat. As you bring the thighs closer to the chest, the femurs move closer to the

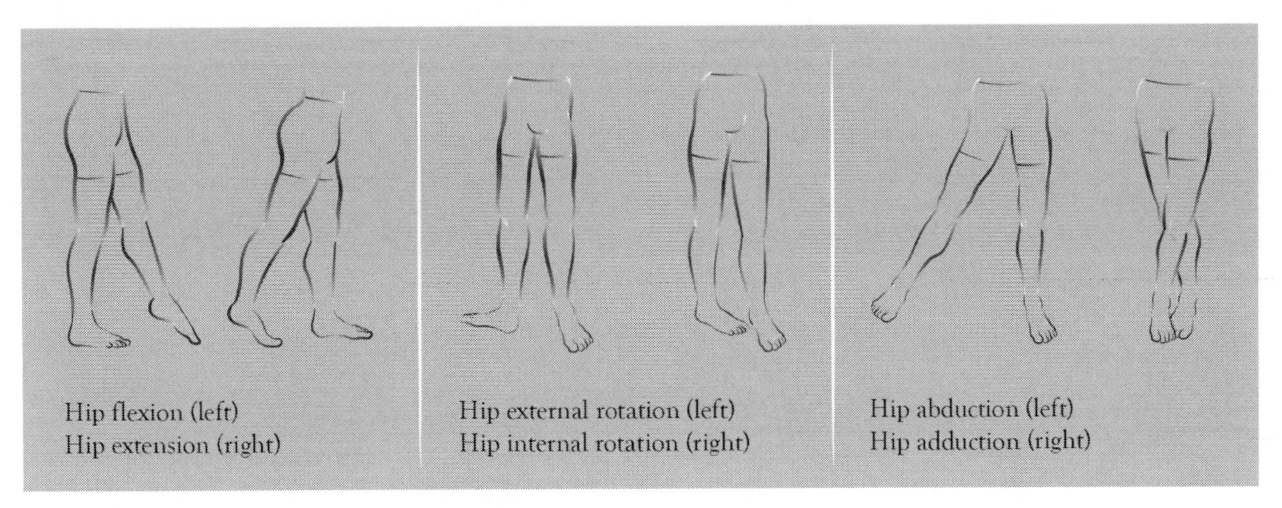

Hip flexion (left)
Hip extension (right)

Hip external rotation (left)
Hip internal rotation (right)

Hip abduction (left)
Hip adduction (right)

front of the pelvis, decreasing the hip joint angles. Notice any sensations that arise as you make this movement. In Yin Yoga postures, we experience hip flexion in a variety of positions, such as when we lower the upper body over the legs in a forward bend.

3. Extend the legs down the mat once again. To create internal rotation at both hips, begin to rotate the thighbones and knees inward toward the midline of your body, turning the legs in. Notice how this action feels as your inner thighs and inner knees roll downward toward the mat.

4. External hip rotation is the opposite action. To explore, now rotate both thighbones and knees outward and away from the midline of the body so the fronts of your thighs roll away from one another.

5. Move back and forth between internal and external hip rotation gently and slowly by turning your legs inward and then outward a few times. Notice any sensations arising within the hip sockets and legs as the femur bones rotate. Do you feel a refreshing flow of circulation or a bit of relief in the hips? Come back to stillness with both legs at ease and extended in front of you.

6. To create hip abduction, slide both of your legs laterally away from the midline of the body, creating a gentle V- shape with the legs. By bringing your legs outward to the sides in this way, you've abducted your legs at the hips. Notice how this feels.

7. To adduct the legs, simply bring them back toward each other and the midline of your body.

8. In Yin Yoga postures, we have many opportunities to fine-tune sensations in our hips and legs by laterally drawing legs closer together or moving them further apart to adjust the degree of hip adduction or abduction.

9. For one more hip abduction-adduction exercise, slide your left leg outward to the left side just a few inches, abducting the left leg at the hip. Next, to create a deeper hip adduction of the right leg, slide the right leg across your midline and toward the left leg. Your legs might touch. If the hips and legs allow, you could increase this adduction further by crossing the right leg over the left. Do you feel any sensations? Perhaps experiment with this lying on your back to see how these movements feel while supine, noting any differences in the sensations that arise.

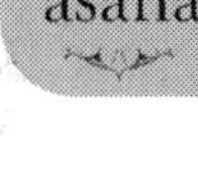

10. Uncross the legs and slide them one at a time back to your starting position with your legs extended in front of you.

11. For a very simple example of hip extension, come to a standing position on your mat. You are already in hip extension.

12. To increase the degree of hip extension, bring the right leg behind you a few inches, touching right toes to the mat. By bringing your leg further behind you from this position, you're extending, or opening, the hip joint angle more as the front of thighbone moves further away from the front of the pelvis. Switch legs to explore hip extension on the other side and notice if you feel any differences between the left and right sides.

13. In Yin Yoga postures, you'll have a chance to experience hip extension from a variety of foundations, such as kneeling, supine, and prone.
14. Oftentimes, we'll experience two or even three joint hip movements simultaneously in a pose. Some poses, such as Deer pose, are asymmetrical and concurrently offer different joint movement options for either hip, for example bringing internal rotation to one hip while the other hip enjoys external rotation.

General Hold Time

- Average of three to five minutes, perhaps lingering longer as your practice continues to evolve, while newer practitioners might begin with one to three minutes and lengthen over time

Yinpression: One-Legged

Many of our symmetrical two-legged Yin postures are transformed relatively easily into one-legged versions. In this Yinpression, one leg is simply doing its own thing!

Whether enjoying seated, supine, prone, or wall-based postures, the versatility of the One-Legged Yinpression affords us freedom to innovate, intuit, and discover ways to serve our unique skeletal structure and the changing needs of our body each time we come to the mat.

Potential Areas of Sensation

- It depends. The leg doing its own thing might receive more or less stimulation than the other leg, or none at all if the one-legged option moves the stresses into other tissues. The quality of the sensations could also change.

Remember: The potential areas of sensation are primary areas of benefit and precaution. In the case of injury/special conditions in these areas, consult your healthcare team and/or avoid.

Additional Safety Watch-Outs ⓘ

Tight hips/hamstrings or tender knees, consider:

- Increasing bend of the knees and/or placing a rolled blanket or bolster underneath knees or hamstrings for support
- Building height by adding prop/s under your seat
- Adjusting the leg angles slightly, perhaps moving the legs further from or closer to the body or each other

Basic Guidance

In addition to all the varieties of muscular tensions we hold, we also are likely to have structural differences between each side of the body. This varying interaction of tensions and skeletal variations can limit our movement into a pose. If you find a two-legged pose isn't accessible, try one-legged instead.

As you explore the One-Legged Yinpression:

1. Approaching the posture one leg at a time could allow for small shifts in the orientation of the pelvis, opening up a bit of space to soften tensions or potentially move around a physical impasse, such as an uneven edge of bone. Exercising one leg and then the other could make the posture more accessible for both sides of the body.
2. One-legged versions can help to accommodate an area of sensitivity or injury. Sometimes the limitation of a temporary injury invites us to find new avenues to work compassionately with the state of the body. Immediately following an injury on my left side, my ankle, knee, and hip were too compromised to do much Yin Yoga exercise on that side. Fortunately, during that fragile time, I was still able to find a good amount of relief on my non-injured side thanks to the one-legged options available in so many of the Yin Yoga poses.

3. If you notice one side of the lower body is asking for more attention, one-legged options give you a chance to spend a little more time exercising that side. Hold the pose an extra minute or two for that side or exercise it a bit more frequently for added release and to help better balance the body as a whole.
4. As you play with the One-Legged Yinpression, you might uncover new ways to move the exercise of the pose into other parts of the body or shift sensations into different nooks and crannies not always available in its two-legged counterpart.
5. In the straight leg, experiment with the positioning of the toes. To emphasize the stimulation along the inner thigh tissues, try turning the toes and thighbone slightly outward to bring external rotation into the hip. Conversely, to induce a light stimulation along the outer hip and thigh area, angle the toes and thighbone slightly inward toward the midline for internal rotation.
6. As you make one adjustment at a time, stay observant and notice the overall effects of each new position to ensure the benefit you're bringing to one part of the body also honors the needs of the whole.

General Hold Time

- Average of three to five minutes, perhaps lingering longer as your practice continues to evolve, while newer practitioners might begin with one to three minutes and lengthen over time

Yinpression: Side Bend

Bending the spine laterally toward the left side or the right; tilting sideways

When in a side-bend, what you're able to see happening along the outer line of the upper body is also happening along the spinal column deep within those areas. The tissues on the side you're bending toward enjoy compression, while the opposite side's ribs, waist, and spinal joints are being decompressed to create a sensation of opening and release. Lateral flexion of the spine also increases room for the diaphragm to expand and contract within the rib cage, facilitating deeper, more easeful breathing which aids physical and mental relaxation.

Potential Areas of Sensation

- Sides of upper body, including the *obliques* and the *intercostal* muscles between the ribs
- *Erector spinae* muscles along the vertebral column
- Lumbar area, where the *quadratus lumborum* (QL) attaches on either side of the spine. A tight QL is a primary source of back pain, so stretching out tension through lateral bending can bring beneficial relief.

Remember: The potential areas of sensation are primary areas of benefit and precaution. In the case of injury/special conditions in these areas, consult your healthcare team and/or avoid.

Additional Safety Watch-Outs (!)

Low back concerns, consider:

- Maintaining a softer level of sensation in this area by not bending as deeply

Shoulder sensitivities or tingling/numbness, consider:

- Altering angles by bending elbows, using a blanket underneath arms and shoulders, or lowering the arms

Neck concerns, consider:

- Maintaining a neutral neck if the cervical twist doesn't feel appropriate by keeping your neck in line with the rest of your spine and/or supporting your head with prop(s)

Basic Guidance

Side bends integrate well with many seated poses in addition to some supine postures, including those on the wall.

To explore the Side Bend Yinpression while in upright seated poses:

1. Start in an upright seated Yin Yoga posture, find a neutral pelvis position (for a refresher, see "Establishing a Neutral Pelvis in Seated Postures," p. 68). Take a moment to feel for the natural curvature of the spine as your attention glides through its elegant and efficient S-shape from the base of the tailbone to the top of the crown.
2. Let's begin with a side bend to the right. If your legs are crossed, twined, or bent, place a block or bolster beside the right outer hip and proceed to step four.
3. If your right leg is outstretched, place a bridged bolster either on top of or alongside the outside of the leg. Turn your upper body to the left so that the center of the chest faces the left leg.
4. Place your right hand on the prop near your right outer hip for stability. Lift the left arm straight up with your fingertips pointing to the sky so that the left bicep is in line with your ear. On the inhale, actively reach upward through your left fingertips to lengthen through the left side, keeping the left sit-bone sealed to the earth as you reach.

5. With the exhale, begin to bend your upper body to the right. As you bend, keep your left shoulder aligned over your right shoulder to avoid slumping or curling forward. Keeping the chest open will help keep you in a lateral bend rather than a forward fold.
6. If you don't feel enough sensation along your sides, bend your elbow and place your right forearm onto the prop. If you need more sensation, remove the prop and place your right hand or forearm onto the earth beside your hip. If bent over your leg, you might rest the side of your rib cage directly onto the leg or more toward its inside or outside.
7. If a shoulder injury prevents holding the left arm overhead without pain, keep the arm lowered, hand resting on the waist or upper leg. If the left shoulder joint allows, dangle the top arm freely over the head to bring more stimulation there. You could also bend your left elbow and let the back of your head rest gently into your hand or the crook of your forearm. If the right arm is free, you could interlace the fingers of both hands behind your head, leaning the back of the head into the cradle of your palms. If you start to experience a tingly numbness in either shoulder or arm, you may be compressing a nerve or blood vessel and you'll need to adjust. Soften the shoulder joint angle(s), and if this doesn't provide relief, lower the arm(s) down to your side to reopen the flow of energy and blood.
8. As you make adjustments in your side bend, here are a couple of spot checks to help ensure you receive the deepest physical benefits: Is the sit-bone opposite the side bend still rooted to the ground? Are the shoulders still stacked with the top shoulder aligned over the bottom?
9. To add a twist for the neck, first lengthen the neck and then slowly rotate your head to the right and tilt your gaze down to the earth. Hold this head position for a handful of breaths, then rotate the head back through center and perhaps to the left to gaze toward the sky. Pause and hold this neck twist for several breaths. You could also explore neck angles anywhere in between that feel best. In the case of a neck injury or if the cervical twist just doesn't feel appropriate, maintain a more neutral neck position by keeping your neck in line with the rest of your spine and gazing directly in front of you. Support your head with props or bend your bottom arm with elbow resting on the earth, and place your head on your palm, as needed.
10. While you stay in the side bend, the intensity of sensations may increase or diminish. Continue to take notice and adjust as your body requests to keep the sensations just right.
11. To ease out of a side bend, return your gaze in front of you, if not already. Lower the left arm and place the hand onto your left hip. Lower the right arm, if raised.
12. Press the right hand on the mat to slowly lift yourself back up, centering your head between your shoulders and over your hips.
13. When you're ready, move to the other side.

To explore the Side Bend Yinpression while in seated forward bends:

If you're in a seated forward bend and would like to add a lateral bend to open the sides of the upper body and spine, it's relatively simple. Practitioners with a sensitive spine/back should take precaution when exploring this option.

1. Reach arms forward and press finger pads into the floor to hover your upper body slightly just above the thighs.
2. Keep the left sit-bone rooted to the ground and begin to walk your fingers to the right to help move your upper body diagonally to the right into a folded side bend.
3. The front of your shoulders should remain relatively square to the earth to get the most benefit through both sides of your upper body and spinal joints.
4. If your upper body is dangling in space rather than resting directly onto the legs and floor and this feels OK, feel free to remain there. Otherwise, support the weight of your upper body with a bolster, blocks, or blankets.
5. Rest your forehead onto folded forearms or let your head dangle freely, if it feels appropriate.
6. For more stimulation, reach your arms in front of you onto the floor if they aren't already.
7. Hold for a minute or two and then slowly crawl your fingers and upper body back to center, then to the other side when ready.

To explore the Side Bend Yinpression while in supine poses:

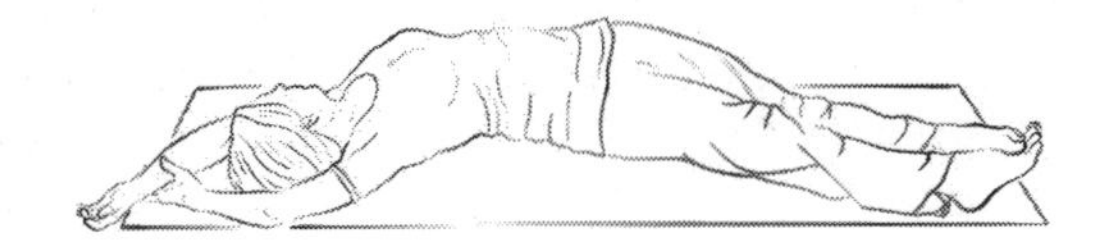

You might also explore a side bend when lying on your back in a variety of postures, including while practicing postures on the wall. Though supine versions tend to be gentler than their seated counterparts, back/shoulder sensitivity precautions still apply here.

1. Lift your upper body a couple of inches off the mat and then slowly move it to the right while keeping the front of the chest and shoulders parallel to the earth and sky. Once you've created a soft curve through the upper body, lower yourself back down onto the mat.
2. If the lateral bend is too deep, the left shoulder may lift off the ground and bring you into a twist instead of a side bend. If this happens, gently scoot your upper body back to the left until the shoulders are relatively square with the mat. If there's still a slight space between the back of the left shoulder and the mat, you could place a folded blanket underneath it, if that would allow your muscles to relax more.
3. Hold this side for half the total pose time, then switch to the other side.

General Hold Time

- Average of one to three minutes per side, perhaps lingering longer as your practice continues to evolve, while newer practitioners might begin with a minute and lengthen

Yinpression: Twist

Rotating the spinal column

Many Yin Yoga postures offer the chance to explore twists from both seated and supine positions. Twisting engages the spinal column through its natural movement of rotation, diminishing tightness through the back muscles, including the deep spinal musculature and the fascia enveloping it. Spinal rotation also produces gentle compression and decompression through the ribcage *intercostals* as well as the *obliques*. Keeping these tissues healthy supports good posture and rotational flexibility and stability and reduces pressure on the spine, potentially relieving back pain.

In addition to helping to maintain the flexibility and integrity of the spine, twists provide a gentle massage for the abdominal organs. Twists may improve the circulation of blood while encouraging energetic flow along the spine. Twisting also stimulates the vagus nerve, which has a grounding emotional effect, helping to unwind anxiety and emotional tensions. All of this work benefits from our deep, conscious breathing while holding the twist. Because twists impart a sense of reorganizing and rebalancing in the spine, they generally feel refreshing after forward and backward bending postures.

Potential Areas of Sensation

- Length of the spine, including the low back
- Shoulders
- Sides of the upper body
- Outer hip area

Remember: The potential areas of sensation are primary areas of benefit and precaution. In the case of injury/special conditions in these areas, consult your healthcare team and/or avoid.

Additional Safety Watch-Outs (!)

Back tenderness, consider:

- Lessening your twist to maintain a softer level of sensation

Neck, consider:

- Whenever twisting the neck, be watchful for lightheadedness and dizziness, as you may be compressing one of the major arteries flowing through that area. Should you experience anything inappropriate, bring the neck back to a neutral position or take a break if it doesn't resolve.

Pregnancy, consider:

- Replace closed twists after first trimester with easeful open twists to avoid compressing the belly. Lessen your open twist to maintain a softer level of sensation.

Basic Guidance

To explore the Twist Yinpression while in upright seated poses:

1. Start with awareness of your spine. Before twisting, you want to ensure your pelvis is in its neutral position (for a refresher, see "Establishing a Neutral Pelvis in Seated Postures," p. 68). As we've discussed, this is the foundation for finding your spine's natural curves. There is a tendency to undershoot the height of our seat, which could cause a posterior tilt of the pelvis and flatten or round the lower back. If necessary, take a moment to elevate your seat with props to find this healthy spinal position. A well-positioned spine is particularly important in seated twists to prevent us from twisting with a rounded back, which can cause injury.
2. Place a block behind the right outer hip and then root both sit-bones to the earth. As you breathe in, lengthen a bit more through your spine all the way to the crown of your head, feeling the spinal column become spacious and tall.
3. Lightly engage your abdominal muscles, and as you exhale, begin to slowly rotate your upper body to the right. Initiate the twist with your pelvis first, allowing it to turn just slightly in the same direction as the twist.

This is generally a bit softer on your SI joints, and it's OK if your left sit-bone lifts a tad to accommodate this.

4. It's helpful to create the twist from the low spine because rotational freedom increases through the thoracic area, with the cervical spine having the greatest rotational range. Starting your twist from the top can lead to inadvertently over-twisting, forcing the rest of the spine to chase the neck. As you twist, maintain the chin centered between your shoulders to keep the neck neutral.
5. Place your left hand to your right leg and your right fingertips or palm onto the block behind your seat as anchors of support. If your right arm is relatively straight in this position, keep the block there. If not, remove the block and place your hand directly on the mat as long as you can do so without over-reaching or straining. As you press through your right hand, feel your arm solid and strong, serving as a sort of kickstand to keep the spinal column tall.
6. Draw your front ribs slightly inward rather than puffing them outward and upward. This keeps the core muscles lightly activated, lengthens your spine, and supports the lumbar arch's natural curvature rather than causing an exaggerated anterior pelvic tilt.
7. If your neck is sensitive, twisting it may not feel right and you'll want to keep the chin centered with the chest. Otherwise, slowly turn your head to look behind you and over your right shoulder to the degree that creates a mild amount of sensation along the neck's length. Feel for a cervical twist that offers a gentle compression to the right-side neck while decompressing and opening the left side.
8. It's essential not to push or force the twist in any way anywhere along the spine. To help with this, find a place that balances sensations along the length of the back and spine and ensures you're able to continue breathing well. Deep, intentional breathing will also support an abdominal massage.
9. If you'd like to open the front of right chest and shoulder a bit more, perhaps add a One Arm Behind the Back Bind (see "Yinpression: Shoulder-Arm Binds," below) to complement the work of the twist.
10. To come out of the seated twist, breathe in, and as you exhale, lift the hands and untwist the neck so it's centered between the shoulders. From there, untwist the whole of your spine as you circle back around the axis of your vertebral column. Rest a few moments, then give the other side a go.

General Hold Time

- Average of one to three minutes per side, perhaps lingering longer as your practice continues to evolve, while newer practitioners might begin with a minute and lengthen

Yinpression: Shoulder-Arm Binds

Binds here refer to positions where one or both arms are twined, holding one another, or holding onto a different part of the body

Although the primary focus of Yin Yoga is the spine and the region between the navel and knees, many of the Yin Yoga postures offer us a welcome chance to nourish and maintain the wellbeing of tissues in the shoulder joint areas.

If your arms are free and the sensations in the body are appropriate and steady, you might enjoy incorporating shoulder-arm binds into a wide range of poses, including supine, seated, upright kneeling, prone, or while at the wall. Shoulder-arm binds help release tightness in the musculature and fascia in the middle and upper back, front chest, and shoulders, potentially improving mobility. Binding generally adds a bit of stability, making it easier to more fully relax the muscles and soften into the support of the shape.

The shoulders are the most mobile joint areas of the body, granting the upper arms the ability to

Shoulder-Arm Binds

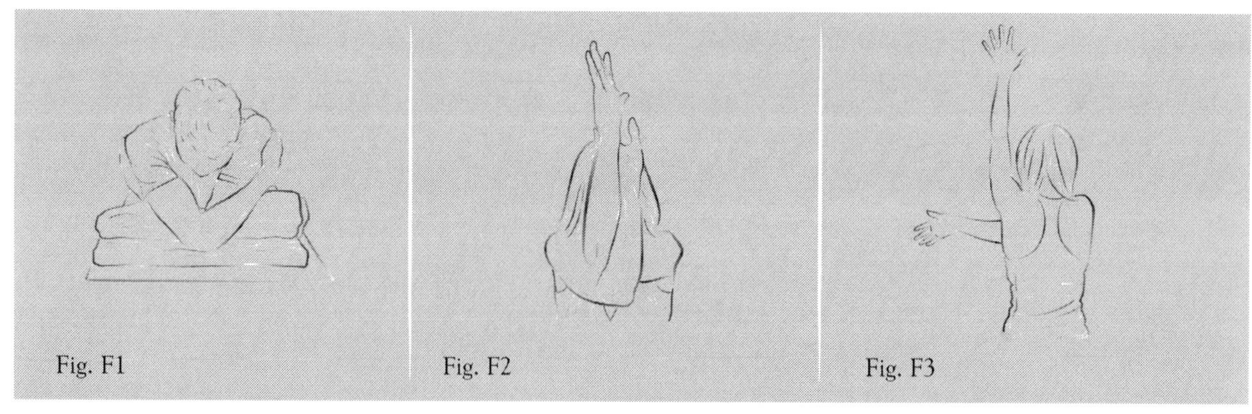

Fig. F1 Fig. F2 Fig. F3

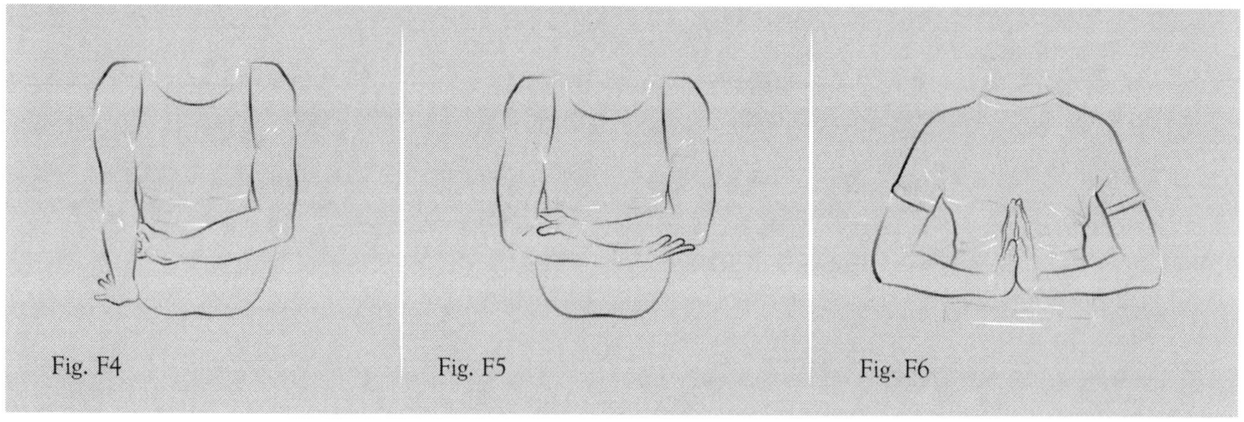

Fig. F4 Fig. F5 Fig. F6

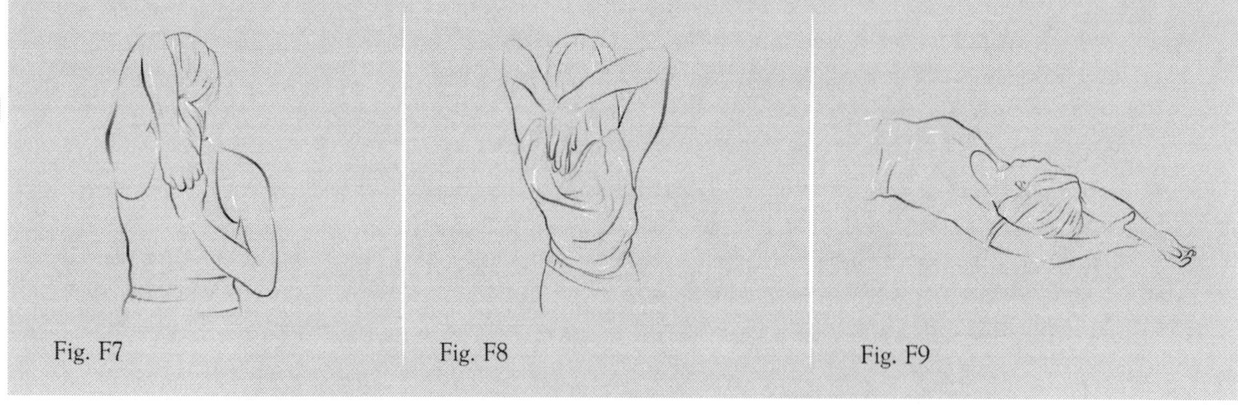

Fig. F7 Fig. F8 Fig. F9

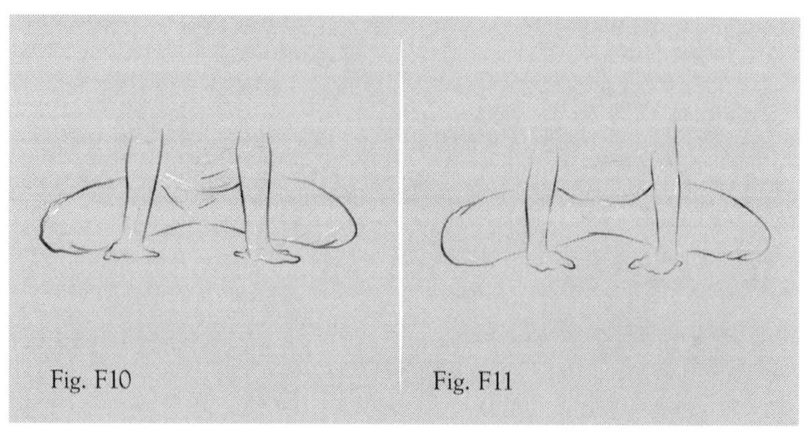

Fig. F10 Fig. F11

move in, out, up, down, and around as well as to rotate both internally and externally. This complex collection of joints offers ample opportunity for the release of tensions with the additional scapular movements of shrugging upward and downward, spreading outward and drawing together, and slightly tilting forward and backward.

Given their prominent role in so many of our daily activities, the shoulders and upper back often store muscular tension. With many of us spending much of the day sitting at desks or hunching over devices, taking time to offer some extra nurturing to the muscles and fascia supporting the shoulder area can bring welcome relief!

Potential Areas of Sensation

- Upper body: shoulders and arms, neck, chest, middle/upper back, wrists, hands, and fingers

Remember: The potential areas of sensation are primary areas of benefit and precaution. In the case of injury/special conditions (e.g., rotator cuff injury, carpal tunnel syndrome) in these areas, consult your healthcare team and/or avoid.

Additional Safety Watch-Outs (!)

Shoulder tenderness or tingling/numbness, consider:

- Softening the shoulder-arm angles by not binding so deeply or perhaps using a strap between the hands to bridge the gap between them
- Choosing to try the shoulder-arm bind lying on your back or standing at the wall, where possible, to minimize the weight of the upper body putting unwanted pressure into the shoulder joints

Neck sensitivities, try:

- Maintaining a neutral neck if twisting, flexion, or extension doesn't feel appropriate by keeping your neck in line with the rest of your spine and/or supporting your head with prop(s)

Basic Guidance

Below you'll find some basic guidance for a number of possible shoulder-arm binds.

Hugging Arms: *Integrates well with seated, supine, and prone poses (Fig F1)*

To try it out in a comfortable seated position:

1. Inhale to stretch your arms wide out to your sides at shoulder height with your palms facing forward.
2. On the exhale, wrap your arms in front of you and across your chest with right arm bound just below left. Reach the arms around you and settle the palms of your hands onto your upper back, giving yourself a giant, warm hug.
3. You also have the option to add a strap to bind the arms by placing the strap around the upper back. Take an end of the strap in each hand for the additional support in this bind.
4. If you have a neck sensitivity, be cautious in attempting the following neck options, or it may be best for you to keep your neck lined up with the rest of your spine. If the neck allows, explore dropping the chin toward the chest, bringing flexion into the neck to open its back line. Feel for mild sensation through the back of the neck and between the shoulder blades, aiding the release of tension within the two large triangular-shaped *trapezius* muscles. These large muscles reside along the mid and upper back into the neck and help to stabilize and move the shoulder blades. As you hold, feel each breath filling the space between your abducted shoulder blades, easing tensions and inviting release. After a few moments, lift the head back up.
5. You could also extend the neck by tipping the head back, but take extra care to not let the head drop too far backward given the sensitivities of compressing the back of the neck. First, make sure the neck is long, and then let the head drop slowly back to a degree of extension that feels reasonable and creates a gentle opening along the front of the throat. Hold for a few breaths, then lift the head back up. Turn your head to one side, pause to breathe

into sensations a few moments, then bring the twist to the other side.

6. To ease out, slowly turn your head back to center and unravel the arms, placing hands to thighs to rest the shoulders. When you're ready, switch the cross of the arms and repeat.

Twisted Branches: *Integrates well with seated, supine, and prone poses (Fig F2)*

To try it out in a comfortable seated position:

1. From the position of the Hugging Arms bind (above), move into this deeper shoulder opener if you need more sensation and your shoulder joints allow.
2. Keep the cross of the arms in front of your chest and lift the hands in front of the face.
3. Move the backs of hands toward one another. It's OK if they do or don't touch.
4. If the wrists permit, continue to entwine your arms by crisscrossing the wrists, bringing the palms toward each other and perhaps pressing together.
5. Play with the positioning and angles of your elbows, neck, and hands and see where the sensations emerge as you explore. For example, lower your elbows and chin onto your chest and slide the hands forward. Another option is to keep the neck straight in line with the rest of the spine, lift the elbows in line with the chin, and move your hands away from your face.
6. As you explore, notice how even these subtle shifts may change the location and intensity of sensations along the backs of your shoulders, arms, upper back, and neck.
7. To release, mindfully unbraid your arms and relax your hands to your thighs to rest. When ready for the other side, repeat by crossing the left arm under the right.

Threaded Needle: *Integrates well with seated, supine, and prone poses in addition to standing at the wall (Fig F3)*

To try it out in a standing position:

1. Threaded Needle binding induces a slight twist in the spine, so as you explore this bind, take caution with any back issues.
2. Stand facing the wall a few inches away from it.
3. Place your hands onto the wall in front of their respective shoulders with your fingers pointing toward the ceiling. Slide your palms up the wall to straighten the arms.
4. Keep the left palm on the wall. To thread your right arm, lift the right hand from the wall, bend the right elbow so that your right palm is in front of your right upper chest and the back of your right hand and forearm lean lightly onto the wall.
5. Press your left palm gently onto the wall. While maintaining light contact between the wall and your right forearm, slide your right arm across the upper chest, threading the arm in front of your left armpit.
6. Keeping your right arm threaded, gently lean your upper body against the wall.
7. The straighter the right arm, the deeper the intensity of the sensations in the focus areas of the right outer shoulder and right upper back. To increase sensations in these areas, reach your right arm further to the left. Be cautious not to over-pull the arm in any way. Remember, we want to feel light diffuse sensations, so nothing sharp, stabbing, too localized, or pointed is appropriate – no pain allowed. Experiment with the right palm facing toward you or away from you.
8. If supportive, rest your forehead onto the wall or rest your chin onto your upper right arm. If the neck permits and you'd like to add a cervical twist, turn your head to the left and hold there, or, for greater emphasis, turn it to the right.
9. Stay with the Single Threaded Needle bind, or, if the shoulders allow and you wish to go deeper, try the Double Threaded Needle by bringing your left arm to cross above your right arm. The arms may be touching. To build more sensations through the backs of shoulders and middle- and upper-back, straighten your arms more to thread more deeply and vice-versa.
10. Keep your head straight here, or if the neck allows, turn it in either direction to find what feels like the appropriate cervical twist for you.

11. Whether in a Single or Double Threaded Needle, choose to have your palm(s) facing toward you or away from you.
12. When you're ready, turn your head back to center and unthread your arms one at a time by sliding each back across the front of your upper chest.
13. Rest both arms down along your sides. After a few moments of recovery, do the other side.

To try out Threaded Needle in a seated upright position or while lying on the back:

1. From either position, begin with your arms relaxed by your sides.
2. Cross your right arm in front of your upper chest and outward to the left while keeping the arm relatively straight.
3. With the left palm facing up, lift your left arm to meet the right forearm, then bend your left elbow to wrap the right forearm into a gentle cradle.
4. Press your left arm gently toward your body to the degree it feels appropriate for your right shoulder, keeping the shoulders squared.
5. Face your right palm toward you or away from you. Play with each to see which you prefer, then hold for a minute or two.
6. To release the arm bind, unbend your left arm and relax both arms down by your sides. When ready, do the other side.

One Arm Behind the Back Bind: *Integrates well with seated twist and seated side bend poses (Fig F4)*

To try it out in a comfortable seated position:

1. Start on the right, reaching the right arm straight out to the right by lining it up with the right shoulder.
2. Create an internal rotation of your right arm by slowly turning the whole right arm in a counterclockwise direction so that the inner elbow faces downward.
3. Keep the internally rotated right arm relatively straight and reach it behind you until you feel a mild edge of resistance in the shoulder and arm.
4. While maintaining the internal rotation, bend your right elbow and place the back of your right hand anywhere along the lower or middle back.
5. Play with your hand's position on the back to give rise to sensations where you most want to feel them along the front and back of the right arm, shoulder, and chest.
6. To release the bind, simply lower your right arm and let it rest. Notice the effects. When you're ready, do the left side.

Double Arm Behind the Back Bind: *Integrates well with seated and upright kneeling poses (Fig F5)*

To try it out in a comfortable seated position:

1. Reach both arms straight out to the sides and lift each to shoulder height to form a T-shape with your arms and body.
2. To internally rotate your shoulders, slowly turn both arms so your inner elbows point toward the mat and palms face behind you. Feel for a gentle twisting up through your arms and into the shoulder joints.
3. Keep this internal rotation as you move your arms behind you and then bend the elbows to reach across your lower back and clasp opposite hands to opposite wrists, forearms, or elbows, wherever the hands reach. Avoid forcing, but allow for mild sensations to arise along the front of your shoulders, arms, and the upper back's bones.
4. To unbind, simply unclasp your hands and let your arms rest down by your sides.

Prayer Hands on the Back: *Integrates well with seated and upright kneeling poses (Fig F6)*

This bind works the wrists particularly deeply. Given the relatively small size and delicate structure of the wrists, take extra care that sensations there remain mild. Hold times are shorter – just a minute or so will do.

To try it out in a comfortable seated position:

1. Reach both arms straight out to the sides and lift each to shoulder height to form a T-shape with your arms and trunk.
2. To internally rotate the shoulders, slowly turn both arms so your inner elbows face the mat and your palms face the wall behind you. Feel for a gentle twisting up through your arms and into the shoulder joints.

3. Keep your shoulders internally rotated as you reach behind you and then bend your elbows to bring the palms behind your back and toward each other while keeping all ten fingers pointed toward the earth. With fingertips still facing downward, slowly bring each hand's fingertips to touch one another.
4. Gently begin to rotate your sealed finger pads toward your spine so that the tent of your fingers points to the lower back.
5. As the wrists allow, continue to rotate the fingertips to face skyward so the pinky sides of your hands are resting on your mid-spine in prayer position.
6. If it doesn't strain any natural boundaries in your wrists, soften the heels of your hands more toward each other. The palms may or may not meet, depending on what feels best for your wrists.
7. To release the bind, turn your fingertips to point toward the spine and then downward, unraveling the wrists. Lower your arms slowly and let them rest along your sides.

Cow-Faced Arms: *Integrates well with seated and upright kneeling poses (Fig F7)*

To try it out in a comfortable seated position:

1. Place a yoga strap or a long towel or scarf over your left shoulder so that half of it drapes down the left side of the chest and the other half falls straight down your back.
2. Reach both arms straight out to your sides and lift each to shoulder height to form a T-shape with your arms and body.
3. Internally rotate the right shoulder by slowly turning your right inner elbow to point toward the floor and the palm to face the wall behind you.
4. Externally rotate the left arm by turning your left inner elbow and palm to face the sky.
5. Lower your internally rotated right arm to your side. Raise your externally rotated left arm straight overhead so the left upper arm lines up with your left ear.
6. Bend your right elbow and bring the back of your right hand to your middle- and upper-back area with fingers slightly angled upward. Take hold of the strap along the spine with your right hand.
7. Bend your left elbow, bringing the palm of your left hand to your middle- and upper-back area with your fingertips pointed downward and grab hold of the strap.
8. To the extent that it feels appropriate, pull the strap taut. To lessen the intensity of shoulder-arm sensations, walk your hands further apart along the strap. To deepen the intensity of stimulation, bring them closer together.
9. If the fingers reach one another without straining, release the strap and clasp your fingers together to bind your arms.
10. When exploring this bind in a seated asana, for more stimulation, you could add a forward bend to enhance both upper and lower body sensations, as needed.
11. To ease out, release the straps from your hands, and one at a time, slowly lower each arm back down to your sides. Repeat it on the other side for balance as you exercise the internal and external rotation of both shoulders.

Prayerful Hands: *Integrates well with prone proses and some forward bends (Fig F8)*

To try it out in a comfortable seated position:

1. Reach both of your arms overhead so your fingertips point skyward and your biceps are beside your ears.
2. Turn your palms to face each other and bring them together.
3. Bend your elbows and lower your sealed hands behind you to the back of your head or neck, resting the thumbs wherever they most comfortably reach.
4. Hold a few moments, and to ease out, simply unbend your elbows and lower your arms to your sides.

To try it out in a prone position:

1. Place two blocks at the front of the mat off to the side within reach.
2. Lie on your belly and reach both arms onto the floor in front of you.
3. Turn your palms to face each other and bring them together.

4. Bend your elbows and lower your sealed hands behind you to the back of your head or neck, resting your thumbs wherever they most comfortably reach.
5. To soften the sensation, separate your hands and place your right palm to the right upper back and the left palm to left upper back. Similarly, you could hold a block widthwise between your hands to help lessen the demands on the shoulder joints as your palms rest into its support.
6. To accentuate the sensation through your shoulders and arms, first unbend your elbows to come out of the bind. Reach both of your arms onto the floor in front of you and then place a block at the lowest height under each elbow. Re-bend your elbows to form Prayerful Hands again, returning the thumbs to the back of your neck. For greater intensity, increase the block height in increments as needed.
7. To release, unbend your elbows and rest with your arms by your sides.

Overhead Binding: *Integrates well with supine poses (Fig F9)*

To try it out while lying comfortably on your back:

1. Raise your arms straight up and then lower them onto the floor behind you with your palms facing the sky.
2. If your arms are hovering above the floor, you could slide a blanket underneath for more support.
3. Bend both of your elbows and clasp opposite hands onto opposite wrists, forearms, or elbows. Stay with this double arm bind or explore a one arm option.
4. To explore a one-arm overhead bind, straighten the right arm. Use your left hand to hold your right arm just below the right wrist. With your left hand, tug lightly on your right arm to generate a line of opening from your right shoulder down through the right-side rib cage. Hold for a minute or two, then switch sides.

Wrist Press: *Integrates well with seated poses (Fig 10 extension, Fig 11 flexion)*

Given the relatively small size and delicate structure of the wrists, take extra care that sensations there remain mild. Hold times are shorter – just a minute or so will do.

To try out Wrist Press in an upright seated position:

1. Begin with wrist joint extension by reaching your arms forward in front of you with your palms facing the sky.
2. Bend your elbows and bring them toward the sides of your rib cage. Lower your hands until the tips of your middle fingers lightly touch the ground and the backs of your hands rest gently against the shins. Your palms should face away from you.
3. As the wrists allow, gently lower the heels of your hands forward and down toward the floor, stopping at the point of mild sensation through the wrists, hands, and fingers. This means the heels of your hands may be hovering above the floor.
4. As you extend the wrist joints, avoid forcing. Just find a sensation that feels stay-able and stop there. For greater intensity, slide your hands a little further away from your body and lean forward a bit more. For less, keep your hands closer to you and lift the heels of your hands away from the floor, as necessary.
5. Hold relatively still for just a minute or so, then slowly lift your hands off the floor. Allow your wrists to rest onto your thighs for a few moments in recovery.
6. To explore wrist joint flexion, reach your arms forward in front of you with your palms facing the mat.
7. Bend your elbows and bring them toward the sides of the rib cage. Lower your hands until the tips of the middle fingers lightly touch the mat and the palms of your hands rest gently against the shins.
8. As the wrists allow, gently rock the wrists forward over your fingers so that your fingernails and the backs of your hands move slowly toward the mat.
9. Lower the backs of your hands only so much as to give rise to diffuse sensation within the

wrists, hands, and fingers. If you're not feeling enough sensation, slide your hands a little further away from your body. For less, keeps the hands closer to you and lift the backs of your hands away from the floor, as necessary.

10. Hold in stillness for a minute or so. To release, gently peel your hands slowly away from the earth and bring them to rest onto your lap as you take in the effects of the wrist work.

General Hold Time

- Average of one to three minutes, perhaps lingering longer as your practice continues to evolve, while newer practitioners might begin with a minute and lengthen over time. Shoulder and arm joints are complex but more delicate than larger joints such as the hips, so holds aren't quite as long.
- Wrists are another exception and hold times are even shorter, up to one or one and a half minutes due to their more delicate nature.

YINPRESSION: INVERSION

Positions in which the pelvis-hips and/or hips-legs are above the heart and head

Inversions can be refreshing, nurturing, and relaxing postures. Using the benefit of gravity, they support the return of built-up fluid from the lower extremities into the lymph network. While there aren't many inversions in Yin Yoga, there are a handful, including supine and kneeling postures. Supine wall poses in which we choose to elevate the hips with a bolster are also considered gentle inversions. With the exception of Snail pose, Yin Yoga inversions are generally milder than their yang counterparts and though not for everyone, they could be more accessible for some bodies.

Potential Areas of Sensation

- It depends. Refer to individual Yin Asana Spotlights for pose-specific areas.

Remember: The potential areas of sensation are primary areas of benefit and precaution. In the case of injury/special conditions in these areas, consult your healthcare team and/or avoid.

Additional Safety Watch-Outs (!)

Inversions should be avoided by those with:

- High blood pressure and conditions exacerbated by increased blood pressure, such as eye conditions or diabetes
- Inner ear conditions, such as vertigo
- Low back conditions/concerns, including spinal disc issues, that are worsened by spinal flexion
- Neck and shoulder issues

Pregnancy, consider:

- Inversions may or may not be advisable during pregnancy, depending on a number of factors, including prior practice of inversions and how far along pregnancy is. The best approach should be agreed with your physician.

Also consider:

- Inverting while menstruating depends on what feels most appropriate for you.

Basic Guidance

1. When inverting, stay watchful of the weight of the upper body causing too much pressure in the shoulders or neck.
2. To protect the neck, do not turn your head in supine inversions.
3. If at any time you find yourself feeling woozy, dizzy, or nauseous, slowly come out of the pose and rest.
4. If something doesn't feel right, it isn't, and an adjustment or exit is necessary.
5. While there's no absolute rule that says you have to take a rest after every Yin Yoga pose, inversions are a good exception. A rebalancing break in stillness close to the ground can be nice immediately following your inversion to prevent any dizziness which can happen if you rise to quickly. Good counterpose options include Savasana, Beetle, Constructive Rest, or other gentle supine or side-lying

shapes you'll find in the Yin Asana Spotlights.

6. Individual inversion pose details are included in the Yin Asana Spotlights, as well as in "Yinpression: On the Wall."

General Hold Time

- Average of three to five minutes, perhaps lingering longer as your practice continues to evolve, while newer practitioners might begin with one to three minutes and lengthen over time

Yinpression: On the Wall

Supine positions with lower body supported on the wall

Postures on the wall can be restful, offering unique angles of support using the wall and floor as props. As with the other Yinpressions, wall postures may not be appropriate for all practitioners all the time, depending on tightness in hips and hamstrings or knee sensitivities. When accessible to the body, the legs let go into the wall's support as the earth provides a solid foundation for the weight of the head, arms, and torso. In wall postures, we're also able to creatively use bolsters, blocks, and rolled blankets to offer additional support for the legs. Supine wall postures can easily transform into gentle inversions by employing a bolster under the hips. Being held close to the earth with legs supported by the wall may feel grounding and especially calming.

Potential Areas of Sensation

- Lower half of the body, in general. See the Yin Asana Spotlights for pose-specific areas.

Remember: The potential areas of sensation are primary areas of benefit and precaution. In the case of injury/special conditions in these areas, consult your healthcare team and/or avoid.

Additional Safety Watch-Outs (!)

Tight hamstrings or tender knees, consider:

- Increasing the bend of the knees or positioning the hips further from the wall

Tight hips, consider:

- Positioning the hips further from the wall

Also consider:

- If inverting on the wall, see "Yinpression: Inversion" above for additional watch-outs.

Basic Guidance

The position from which to enter the majority of supine wall poses is Wall Caterpillar pose.

To explore Wall Caterpillar:

1. Lay your mat onto the floor with the short edge along the wall so the mat and wall form a T-shape. Spread a single-folded blanket across your mat about two and a half feet from the wall to serve as a cushion for your head once you've reclined. Position the bolster just off to the right side of your mat so the long side is against the wall. Place two blocks and a blanket off to the side of your mat within reach.
2. Sit onto the left edge of your mat between the blanket and the wall with your right outer hip parallel to the wall. Bend your knees a little and place the soles of your feet onto the floor. Keeping a slight bend in the knees, slowly lie onto your left side, coming into a side-lying fetal position, or Sideways Beetle pose. Here the soles of your feet will be against the wall. If your knees, hips, or back feel tight, come back to seated and position the hips a little further from the wall to help soften the joint angles, then lie back down onto your left side.
3. While keeping your knees in toward your chest, engage your core as you press your right hand to the floor and roll onto your back as one unit. Position the back of your head onto

the blanket and position the soles of your feet on the wall so the toes point toward the sky.

4. Slowly unbend the knees and stretch your legs up the wall to enter the general L-shape of Wall Caterpillar pose. Place your feet about hip-width distance apart and rest your heels onto the wall. Keep the legs straight or bend the knees a bit, depending on what feels best for the backs of your legs.
5. This is another good check-in point. If sensations are either too intense or too faint anywhere along the back line of the body, or if your knee joints become strained, you could exit the pose to adjust or slowly scoot yourself closer or further from the wall by lifting the hips and using your upper arm strength. Hips closer to the wall tends to generate more sensation, while hips further from the wall likely lessens sensation. If choosing to exit the pose, bend your knees, slide your feet down the wall, and roll back onto your left side. Rise to seated and adjust your hip position relative to the wall based on what your body needs, then reenter Wall Caterpillar following steps two through four.
6. As you rest into Wall Caterpillar, allow the weight of your legs to lean into the wall and release tension through the hamstrings and calf muscles. While holding the posture, if you start to experience any painful compression in your feet, toes, or ankles from the pressure of the wall, wrap a small blanket around them to give a soft cushion. Wall Caterpillar makes a lovely opening posture for a wall Yin Yoga practice, offering space to enjoy a body scan, mindful breathing practice, or other meditative techniques.
7. From Wall Caterpillar, you are well-positioned to move into the other supine wall postures. You'll find their details highlighted throughout the Yin Asana Spotlights.
8. There is also the additional option of transforming the supine wall postures into mild inversions. Though relatively gentle, the same inversion benefits and precautions apply while on the wall. For safety considerations, please reference "Yinpression: Inversion" above. Wall Caterpillar transforms into the inversion Elevated Wall Caterpillar when a bolster is slid under the hips. To proceed into Elevated Wall Caterpillar, bend your knees enough to comfortably position the soles of your feet onto the wall. To protect your neck, be sure not to turn your head as you make this transition or while you're holding the inversion. Press both feet into the wall to lift your hips just enough to slide the bolster underneath you, then rest your hips down onto the bolster. Just as Wall Caterpillar is a good starting point for other wall postures, Elevated Wall Caterpillar is a fine base from which to elevate additional wall postures into mild inversions, which we'll cover in the Yin Asana Spotlights.

9. While enjoying the various supine wall postures, remain attentive to changing sensations throughout the body and make adjustments as necessary, including moving your hips closer to or further from the wall. If your hips lift off the floor or bolster in any of the poses, it's OK as long as it feels good for you. If not, shift your hips away from the wall a little more to allow them to release onto the floor or prop.
10. To exit Elevated Wall Caterpillar, bend your knees and press your feet into the wall to lift your hips just above the bolster. Roll the bolster toward the wall if there's enough room or slide it off to the side. Lower your hips onto the mat, returning to Wall Caterpillar.
11. To exit Wall Caterpillar, simply slide the feet down the wall, and with your knees bent, roll gently onto your preferred side.
12. Rest for a minute or two on your side with your knees pulled loosely in toward the chest in Sideways Beetle pose, perhaps using your forearm or a blanket under your head as a

cushion. After coming down from the wall, rising to a seated position too quickly can cause dizziness, so this position is an invitation to pause and feel the pose's effects. Allow your body ample time to adjust, letting yourself steep in the rest.

General Hold Time

- Average of three to five minutes, perhaps lingering longer as your practice continues to evolve, while newer practitioners might begin with one to three minutes and lengthen over time

Yinpression: Backbend

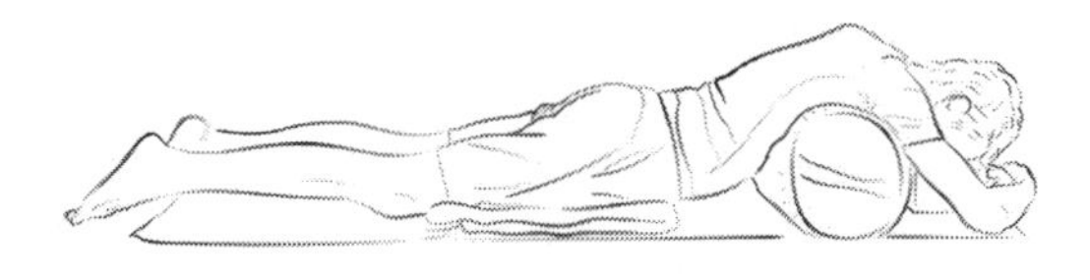

Bending the upper body away from the front of hips/thighs; bending backward, extending the spine

Among so many daily activities that cause slouching, bending backward offers us a complementary counterbalance in support of the mobility and wellbeing of the spine. These energizing postures can serve as natural mood boosters. Backbends stimulate the area of the lumbar spine and harmonize the Kidney Qi flowing through it, helping to dissolve fear and replace it with our innate courage and resolve. They also open the front of the body, revealing our confident, loving heart.

Potential Areas of Sensation

- Length of the spine, including the lumbar spine and the neighboring tissues
- Shoulders and chest, with the potential to reach down to the abdominal area
- Front of hip/thigh, including quads and hip flexors

Remember: The potential areas of sensation are primary areas of benefit and precaution. In the case of injury/special conditions in these areas, consult your healthcare team and/or avoid.

Additional Safety Watch-Outs ⓘ

Consider:

- If inverting in a backbend, see "Yinpression: Inversion" above for additional watch-outs.

Basic Guidance

Backbends build strength and suppleness into the low back, the area of our spine most at risk for compromise given its mobility and weight bearing responsibilities. It's a great idea to consider regularly integrating backbends into the practice given the amount of time we bend forward over desks and devices. While there aren't a large number of backbends in Yin Yoga, helpfully, we don't need to have twenty different varieties, just one or two that work well. As the esteemed late U.S. Supreme Court Justice Ruth Bader Ginsburg noted, there's no need to use four words when three will do!

1. In addition to serving the lumbar area, backbends offer an opportunity to consciously open the chest and shoulders along the front line of the body and extend stimulation through the thoracic spine. Feel for diffuse sensations along the spine's length and its surrounding tissues, avoiding anything pinching, isolated, or sharp.
2. If you're experiencing a bit too much sensation in the lower back, pick a gentler phase of the shape or slightly lengthen the tail bone toward the heels which can help spread and soften the sensations.
3. Take care to recruit your core muscles during your slow transition out of backbends; this helps protect the low back in its temporarily fragile state.
4. To support mindful recovery in these tissues after the spinal extension of a backbend, choosing a counterpose with a more neutral spine can be especially nurturing. Savasana pose (p. 179), makes a wonderful resting position as you soak in the grounding energies of the earth. If the low back is particularly sensitive, Constructive Rest pose (p. 204), is another soothing option.
5. Sometimes we unintentionally hold our breath in backbend postures, so these are particularly potent times to encourage slow,

mindful breathing, perhaps integrating a supportive directed breathing technique such as breathing into any sensations arising in the lumbar spine. When breath flows, Qi flows!

6. Revitalizing and refreshing, backbends are great pick-me-ups when you're feeling fatigued or low energy.
7. Individual backbend pose details will follow in the Yin Asana Spotlights.

General Hold Time

- Average of three to five minutes, perhaps lingering longer as your practice continues to evolve, while newer practitioners might begin with one to three minutes and lengthen over time

Yinpression: Supine

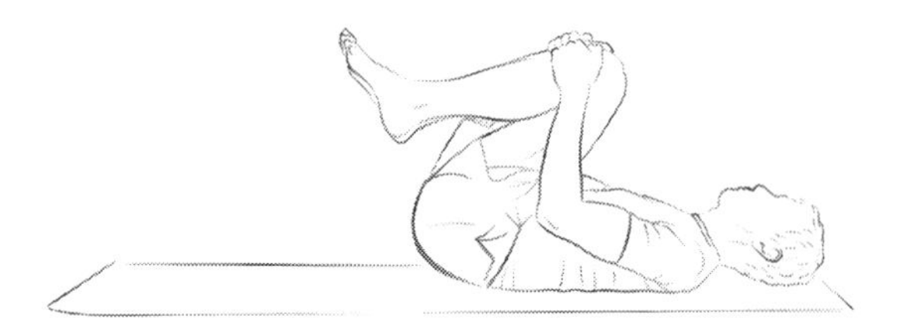

Lying on the back; reclined on the mat

Supine postures are a viable option to consider whenever we desire a little less sensation in general. While not always the case, postures incorporating this Yinpression are often gentler than many of the seated and kneeling positions. You might consider including supine postures into your practice anytime you feel especially fatigued after a long day's work or in the evening when wanting to quietly wind things down. If you find yourself moving through difficult times, these variations may offer helpful emotional support and steadiness by bringing you closer to the earth. A reclining posture can quiet the mind and body as a lovely prelude to your closing Savasana relaxation.

Potential Areas of Sensation

- It depends. See the Yin Asana Spotlights for pose-specific areas.

Remember: The potential areas of sensation are primary areas of benefit and precaution. In the case of injury/special conditions in these areas, consult your healthcare team and/or avoid.

Additional Safety Watch-Outs ⓘ

Pregnancy, consider:

- Swapping with side-lying or seated variations

Basic Guidance

1. During set up, place a single-folded blanket on the back of your mat to serve as a cushion for your head once you've reclined. Place the rest of your props near the middle of your mat off to the side within reach.
2. The relative soft and supportive nature of supine poses like Savasana (p. 179) and Supine Butterfly (p. 143) makes them good session starters, letting us give the weight of the body and any worries of the mind over to the earth as we arrive to the mat. Their simplicity offers space for us to refresh on the practice principles or to share them with practitioners if we're teaching.
3. If there are any sensitivities or injuries in the areas of the neck, spine, or knees that make the seated pose version inaccessible, going supine may take the strain out of those areas and open new possibilities for working with your body.
4. While supine, perhaps you try out various bind options to open the shoulders, such as Overhead Binding or Threaded Needle (see "Yinpression: Shoulder-Arm Binds"). For a peaceful effect, place your hands over your heart or one hand on the heart and the other on the belly.
5. As in seated postures, if there's too much stimulation in your hips, legs, and/or knees, place a block or rolled blanket underneath the outer thigh/knee area to soften the intensity levels and keep sensations reasonable.
6. Individual supine pose details are included in the Yin Asana Spotlights.

General Hold Time

- Average of three to five minutes, perhaps lingering longer as your practice continues to evolve, while newer practitioners might begin with one and a half to three minutes and lengthen over time

Yinpression: Prone

Lying on the belly

Low to the ground, prone positions bring us face to face with the yin energy of the earth. With the back of our body bathed in the yang energy of the heavens, we give ourselves over to the stability of the earth, transitioning our attention inward. You might enjoy exploring prone postures for the Savasana final relaxation at the end of class as well as in counterposing. In general, prone positions are relatively mild and supported, making them useful alternatives to some of the seated or supine postures. They can be a quieting way to open class, encouraging us to let the busy-ness of the day fall away. We can completely release all muscular holding, putting our full attention on the body lying on the earth and on the movement of the flowing breath, steeping in the beauty of the present time.

Potential Areas of Sensation

- Lumbar spine
- Shoulders
- Cervical spine, if twisting the neck

Remember: The potential areas of sensation are primary areas of benefit and precaution. In the case of injury/special conditions in these areas, consult your healthcare team and/or avoid.

Additional Safety Watch-Outs (!)

Pregnancy, consider:

- Swapping with side-lying or seated variations

Neck or shoulder sensitivities, consider:

- Keeping neck in line with the spine by supporting head with a prop
- Supporting upper body with blanket or bolster

Low back sensitivity, consider:

- Decreasing angle of spinal extension using a blanket under the front of the hips

Basic Guidance

1. To set up, place a single-folded blanket on the middle of your mat to serve as padding for the hips, helping to avoid any painful compression of the frontal hip bones. Place the rest of your props at the front of the mat off to the side within reach.
2. Kneel in Tabletop position with hands on the mat in front of the blanket and knees behind it. Walk your knees backward several inches. Bend your elbows and lower onto your belly, adjusting the blanket so it cushions the fronts of your hips. If lowering in this way starts to cause too much strain on the shoulders or back, sit onto your side with knees bent, stretch out side-lying, and roll onto your belly.
3. Lying flat on the belly may bring a gentle compression to the lower back. If this doesn't feel good, place another blanket or two under the front of your hips and lower abdomen. Should this transfer unwanted pressure into your neck or shoulders, try sliding a blanket under your chest/shoulders/neck.
4. To keep your neck in line with the rest of the spine, slide an extra blanket underneath your forehead or cheek. Keep your forehead on the mat or blanket, or for a cervical twist, rest onto a cheek.
5. To help prevent any painful compression of the top of the foot on the floor, position a rolled-up blanket under the tops of your ankles to soften the angles as needed.
6. Individual prone pose details are included in the Yin Asana Spotlights.

General Hold Time

- Average of three to five minutes, perhaps lingering longer as your practice continues to evolve, while newer practitioners might begin with one to three minutes and lengthen over time

Yinpression: Qi Charting

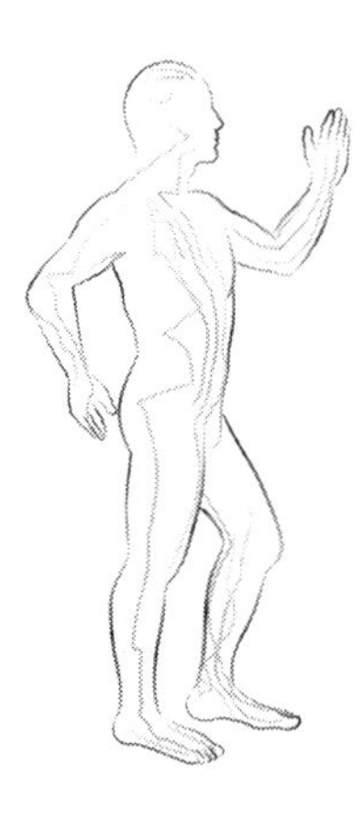

Selecting focus areas for the purpose of stimulating Qi channels

As we've discussed in "The Energy Layer," there are twelve Qi channels that feed our yin-yang Organ pairs. When we exercise the yin tissues of the body through which a Qi channel runs, we help to clarify and strengthen the flow of energy through it, nourishing its Organ System and supporting the related physiological and emotional functions the Organ oversees. When we understand the relationships between the physical areas of exercise and the chart of energy channels within us, we can intentionally select poses and sequences that target specific Qi channels/Organs. We have a lot of flexibility and freedom to explore Yinpressions within our postures to exercise the physical tissues and Qi channels we want to nurture.

Potential Areas of Sensation

- Use the Yinpression reference summary to identify the areas of potential sensation and Qi channel(s) reached in each Yinpression. When we stimulate a yin channel, remember that its yang counterpart is also stimulated, and vice versa.

Basic Guidance

In the "The Energy Layer," we moved through a more comprehensive energetic scan. Following is a reminder of the general pathways the Qi channels take through the body. Understanding their locations helps us associate the physical focus areas of exercise with the channels we're activating, based on where we're feeling sensations.

Lower Body Qi Channels

1. The lower body yin-yang Qi channels originate or end in the toes and include the yin Kidney & yang Urinary Bladder, yin Liver & yang Gall Bladder, yin Spleen & yang Stomach.
2. All three lower body yin channels run from the toes upward along the inner legs. The Kidney channel enters the torso at the base of the spine and continues up the bones of sacral and lumbar spine before entering the Kidney and then continuing to branch. The Liver channel continues up the legs, entering the torso at the groin. The Spleen channel flows along the inner shins and inner knees, then the top of the thighs on its way into the torso.
3. The three lower body yang channels all run from the head and flow downward and land in the toes. The Gall Bladder channel traces through the lateral torso and down the outer hip/leg/shin. The Stomach channel travels through the front of the torso and the tops of the thigh and shin. The Urinary Bladder channel flows through the length of the back on either side of the spine, through the backs of the buttocks and down along the backside of the legs.

Upper Body Qi Channels

1. The upper body yin-yang Qi channels originate or end in the fingers and include the yin Lung & yang Large Intestine, yin Heart & yang Small Intestine, yin Pericardium & yang Triple Burner.
2. All the upper body channels travel through the torso, shoulders, arms, and fingers. As the arms are often positioned overhead in the traditional Chinese energy map, the yin

Yinpression Summary for Qi Charting

Yinpression	Areas of Potential Sensation with Qi Channels
Seated Forward Bend	♦ Back of spine/back of leg: Urinary Bladder, Sea of Yang ♦ Lower back: Kidney
Hip-Leg Work, One-Legged	♦ Inner leg: Kidney, Liver, Spleen (lower inner leg/inner knee) ♦ Back of hip/buttock/back of leg: Urinary Bladder ♦ Outer hip/lateral thigh: Gall Bladder ♦ Front of hip/front of thigh: Spleen
Side Bend	♦ Side of torso: Gall Bladder ♦ Back of spine: Urinary Bladder, Sea of Yang ♦ Shoulders/arms: all upper body channels
Twist	♦ Back of spine: Urinary Bladder, Sea of Yang ♦ Front of spine: Sea of Yin ♦ Side of torso: Gall Bladder ♦ Chest/shoulders/arms: all upper body channels ♦ Outer hip/lateral thigh: Gall Bladder
Shoulder-Arm Binds	♦ Chest/shoulder/arm: all upper body channels ♦ Middle/Upper back: Urinary Bladder, Sea of Yang
Backbend	♦ Lower back: Kidney ♦ Back of spine: Urinary Bladder, Sea of Yang ♦ Chest/shoulder/arm: all upper body channels ♦ Front of torso: Spleen, Stomach ♦ Front of hip/thigh: Spleen ♦ Front of spine: Sea of Yin
Wall, Inversion, Prone, Supine	♦ Where you feel sensation will depend on the posture, see the Yin Asana Spotlights for pose-specific areas and associated Qi channels.

channels of Lung, Heart, and Pericardium begin in the torso and flow upward along the inner arms to the fingers. The yang channels of Large Intestine, Small Intestine, and Triple Burner begin in the fingers and flow down along the outer arms to the back of shoulder before continuing to branch.

Sea of Yin and Yang

1. The general path of the Sea of Yin (Conception Vessel) runs along the front of the spine while the Sea of Yang (Governor Vessel) flows along the back of the spine. Serving as reservoirs for the body's overall yin and yang energy, these two vessels work collaboratively to promote a balanced flow through all twelve of the primary yin-yang channels and their Organs.

General Hold Time

- ♦ Because hold times vary based on the areas of sensation, reference individual Yinpressions.

Qi Channels

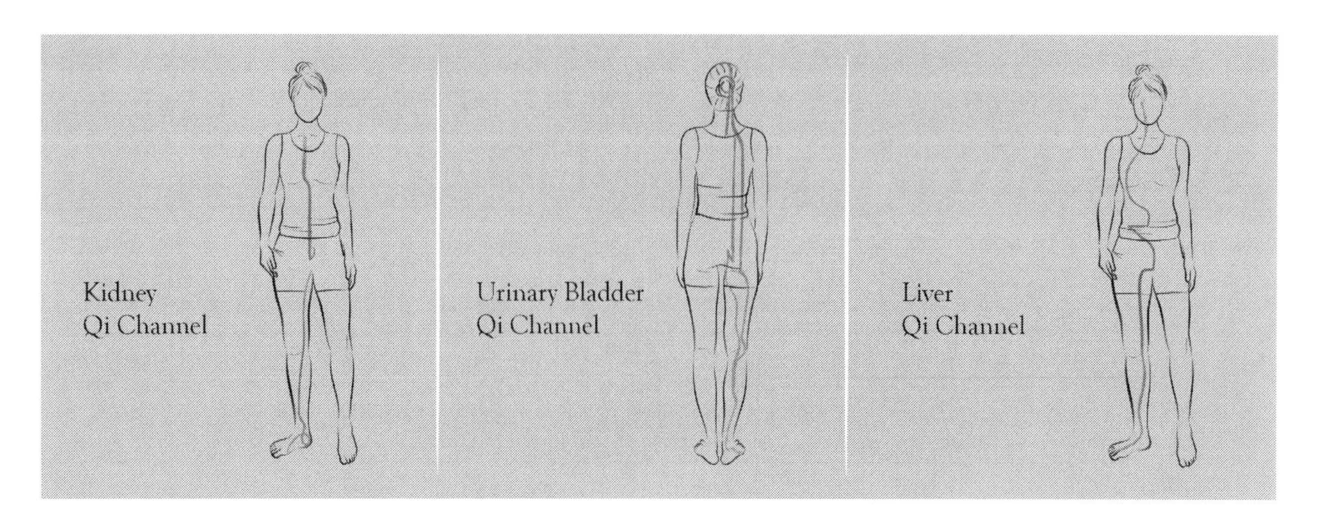
Kidney
Qi Channel
Urinary Bladder
Qi Channel
Liver
Qi Channel

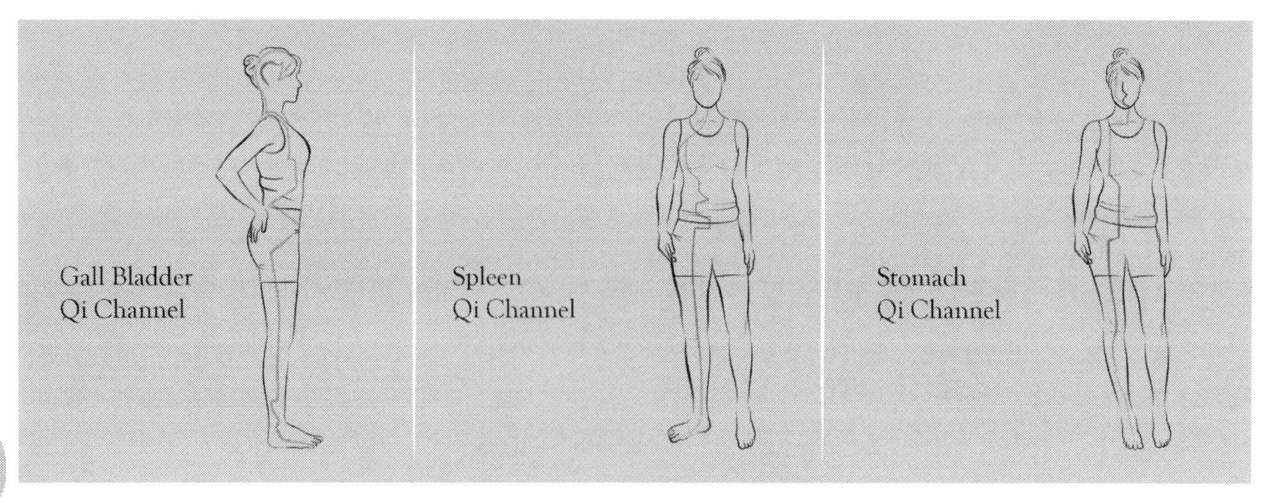
Gall Bladder
Qi Channel
Spleen
Qi Channel
Stomach
Qi Channel

asana

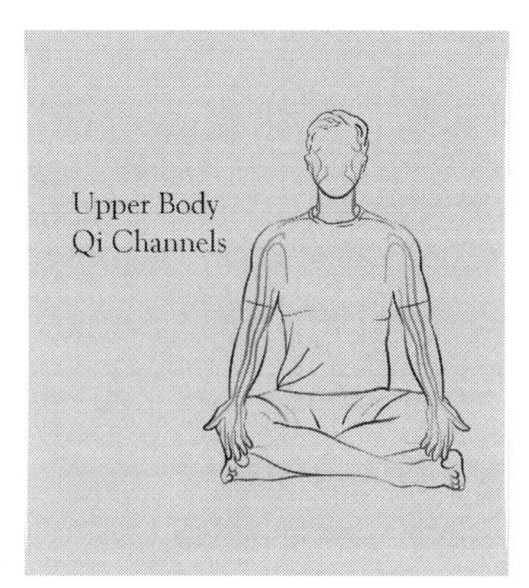
Upper Body
Qi Channels

CHAPTER 10

YIN ASANA AND COUNTERPOSING

The Yin Asana Spotlights presented here include a wide assortment of Yin Yoga poses which are alphabetized to help you locate them readily. Though some poses in this practice may be visually similar to their yang counterparts, the names are typically modified in Yin Yoga to highlight their more yin-like intent and approach. Many of the names are also nature-based, echoing the inspiration and wisdom of the natural world.

While the "Asana Yinpressions: Patterns and Potentials" section is designed to offer a fundamental and more holistic understanding of the postures and the many possibilities they contain, the individual Yin Asana Spotlights are intended to provide more pose-specific instructions. These sections are offered together to help build your technical and intuitive understanding of the Yin asana series as you continue to discover how to make each pose best fit your individual needs as well as the needs of your students.

WHAT TO EXPECT IN THE YIN ASANA SPOTLIGHTS

You will find several subsections to help guide you safely and effectively into, through, and out of each posture. The pose instructions are written step-by-step, with the starting point typically representing the gentlest expression of the shape. The subsections include:

Physical Focus – This section lists the primary areas of the body where you're likely to feel sensations in the pose. As we've learned, these areas are therefore the primary areas of benefit and precaution. The Physical Focus section can help you select poses according to your needs and intention and is meant to be a starting point for your observations. In the pose, you might not feel anything or you might feel sensations in other parts of the body not mentioned, and both are equally OK! What's important is feeling sensation in your desired area(s) of focus.

Qi Charting – A quick reference to help you choose poses that stimulate specific yin-yang Organs/Qi channels. More detailed information about the energetic pathways can be found in "Yinpression: Qi Charting" and "The Energy Layer."

Finding Your Expression of the Shape – No two expressions of a pose will likely look exactly alike, and our needs often change day to day. In this section, you'll find guidance on ways to experiment with each posture to find the shape that best suits you each time you approach it, including:

- *Setting Up*: Suggestions for prop selection and placement to keep them within easy reach as you enter the posture and try different variations of the pose.
- *Easing In*: Instructions for moving mindfully into the phase of the pose that works for you. At the end of pose guidance, italicized Yinpression indicators (Yp) list the Yinpressions experienced in that pose.

- *Yinpressions for Exploration While You Stay*: A selection of additional Yinpression options to experiment with while holding the pose.
- *Easing Out*: Instructions to safely emerge from the pose.
- *Substitutions for Consideration*: Suggestions for alternate postures to consider if a particular pose isn't accessible or you want to gain access to another part of your body. Yinpression indicators (Yp) list the Yinpressions experienced in that pose as well as additional Yinpression options to explore while you stay.
- Use the Yp designators to reference back to the Yinpression section guidance anytime a refresh would be helpful, whether for safety and efficacy reminders or to reflect on their patterns and potentials.

Images – A selection of photographs to demonstrate some of the many phases and variations for the spotlighted postures. Some images include extensive prop setups while others show few or none. They're offered here as ideas to consider as you find the perfect option for you.

Meditative Yinquiry for the Mat – Brief meditative prompts for your contemplation grounded in Yin Yoga & Meditation Mandala Map. You might reflect on them as you arrive to the mat, within poses or counterposes, or following your practice to spur insights. Perhaps you'll find inspiration in using them as foundations to creatively blossom them into your unique Yin Yoga & Meditation session themes.

asana

Counterposes – A sampling of counterposes with considerations and instructions to incorporate rest and recovery throughout your Yin Yoga & Meditation session.

Here are a few recommendations to help you get acquainted with each pose:

1. Read through the guidance in the Yin Asana Spotlight for the pose you want to learn about, using the photographs to help you visualize the posture and its variations.
2. Review the "Setting Up" information and arrange the relevant props on your mat.
3. Before entering the pose, briefly revisit the "Easing In" and "Easing Out" instructions.
4. Try easing in, stopping at the phase that's right for you. If it feels inaccessible, try swapping with a suggested substitution pose.
5. Ease out of the pose.
6. Once you're familiar with the pose, you can reference the "Yinpressions for Exploration While You Stay" subsection to explore incorporating additional Yinpressions.
7. If it would be helpful to you, you could record the pose guidance just as it is written into your phone or other recording device. Read the instructions at a pace which will allow you to mindfully follow along on the mat.
8. Consider jotting down any observations of your experience in your practice journal after exiting the pose.

Beetle

Physical Focus

Releases lower back with the opportunity for freedom in the whole spine, massages abdominal organs, works into hip adductors of the inner thighs, and extends the tops of ankles.

Qi Charting

Kidney-Urinary Bladder
Liver-Gall Bladder
Spleen-Stomach

FINDING your Expression of the shape

Setting Up: Place a bolster on your mat lengthwise and a single-folded blanket on your mat behind the bolster to serve as padding for your knees and shins. Place two blocks and a blanket near the middle of your mat off to the side within reach.

Easing In: Kneel onto the blanket with the bolster in front of you and then place hands to the floor to come into Tabletop position, stacking shoulders over wrists and hips over knees. Further separate the knees toward the outside edges of your mat until you feel a light sensation of pulling through the inner legs. Bring your big toes together behind you and lower your hips toward your heels to the degree that your body allows, resting the hips onto the feet if that's accessible. Place the bolster lengthwise between the knees. As you inhale, lengthen your spine. As you breathe out, keep the hips weighted back and down as you fold forward, draping your upper body onto the bolster to come into **Wide Knee Beetle** pose (Fig A). Stay mindful of low back issues that might be exacerbated by the rounding of the lower back.

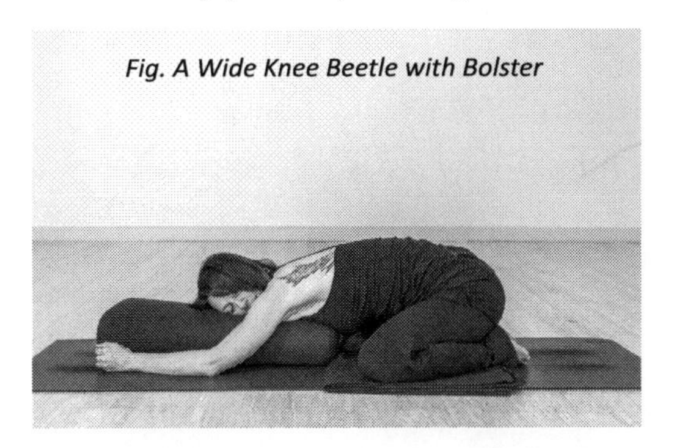
Fig. A Wide Knee Beetle with Bolster

If the hips lift off the heels, try slipping a rolled blanket between the calves and the backs of the thighs to aid the muscular release in the lower body. If there's too much strain in the neck, shoulders, or knees anywhere along the way, soften the depth of the fold by placing a block underneath the bolster's top edge to angle it upward and closer to you. If there's not enough release through the back and hips, remove the bolster from underneath the chest and rest your upper body onto the mat. Fold your arms under your forehead or stretch them long onto the mat in front of you. Play a bit with the positioning of your knees. With knees wider, the greater abduction of the hips will likely generate more sensation in the hips and inner thighs. If there's painful groin compression at the front of the hips, separating the knees a touch more sometimes alleviates this undesired pressure.

Fig. B Closed Knee Beetle

Alternately, create a more rounded lower back release by bringing the inner knees together. In this **Closed Knee Beetle** shape (Fig B), you could rest your arms by your sides and hold your feet with your hands, tucking deeper inward. Feel for how the fold creates a soft compression of the internal organs of the abdomen that's enhanced through mindful breathing. If at any time the hips lift above the heart and head, this becomes a gentle inversion.

Postures of a relatively uncomplicated nature like Beetle require fewer verbal cues, making them excellent candidates for class-starter poses to revisit the practice principles for a safe and effective experience. Delivering these tenets early in the session helps establish a supportive environment and encourages a mindful practice. (Yp: *hip-leg work*)

Fig. C Threaded Needle Beetle

⦿ **YINPRESSIONS FOR EXPLORATION While You Stay:** *side bend, shoulder-arm binds: threaded needle (Fig C), prayerful hands*

Easing Out: To mindfully emerge from Beetle, place your hands to the floor and walk them toward you as you slowly press yourself upright. If the knees are separated, bring them together and then slowly sweep the legs around in front of you and come to seated.

Substitutions for Consideration

Tipped Beetle/One-Legged Tipped Beetle (below), Sitting Beetle (below), Sideways Beetle (below), Supine Butterfly (p. 143)
The supine variations may be easier on the hips, knees, and spine.
Seated and sideways variations can take pressure off the neck and knees.

Fig. D Tipped Beetle

Tipped Beetle: Lie on your back with a single-folded blanket under your head for comfort. While keeping the sacrum flat to the floor, draw both knees in toward your chest. Place your hands on the tops of your knees or wrap your hands or arms around the shins (Fig D). If the hands do not comfortably reach the legs, wrap a strap around the backs of both thighs, holding a tail of the strap in each hand. To help bring ease to the head, neck, and shoulders, adjust your hand positions on the strap until it holds the knees toward the chest while also allowing the back of your shoulders and head to rest on the mat. Gently rock side to side to smooth out any tensions in the sacrum. After swaying a bit, pause in stillness and circle the knees in a clockwise direction several times slowly, as if you're using them to draw circles on the ceiling.

Repeat this going counterclockwise. If rounding the lumbar spine feels OK, play with rolling the hips upward and off the mat. Curling into this tighter Beetle shape offers a deeper opening for the lower back. If your neck allows, perhaps lift your head off the floor to touch your forehead to your knees. After a few moments of holding, return your head to the floor. Release your hands from your knees and place both feet to the floor hip-width distance apart with the knees stacked over the ankles. From this position, you might also try a **One-Legged Tipped Beetle**. Draw the right knee into the chest. Interlace your fingers and wrap your hands around the upper shin, cradling the right leg. If not within comfortable reach, loop a strap around the back of the thigh, holding a tail in each hand. Extend the left leg straight down the mat for a deeper low back opening (Fig E). To transition out, place your feet to the floor one at a time hip-width distance apart, stacking knees over ankles, then switch sides. (Yp: *supine, hip-leg work, one-legged*)

Fig. E One-Legged Tipped Beetle

Sitting Beetle: Sit on your mat on top of a folded blanket with legs extended in front of you. Find a slight anterior tilt in the pelvis (for a refresher, see "Yinpression: Seated Forward Bend," p. 109) using additional props under the sit-bones as needed. Bend your knees and place the soles of your feet to the floor in front of you. Adjust the distance between the feet and your body for overall comfort. Rest your hands on top of your knees or wrap your arms around your shins. Keep the spine tall through the crown of the head if more rounding in the back causes irritation. Otherwise, let the whole spine round freely forward and inward, resting your upper body onto your legs as your forehead drops onto your knees. This seated variation can also be enjoyed as a counter-posture for rest and mindful observation between poses. (Yp: *seated forward bend, hip-leg work)*

Sideways Beetle: Lie on your side and bend your knees, stacking one on top of the other. If this causes too much sensation, try separating the knees a bit, or you could place a prop between them until it feels right. If the low back allows for rounding, slide the knees along the floor toward your chest to a degree that creates a comfortable resting position. Wrap both of your arms around your legs. Alternately, rest your head onto the cradle of your arm or add a blanket for extra cushion and neck support. Sideways Beetle also offers a quiet contemplative holding space for a mindful transition point between supine and seated postures. To ease out, place the hand of the arm underneath you to the floor and slowly press yourself up to seated, letting your head hang heavy so it's the last to rise. (Yp: *hip-leg work*)

Meditative Yinquiry for the Mat

"The Five-Minute Reset"

If you arrive into a pose feeling distracted or anxious, frazzled, or fatigued, it's OK. We've all come to our practice in all manner of moods. You might approach the posture as an opportunity for a five-minute reset. Which aspect of you is most in need of nurturing? Is it a particular area of your body? Do you have an unhelpful thought loop racing around the same mental track over and over? Is there a feeling tone holding on from earlier in the day? Notice anything persisting or insisting right now. Name it with friendliness, acknowledge its presence, and take three intentional deep breaths in and out. Give yourself permission in this moment, in this pose, to simply *be*. Let all else fall outside your attention, just breathing here in this small window of time, a chance to reset and renew. As you rest in this way, is anything transitioning or transforming? Meet yourself fully here with kindness and openness...these few minutes are all yours. Let this five-minute reset reverberate all through you, refreshing the body, refreshing the mind, and refreshing the soul.

Bridge

Physical Focus

Supine backbend serving the base of the spine and lumbar area with the chance to clear tension along the frontline of the body, from the tops of the hips, thighs, and abdomen into the chest. Supports a strong and supple spine by counterbalancing unhealthy sitting patterns and complements the many forward bends in Yin Yoga.

Qi Charting

Kidney-Urinary Bladder
Spleen-Stomach

FINDING your Expression of the shape

Setting Up: Place a single-folded blanket on the back of your mat to serve as a cushion for your head once you've reclined. Place two blocks, a bolster, and a blanket near the middle of your mat off to the side within reach.

Easing In: Bridge is a gentle inversion which may be more accessible than vigorous inversions while offering the same benefits. It also has many of the same contraindications to consider. If inverted postures aren't working for your body right now, there are a variety of options to explore in the Substitutions.

Fig. A Bridge

For this backbend **Bridge** pose, begin by lying onto your back with the spine in a straight line. Place your feet onto the floor hip-width distance apart with your knees above your ankles. Press into the feet to gently lift your hips a few inches, then slide a bolster or a block at the lowest height under your sacrum, that bony triangular area just below the arch of the lumbar spine. Use one block at the lowest level, or for more stability, place two blocks side by side. Once the prop support is under the sacrum, relax the hips down onto it (Fig A). If you're not feeling enough compressive sensation through the low back and sacral area, try stacking another block at its lowest level on top of the first to increase the angle of spinal extension. For additional height, layer a blanket on top of the prop support.

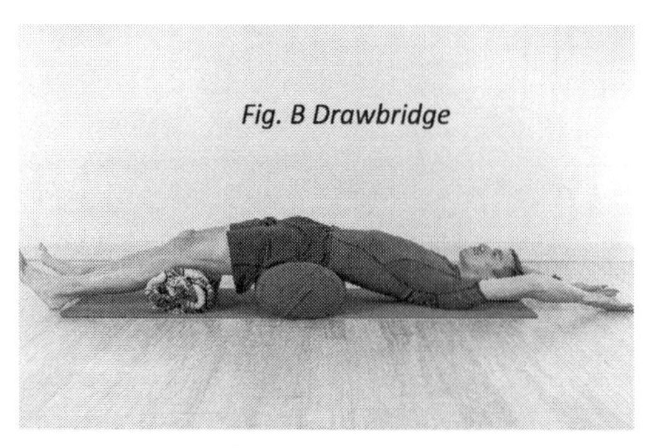
Fig. B Drawbridge

To help open the tops of the thighs, hip flexors, and front of torso, turn Bridge into **Drawbridge.** This elongated variation tends to increase intensity in the lower back. Move slowly as you extend your legs one at a time toward the end of the mat and rest your heels on the earth. Let the toes turn inward or outward and play with the distance between heels. Notice any shifts in sensation and pick the position that feels best. If the knees are strained, place a rolled up blanket underneath them for support. To emphasize the shoulder joints and activate the Lung-Large Intestine, Heart-Small Intestine/Pericardium-Triple Burner channels, reach the arms overhead and lower them onto the mat behind you (Fig B). Keep the arms straight or bend your elbows with hands holding opposite wrists, forearms, or elbows. To help the shoulders and arms relax more and avoid numbness in the shoulder joints, slip a blanket underneath the arms as needed.

With arms settled above your head, feel for a gentle tug along the fascia of the entire front of the body from tips of fingers to tips of toes. Relax the hips, legs, shoulders, and arms, letting a deep and steady breath flow naturally. If relaxation is difficult or the sensation levels are too high, return to a less intense phase of the shape.

If you're looking for a variation that enhances the back-bending stimulation in combination with an inner thigh release, explore **Flyover Bridge**, a deeper version of Bridge created by bringing your hips into external rotation and abduction while extending the spine. To find Flyover Bridge, return to Bridge pose with the feet on the floor hip-width distance apart and knees stacked over ankles. Gently allow the knees to fall out toward either side of the mat as you bring the soles of your feet together to form Butterfly-legs. If the knees are hovering above the ground, you might slip a rolled blanket or block underneath each outer knee to hold the weight of the bones and invite the hip and leg muscles to more deeply relax. The prop underneath the legs can also help absorb extra stress from the knees and inner legs. (Yp: *inversion, supine, backbend, hip-leg work*)

Fig. C One-Legged Bridge

⦿ **YINPRESSIONS FOR EXPLORATION While You Stay:** *one-legged (Fig C)*

Easing Out: If in Flyover Bridge, mindfully ease out by engaging the core and taking your hands to your outer legs to assist the knees together to return to Bridge pose. From Bridge or Drawbridge, lower the arms, engage your core muscles, and if the legs are extended, bend the knees and place the feet to floor one at a time, with knees stacked over ankles. Press your feet into the earth and carefully raise your hips just slightly higher than the prop support under the sacrum so you can slide it out of the way. Slowly lower your hips back onto the mat, allowing the low back to ease restfully onto the earth.

Substitutions for Consideration

Sphinx-Seal (for the lumbar spine and front of torso without inverting, p. 188),
Dragons (for the fronts of thighs and hip flexors without inverting, p. 150),
Fish (for the spine and front of chest without inverting, p. 159)

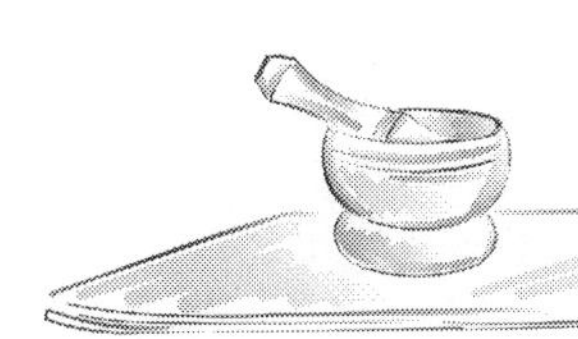

Meditative Yinquiry for the Mat

"The River of Letting Go"

As you encounter thoughts or feelings on your mat, you might visualize the image of a river and its lazy current flowing under the blue of a summer sky. The river flows along with no effort from you, just as your breath flows in and out again and again. Nothing to control, fix, or direct, just enjoy how the river flows on and on. Notice if you place a leaf on the surface of the river in your mind, the river will hold it and slowly carry it along as it flows. Letting go of thoughts and emotions can feel like this, allowing each to come and then to go, carried away like a leaf riding the current of a river. Anything that pulls at your attention in your practice is something available for release. Simply lay it down in the river of your mind, like a leaf landing then floating away as the slow, steady water flows.

Butterfly

Physical Focus

Inward-turning, simple shape that nurtures the hips and inner thigh/groin while you can decompress the whole of the spine and back with a forward fold. Excellent gateway posture to begin practice, supporting an easeful transition away from the busyness of the day into the quiet sanctuary of the mat.

Qi Charting

Kidney-Urinary Bladder
Liver-Gall Bladder
Spleen-Stomach

FINDING your Expression of the shape

Setting Up: Place a single-folded blanket on the mat for your seat. Place two blocks, a bolster, and a blanket near the middle of your mat off to the side within reach.

Easing In: Sit on the folded blanket on your mat and extend your legs in front of you. Begin by establishing your neutral pelvis position (for a refresher, see "Establishing a Neutral Pelvis in Seated Postures," p. 68). As you bring your feet nearer to the body, allow the knees to fall out toward either side of the mat. Play with the distance between the feet and the pelvic floor to moderate the sensations through the legs, hips, and knees. Feet closer to the body creates a short-legged **Butterfly** variation to intensify the opening through the inner thigh/groin area. This can put extra pressure on the knees, so stay attentive to ensure the knees don't grumble. Feet further from the body forms a longer-legged version, which in general tends to bring more sensation to the hamstrings/outer hips and may also soften the sensations in the knees. If the knees still feel too sensitive, place a block or rolled blanket underneath each outer knee or thigh for support. You have the option of separating the feet away from one another a little or a lot to find just the right amount of sensation for your hips and legs. Feel your body as a place of peace in this supportive shape where your physical tissues relax, your mind settles, and the reassuring flow of your breath lengthens and steadies. (Yp: *hip-leg work*)

Fig. A Butterfly with forward bend

Fig. B One-Legged Butterfly with forward bend

⊙ **YINPRESSIONS FOR EXPLORATION While You Stay:** *seated forward bend* (Fig A), *side bend, twist, most shoulder-arm binds, one-legged* (One-Legged Butterfly), *forward bend + shoulder-arm binds* (Bow Tie Butterfly)

One-Legged Butterfly: Follow the same guidance as above to ease into Butterfly, then extend one leg straight in front of you. Rest the opposite foot anywhere along the inner thigh area of the straight leg. One-Legged Butterfly allows you to integrate all the same Yinpressions as Butterfly to work the spine, hips, and upper body but has the additional benefit of emphasizing the release of tensions through the hamstring tissues of the straight leg (Fig B). You could transform Butterfly into One-Legged Butterfly partway through the pose to enjoy the combined effects. To come out of the pose, press hands to the floor to rise slowly. Add a counterpose in between for rest, then repeat, switching sides.

Fig. C Bow Tie Butterfly

Bow Tie Butterfly: From the upright Butterfly position, there is the option of integrating a forward bend with a shoulder-arm bind to form Bow Tie Butterfly. To do so, place the right hand to the floor in front of right shin and the left hand in front of the left shin. Lift your hands a touch off the floor and turn both palms to face up. Begin to slide the backs of hands along the floor toward you underneath each lower leg. Bring your palms into the diamond space between the legs so that each forearm hugs the lower legs as you fold forward (Fig C). This bind is a stabilizer in this position and further opens shoulders, upper back, and arms while stimulating the upper body Qi Channels that flow through these areas. Depending on the depth of your forward bend, rest your head on your feet, a prop positioned on your feet, or let it dangle freely. To release the pose, unbind your arms, press your hands into floor, and slowly press yourself upright.

Easing Out: To come out of the upright Butterfly position, place your hands on your outer knees to assist them gently up and together as you place the soles of your feet to the floor.

Substitutions for Consideration

One-Legged Butterfly (above), Supine Butterfly (below), Wall Butterfly (below), One-Legged Dragonfly (p. 154)
Each of these substitutions has the potential of providing a little more ease for the knees. Supine versions of Butterfly help soothe stimulation on the spine relative to the seated variations.

Supine Butterfly: Place a single-folded blanket on the back of your mat to serve as a cushion for your head once you've reclined. Place three blocks near the middle of your mat off to the side within reach. Lie on your back with the blanket positioned under the head. Place your feet onto the floor hip-width distance apart with your knees above your ankles. Separate your bent knees, dropping them gently outward to the sides to create external rotation and abduction in the hips. Bring the soles of your feet together. If needed, place a rolled blanket or block underneath each outer knee/thigh area to reduce strain in the knees and moderate tension within the inner leg tissues (Fig D). For greater hip abduction, separate the feet and slide a block between them, letting the soles of the feet lean into the support of the block. To ease out, place your hands on your outer thighs to guide the knees together and place your feet to the floor, ankles under knees. (Yp: *supine, hip-leg work*; Yp for exploration while you stay: *side bend, shoulder-arm binds*)

Fig. D Supine Butterfly

Wall Butterfly: Start in Wall Caterpillar (for a refresher, see "Yinpression: On the Wall," p. 127). Slowly bend the knees and begin to slide the feet down the wall a bit. Roll the outer edges of the feet onto the wall, allowing the soles of the feet to come together. Gently wing your bent knees outward to either side to form Wall Butterfly (Fig E). To deepen sensation, continue to slide the heels closer to the body or further away to soften. To ease out, slowly slide the feet back up the wall to unbend the knees. Rest your heels onto the wall hip-width distance apart, returning to Wall Caterpillar. (Yp: *on the wall, hip-leg work*; Yp for exploration while you stay: *inversion, side bend, shoulder-arm binds*)

Fig. E Wall Butterfly

Cat Pulling Its Tail

Physical Focus

Side-lying posture awakening the hip flexors and quads in the front hip/thigh in one leg while also offering access to the glutes and IT band area in the other. In addition to working the hips and legs, has the option of deepening into a supine twist to reach the shoulder and chest while supporting the wellbeing of the spine.

Qi Charting

Kidney-Urinary Bladder
Liver-Gall Bladder
Spleen-Stomach
Lung-Large Intestine
Heart-Small Intestine
Pericardium-Triple Burner

FINDING your Expression of the shape

Setting Up: Place a single-folded blanket on the back of your mat to serve as a cushion for your head once you've reclined. Place two blocks, a bolster, a blanket, and a strap near the middle of your mat off to the left side within reach.

Easing In: To prepare for **Cat Pulling Its Tail**, lie on the mat with your head on the blanket. Position your spine in a straight line from the top of your head to your tailbone. Draw your right knee toward your chest and then interlace both hands around the upper right shin. Place the right hand to the right hip crease and the left hand to the outer right thigh. Using the left hand, guide your right leg across the midline of your body to the left, rolling onto your left side. Place your left elbow onto the earth and rest your head comfortably into your left palm. If needed, slide the bolster under the inner right leg/knee area for support. Stack the right hip over the left and turn the left thigh slightly to face the floor so the thighbone feels cozy in the hip socket. To induce more sensation in the quad of the bottom leg, bend the bottom knee, checking to see that the knee still points straight down the mat. If additional sensation is needed through the quads/front of hip, slide the left thigh behind you a bit more, staying mindful that this adjustment could overload the knee. Play around to find the placement that feels right.

Fig. A Cat Pulling Its Tail

If you wish to pull your cat tail and invigorate the Lung-Large Intestine and Heart-Small Intestine/Pericardium-Triple Burner Qi channels, you can induce a twist to further open the shoulder and chest by binding the bottom leg. Reach your right arm straight up and then behind you to grab hold of your left foot with your right hand (Fig A). Play with internal versus external rotation of the arm to see what settles best within the right shoulder joint. If your foot is out of reach, loop the strap around your foot and hold its ends in your right hand.

Keep the right leg bent or unbend the knee so the leg becomes perpendicular to your upper body. This may amplify sensations through the glute/IT band area and perhaps the hamstrings. The right leg in line with the navel is a good baseline navigation point from which to play. Generally, raising the leg above the navel line intensifies the hip and leg sensations, while angling the leg below the navel tends to soften them.

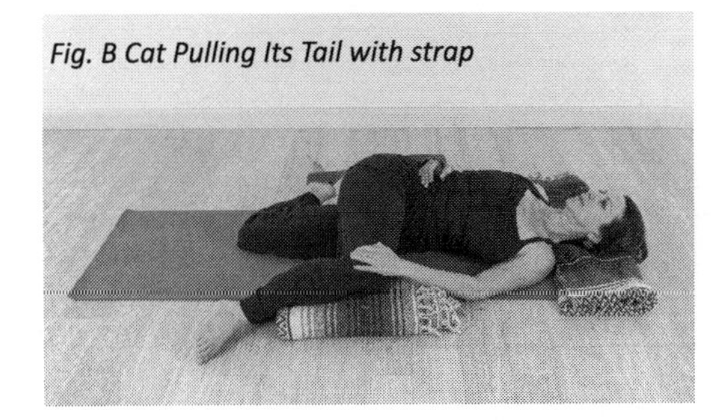
Fig. B Cat Pulling Its Tail with strap

Fig. C Cat Pulling Its Tail holding big toe

Should the body request more opening for the middle/upper-back, chest, shoulders, and neck, rest your upper body gently back onto the mat behind you to deepen the twist and introduce a slight backbend (Fig B). This typically generates sensation through the intercostals and side obliques. Use a blanket as a cushion for your head or the left hand if it's free. The left fingers could bind around the right big toe. (Fig C). To bring more sensation to your neck, turn your head to the right for a cervical twist. (Yp: *twist, supine, hip-leg work, backbend*)

⦿ **YINPRESSIONS FOR EXPLORATION While You Stay**: The multiple phases available for deepening this posture in the legs, torso, and shoulders make Cat Pulling Its Tail nearly a whole-body exercise.

Easing Out: To mindfully untwist, release the feet if you're holding either of them. Look to the left to untwist the neck. Bring the right side of your body over the left as you roll onto your left side, then gently move onto your back or belly. Enjoy a counterpose or go directly into the other side.

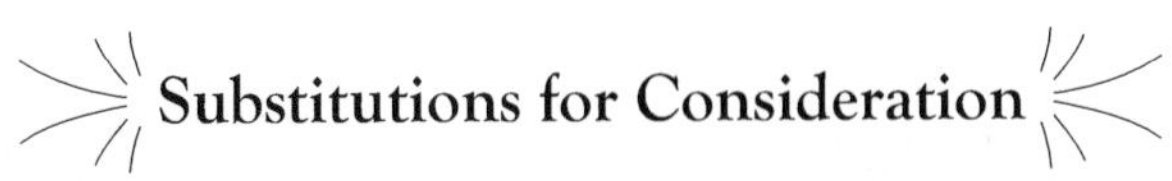

Substitutions for Consideration

One-Twig Twist (p. 196), Two-Twig Twist (p. 196)

Consider weaving these alternative reclining twist options into your practice.

Meditative Yinquiry for the Mat

"Keeping a Light Touch with the Two-Finger Smile"

Ajahn Brahm once shared an assignment given to him by his first meditation teacher. Each morning he was to look in the mirror and smile, and if a smile didn't come naturally, his teacher advised him to stick his two index fingers on each corner of his mouth and push up. His teacher looked ridiculous demonstrating this, and Brahm chuckled, giving it a try himself. The next morning, he woke especially tired. Dragging himself to his mirror, Brahm resorted to the two-finger assist. He writes that he saw a silly man making a silly face back at him and couldn't help but smile, which made the man in the mirror smile even more, and eventually they had a good long laugh together! He continued this practice every morning for two years and credits it with building a joyful foundation in his heart. If ever you're not feeling particularly jolly, see how the two-fingered smile works for you. You might bring your smile inside to the parts of your body receiving exercise in your pose and notice: What power does the presence of your smile hold? What transformation does it bring?

Caterpillar

Physical Focus

Folding forward and inward, this shape untightens the whole back seam of the body, helping to maintain the strength and agility of the spinal column and open the backs of thighs. Works into the hips and gently pressurizes the abdominal organs of the digestive system.

Qi Charting

Kidney-Urinary Bladder

FINDING your Expression of the shape

Setting Up: Place a single-folded blanket on the mat for your seat. Place two blocks, a bolster, and a blanket near the middle of your mat off to the side within reach.

Easing In: Sit on the folded blanket on your mat and extend your legs straight in front of you. Begin by establishing a slight anterior tilt in the pelvis (for a refresher, see "Yinpression: Seated Forward Bend," p. 109). If the hamstrings already feel too stiff or sensitive, experiment with bending the knees to various degrees and placing a rolled blanket underneath for extra support to ease the intensity. If sensations remain too strong, consider exploring One-Legged Caterpillar (see "Yinpressions for Exploration While You Stay").

Fig. A Caterpillar with bridged bolster

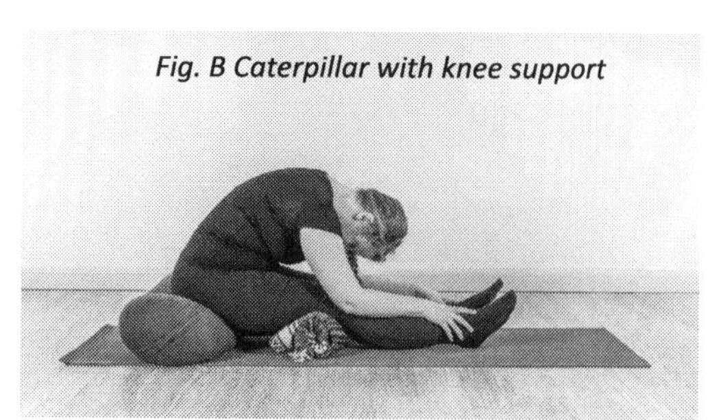

Fig. B Caterpillar with knee support

To proceed into **Caterpillar**, bridge the bolster over your legs to get started. As you inhale, lengthen a touch more through the spine. As you exhale, keep length in the spine and slowly bow over the legs, hinging forward at the hips just enough to bring about sensation along the spine and backs of legs. If your low back permits, allow the spine to round more in the fold. If that isn't appropriate for your back, keep the spine more neutral. Settle your upper body onto the support of the bolster or allow it to hover above or rest directly on the legs (Fig A, Fig B). If the neck is sensitive, it might feel best to keep it in line with the rest of your spine. If so, you could prop your head onto a vertically-angled bolster positioned between slightly separated legs or on top of blocks stacked on the legs. Otherwise, choose to let the head dangle freely, if the neck allows.

If you need more sensation and it's within reach, reach your arms forward alongside your legs and loosely hold your shins or feet with your hands. This might also amplify sensations through the muscles of the middle- and upper-back regions. If the whole of the upper body is resting directly on your legs and you find it's still not enough sensation, separate the legs to carve out space for the upper body to fold between them. If you still need more, try a deeper phase of the pose. To do so, exit the forward fold and return to a seated position. Place a bolster underneath your hips and separate your legs about twelve inches apart. Slide blocks at the same height as the bolster under each heel. Once you feel balanced and stable, ease into your forward bend again by following the guidance above, sinking into the newly created extra space beneath you. (Yp: *seated forward bend, hip-leg work*)

YINPRESSIONS FOR EXPLORATION While You Stay: *shoulder-arm binds: hugging arms, twisted branches, one-legged* (One-Legged Caterpillar, aka One-Legged Butterfly)

Fig. C One-Legged Caterpillar with forward bend

One-Legged Caterpillar: To transform your Caterpillar into a one-legged version, start seated with both legs stretched in front of you. Begin by establishing a neutral pelvis (for a refresher, see "Establishing a Neutral Pelvis in Seated Postures," p. 68). Bend one knee and place that foot anywhere along the opposite inner leg. One-Legged Caterpillar allows for all the same Yinpressions as Caterpillar as well as the benefits of an upright open or closed twist while still stimulating the back of the outstretched leg. If proceeding into a forward bend (Fig C), remember to first establish a slight anterior tilt of the pelvis (for a refresher, see "Yinpression: Seated Forward Bend," p. 109). After exploring options on one side, switch legs and do the other side.

Easing Out: To mindfully emerge, place hands to the earth, walk them back toward your seat, and press down to tenderly lift yourself upright. You'll likely feel sensation along the spine as you rise, so move slowly, there's no cause to rush.

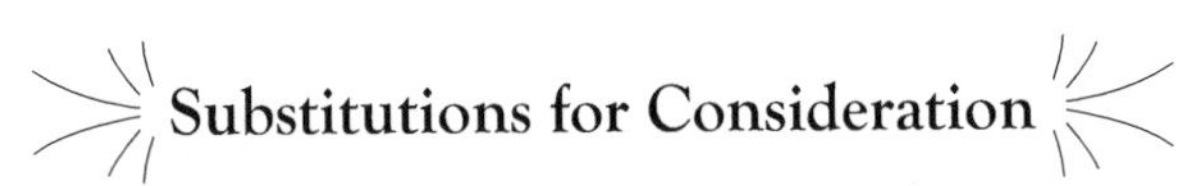

Supine Calf-Hamstring Opener (below), One-Legged Caterpillar (above),
Wall Caterpillar (p. 127) / Elevated Wall Caterpillar (p. 128)

One-Legged Caterpillar may be more accessible for practitioners with tighter hips, hamstrings, and/or knee sensitivities. Supine Calf-Hamstring Opener and Wall Caterpillar offer the chance to work into the hips and backs of thighs while the spine remains supported by the earth and also grant the option of a one-legged version. To simultaneously enjoy a mild inversion, explore Elevated Wall Caterpillar by adding a bolster underneath the hips.

Supine Calf-Hamstring Opener: Place a single-folded blanket on the back of your mat to serve as a cushion for your head once you've reclined. Place a strap near the middle of your mat off to the side within reach. Lie on your back with the back of your head on the blanket. Place both of your feet on the floor hip-width distance apart with knees stacked over ankles. Create a small loop in one end of your strap that's wide enough to fit around your foot.

Draw the right knee toward your chest to loop the strap around your foot, positioning it just below the ball of the foot. Hold the other end of your strap with your right hand. Begin to slowly unbend the right knee, extending the right leg directly overhead until you feel a mild pulling sensation through the hamstrings and calf tissues. To accentuate the sensation, unbend the right leg more as you carefully draw the right thigh closer to your right-side chest. To tone down the intensity, bend the right knee more and move the thigh further from the chest. To open the lower back more, extend the left leg straight down the mat and rest the heel on the floor. Sometimes the loop's position on the foot affects where you feel the stimulation, so you might play with repositioning the loop midway through the pose, sliding it to rest over the heel or at the base of the toes. Adjust as needed to keep the sensations just right. While you hold the posture, invite the muscles of your leg, shoulders, neck, and face to relax as much as possible. To ease out, bend the right knee enough to remove the strap from your foot. Place your right foot to the floor and stretch the right leg down the mat beside the left and rest. When ready, do the other side. (Yp: *supine, one-legged, hip-leg work*)

Deer

Physical Focus

A balancing blend of both internal and external rotation of the hips. Potential of adding twist or forward bend to invigorate whole of spinal column and alleviate tension in the quads and glutes/outer hip area.

Qi Charting

Kidney-Urinary Bladder
Liver-Gall Bladder
Spleen-Stomach

FINDING your Expression of the shape

Setting Up: Place a single-folded blanket on the mat for your seat. Place two blocks, a bolster, and a blanket near the middle of your mat off to the side within reach.

Easing In: Sit onto the folded blanket on your mat and extend your legs in front of you. Establish your neutral pelvis position (for a refresher, see "Establishing a Neutral Pelvis in Seated Postures," p. 68). Bend your knees and bring the soles of your feet together, letting the knees fall gently open to the sides. This is Butterfly pose, which is also a good starting point for **Deer**.

Shift your weight slightly onto your outer right hip and slide the left heel back and toward your left outer hip, bringing your left hip into internal rotation. For many, the toes of the internally rotated leg will naturally point backward. For others, depending on the shape and structure of their bones, the toes could point outward. What's right is what feels best for your knee. There should only be very slight sensations in the knee, if any. If the body allows, slide the left knee outward and back to a degree of hip abduction that feels OK. If your hips become unlevel at any point, slip a blanket underneath you to level them. Keeping the left sit-bone weighted downward, begin to slip your left foot away from the buttock. If too much strain arises in your hips, thighs, or knees, bring the left foot back toward your body until you feel adequate softening.

Fig. A Deer

To increase sensation through the externally rotated right hip, begin to slide the right knee toward the midline of the body. Stay here, or if your knee allows, move the right foot away from your seat to bring the right shin toward being parallel with the top edge of the mat. The only destination is appropriate sensation, so stop anywhere along the way that feels good. Gently curl your right toes back toward the right shin to lend some support for the right knee joint (Fig A). As needed, slide a block or blanket under either or both knees to relax and support the legs. If the sensations are still too great, try bringing one or both feet closer to your body and/or the knees closer together. Sometimes the slightest change has just the right effect, so take time to play with adjustments until you find suitable sensations. If it still feels tweaky, swap with a substitute posture. If staying, let gravity hold you as you surrender the weight of your hips to the earth and allow the breath to be comfortable and full. (Yp: *hip-leg work*)

⦿ **YINPRESSIONS FOR EXPLORATION While You Stay**: *seated forward bend, side bend, most shoulder-arm binds, twist* (Watchful Deer), *twist* (Sleeping Deer)

Fig. B Watchful Deer

Fig. C Sleeping Deer

Watchful Deer and Sleeping Deer: If you'd like to explore a couple of twists, begin in upright Deer (above) with a bolster beside the externally rotated right outer hip. With your torso upright, inhale slowly and reach the crown of the head skyward. As you exhale, slowly rotate your torso to the right, placing your hands on the bolster beside you to enjoy Watchful Deer pose (Fig B). For a cervical twist, expand your watchful scanning by looking over your right shoulder. Choose to stay in this upright twisting variation or experiment with Sleeping Deer (Fig C). To move into this deeper twist, lift the left hip off the floor and rotate through the spine to the right a bit more as you lay your torso over the bolster or onto the ground, depending on what feels best. Play with the positioning of your feet and the degree of bend in your knees, perhaps sliding your left leg perpendicular to your torso and extending your right leg straight down the mat. If your neck would prefer a twist, turn your head to the right. To ease out, first bring your forehead to center to untwist the neck, then slowly bend the legs to loosely stack your knees in front of you. Use your hands to press yourself upright to seated.

Easing Out: To mindfully ease out of the upright Deer position, slowly slide your bent back leg forward and bring both knees toward one another into a loosely stacked position in front of you. Place your hands behind you for support, lean back slightly, and place both feet onto the earth a comfortable distance in front of you. When you're ready, switch sides.

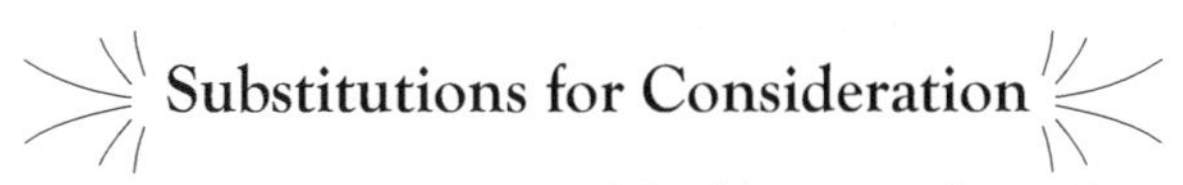

Substitutions for Consideration

Supine Lingering Windshield Wipers (p. 178)

This pose variation offers another chance to create internal and external rotation of the hips while tipped onto the back, a position that can soften the pressure on hips, knees, and spine.

Dragons

Physical Focus

A spirited, versatile collection of poses to enhance strength and mobility of hips and legs with ample occasion to creatively gain access to the front of the hips, tops of thighs, hamstrings, inner legs and even the ankles and toes. Like their legendary namesake, they're not the tamest postures in the Yin series!

Qi Charting

Potentially all channels, depending on pose alterations and chosen Yinpressions

FINDING your Expression of the shape

Setting Up: Place a single folded blanket on the back third of your mat to serve as padding for your knees and shins. Place two blocks at the tallest height at the front edge of your mat several inches apart from each other. Place a block, a bolster, a blanket, and a strap near the middle of the mat off to the left side within reach.

Easing In: Practitioners experiencing SI joint issues will want to take precaution with these asymmetrical Dragon shapes. Begin by kneeling on the blanket on your hands and knees in Tabletop, stacking your hips over your knees and your shoulders over your wrists. To ease into **Baby Dragon**, place your hands on the blocks in front of you and step your right foot forward just to the inside of your right hand, flexing the front hip. Begin with your front knee positioned over your front ankle. Stretch your back leg behind you so the front of the thigh is facing down toward the earth and your toes point behind you. Because these are hip-opening poses, stay especially mindful not to overburden your knees. If there's too much pressure on the back knee, try double-folding the blanket underneath it. If even more cushion is needed, try a block or bolster underneath the back shin to float your knee above the mat. If the knee still doesn't agree, try substituting with Tipped Dragon (See Substitutions) or another hip-opening posture.

Fig. A Baby Dragon with bolster

To increase sensations through the front of the extended hip, scoot your back leg a little further behind you. Keep your hands on the blocks or place your palms on the floor to go deeper. If the sensations are too great on your back thigh, shorten the distance between your legs by gently sliding the back knee a bit closer to you or positioning the bolster lengthwise in front of your back thigh to lean into its support (Fig A). Enjoy Baby Dragon on its own, held for the customary three to five minutes, or leash several Dragons together, holding each for a minute or two before resting, then switching to do the series on the other side. I don't recommend practicing all possible Dragon variations at once, though!

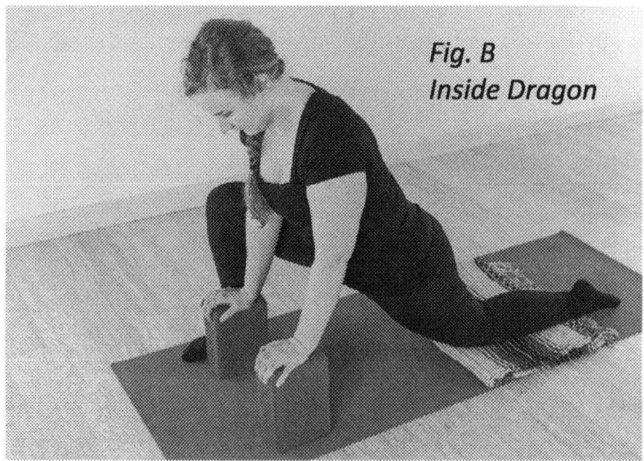

Fig. B Inside Dragon

Fig. C Winged Dragon

Fig. D Dragon Pulling Its Tail

Fig. E Crouching Dragon Hidden Toes Squat

Fig. F Crouching Dragon Hidden Toes Squat

Let's continue our journey through the land of Dragons, letting the Baby Dragon shape transform into **Inside Dragon**. Place both of your hands to the inside of your right foot (Fig B). Keep your hands on the blocks or, if more sensation is needed, lower your hands or forearms onto the mat inside the front foot.

To morph into **Winged Dragon**, toe-heel your right foot toward the right side of your mat and angle your right toes outward about forty-five degrees. Allow your right knee to swing outward and down to the right as you roll onto the outer edge of your right foot. Externally rotating and abducting the leg at the hip in this way spurs more stimulation along the inner thigh/groin area and has the added advantage of possibly helping to release any painful groin compression due to the hip flexion. Keep your hands on the blocks or build more sensations by pressing hands on the mat to the inside of the winged leg. To further build sensation, lower your forearms onto the floor (Fig C).

If it's suitable for your body, you could add a twist. Lengthen the spine first, then twist your torso to the right for **Twisted Dragon.** Hook your right hand onto your right hip and look over your right shoulder to bring a twist into your neck. If you feel steady, you could try a One Arm Behind the Back Bind (for a refresher, see "Yinpression: Shoulder-Arm Binds," p. 119) using your right arm to open the shoulder and chest. To increase sensation through the back thigh, bring your weight slightly forward of your back knee and begin to lift the back foot off the mat to a suitable degree. Bind the leg by reaching your right hand around to catch hold of the foot, if desired. If your foot isn't within reach, lasso your strap around it and hold the tails of the strap in your right hand to form **Dragon Pulling its Tail** (Fig D). To come out, carefully release your hold of the right foot, lower the leg onto the mat slowly, and gently untwist through the torso. Place your hands on the blocks, then toe-heel the right foot back to the centerline of your mat. With the blocks in your hands, position a block on either side of the front foot, returning to Baby Dragon.

From Baby Dragon, perhaps continue your adventure with **Crouching Dragon, Hidden Toes Squat** to open the hamstrings, spine, ankle, and toes. Take the two blocks in your hands, walk them back toward the middle of the mat, and position them on either side of your outer hips. At the same time, begin to draw the right leg toward a straighter position. Align your left hip over the left knee to form Crouching Dragon. If your ankles and toes allow, tuck the left toes under to add Hidden Toes Squat. Stay upright through the spine, or for more sensation in hamstrings and back, inhale and lengthen the spine. On the exhale, gently fold forward (Fig E). Keep your spine long if you have back/spine issues that prevent rounding. If you're close enough to the earth, place your hands on the mat. For the deepest phase of this posture, a variant of One-Legged Saddle, take special care with hips, knees, ankles, and toes as you lower the hips back and down toward the left heel (Fig F). For added stability, slip a block or two under the right sit-bone. To rise, engage your core muscles, press your hands into the blocks, and untuck your left toes. With your hands holding the blocks, walk them forward and re-bend your right knee to bring your hips forward until the right knee stacks over the right ankle to return to Baby Dragon.

To open your ankles, you might give **Overstepping Dragon** a try. While maintaining a light contact between the sole of your right foot and the floor, slowly slip the foot toward the right sit-bone. Slide the foot backward only so far that you generate mild sensation through your ankle and calf tissue while making sure the sole of the foot stays on the floor. Press your hands on blocks for support (Fig G), or to increase sensations, rest them on the mat. To come out, return your hands to the blocks if not already, then press down as you bring your hips up and back until the right knee is aligned directly over your right ankle. Reposition the blocks so they're on either side of your right foot within comfortable reach and scoot your left leg back to return to Baby Dragon.

Fig. G Overstepping Dragon

Fig. H Upright Dragon

For more stimulation through the hips and legs as well as the potential of adding some upper body exercise to the mix, you might experiment with **Upright Dragon**. To create this shape from Baby Dragon, place one forearm at a time on your front thigh. If deepening more feels reasonable, place your palms one at a time on the front thigh, then begin to straighten your arms. While keeping the hips sinking toward the ground, slowly press your upper body away from the front thigh so your shoulders stack over your hips (Fig H). If you're feeling steady, perhaps explore integrating some shoulder-arm work for additional intensity. To ease your way back to Baby Dragon, unbind the arms. Place your hands to your thighs, then lower your torso down and press your hands to the blocks to return to Baby Dragon. (Yp: *hip-leg work, twist, shoulder-arm binds: one arm behind the back*)

⦿ **YINPRESSIONS FOR EXPLORATION While You Stay:** In Upright Dragon: *side bend, twist, shoulder-arm binds: double arm behind the back bind, hugging arms, twisted branches*, and *prayer hands on the back*

Easing Out: To emerge from Baby Dragon, press your hands into the blocks positioned on either side of your front foot. Using your core muscles and shoulder strength to support the weight of your body, slip your right foot behind you until your right knee lands under the right hip, returning to hands and knees Tabletop. Don't forget to enjoy the other side for balance.

Substitutions for Consideration

Tipped Dragon (below), Two-Legged Tipped Dragon (below)

Supine Eye of Needle (p. 157), Supine Butterfly (p. 143), Supine Shoelace (p. 184), Drawbridge (for hip extension and quads, p. 140)

These alternate supine hip and leg opening postures provide extra support for the spine and may be softer on the knee joints. Each pose uniquely engages the body and might feel different each time you come to the mat, so keep your horizons open and stay curious as you find what is most accessible for you.

Tipped Dragon: Place a single-folded blanket at the back edge of your mat and a strap alongside the mat near the center. Lie on your back, resting the back of your head on the blanket. Place your feet on the mat hip-width distance apart with your knees over your ankles. Keeping your right knee bent, bring your right thigh toward your chest without forcing. Hold the back of the right thigh with your right hand. While keeping the right thigh close to your right-side chest, begin to unbend your right knee until the right ankle is more or less stacked on top of your right knee with the sole of your right foot facing the sky. If within comfortable reach, hold your inner or outer right foot with your right hand (Fig I). If the foot is too far to reach, lasso a strap around the sole of your right foot and hold its tails in your right hand.

Fig. I Tipped Dragon

Keep the right leg bent to create sensations through the inner leg. To bring gentle compression to the lower back, extend your left leg straight down the mat, letting the left heel settle on the earth. Play with the position of the right leg. For example, you might let your right foot sway further out to the right a bit while keeping the right thigh close to your body with the right knee bent. To deepen sensation, ease the bent inner knee down toward the mat alongside the outer right rib cage. Go slowly as you investigate subtle adjustments and find the sensations that meet your body's needs. To emerge from this shape, place your left foot on the mat with the knee over the ankle and release the right leg, landing your right foot on the mat next to the left so that your feet are hip-width distance apart. (Yp: *supine, one-legged, hip-leg work)*

Fig. J Two Legged Tipped Dragon

Two-Legged Tipped Dragon: To work both hips and legs simultaneously while releasing the spine, try a Two-Legged Tipped Dragon by following the same instructions as for Tipped Dragon but engaging both legs at the same time instead of just exercising one side (Fig J). If your body allows a rounded spine, perhaps roll your hips up and off the floor. Stay mindful of lower back/SI joint precautions. This may become an inversion should your hips lift above your heart and head. To ease out, bring your bent knees together and slowly stretch one leg at a time down the mat to rest. (Yp: *supine, hip-leg work*; Yp for exploration while you stay: *inversion*)

Dragonfly

Physical Focus

Contributes to freedom of movement in both upper and lower body. Opens inside leg line and groin, backs of thighs, and hips and offers plenty of creative options to spread sensations into the spinal column and musculature of the back.

Qi Charting

Kidney-Urinary
Liver-Gall Bladder
Spleen-Stomach

FINDING your Expression of the shape

Setting Up: Place a second single-folded blanket on the mat for your seat. Place two blocks, a bolster, and a blanket near the middle of your mat off to the side within reach.

Easing In: Sit onto the folded blanket on your mat and extend your legs straight in front of you. Begin by establishing your neutral pelvis position (for a refresher, see "Establishing a Neutral Pelvis in Seated Postures," p. 68). Position a block at the lowest height on the mat just behind each hip. To support an upright spine, place your hands onto the blocks behind you or directly onto the floor if within reach, fingertips pointing in the direction that feels best for your wrists. To proceed into **Dragonfly**, slowly separate your legs to form a V-shape until you feel mild sensation through the inner leg area. Widen the V-shape to increase sensation or narrow it to lessen sensation as you find what feels just right. If the hamstrings or knees object, try bending the knees and sliding a rolled blanket underneath them. You might enjoy adding any of the Yinpressions listed below to your Dragonfly shape for the potential to also stimulate the Lung-Large Intestine, Heart-Small Intestine, and Pericardium-Triple Burner Qi channels. (Yp: *hip-leg work*)

⦿ **YINPRESSIONS FOR EXPLORATION While You Stay:** *seated forward bend (Fig A), side bend, twist, most shoulder-arm binds, one-legged + twist* (One-Legged Dragonfly) (*Fig B*), *one-legged + side bend* (One-Legged Dragonfly) (*Fig C*)

One-Legged Dragonfly: To explore the one-legged version, follow the same guidance as above to ease into Dragonfly and then simply bend one knee and place that foot anywhere along the opposite inner thigh area. One-Legged Dragonfly allows us to integrate all the same Yinpressions as Dragonfly and enjoy their many benefits for the spine, hips, shoulders, and arms. In addition, the hamstrings of the bent leg receive a break, which may at times be just what's needed to allow us to linger longer in the shape. Remember to switch the legs to do the other side.

Easing Out: To mindfully ease out from the upright Dragonfly position, if a leg is bent, slowly unbend it, then place a hand under each knee to draw your legs back together in front of you.

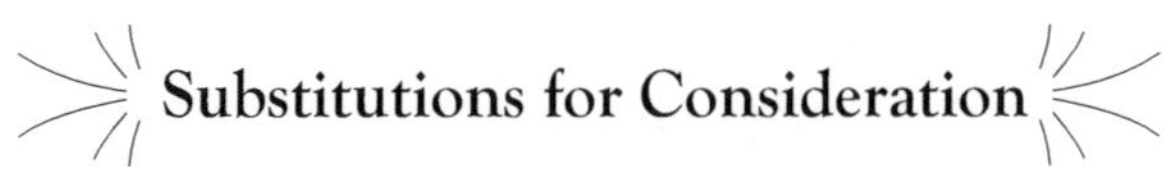

Substitutions for Consideration

One-Legged Dragonfly (above), Wall Dragonfly, (below)
Frog (p. 163)

One-Legged Dragonfly may be more accessible for tighter hips and hamstrings. Frog offers access to inner thighs without the same hamstring requirements of Dragonfly.

Fig. D One-Legged Wall Dragonfly with side bend

Wall Dragonfly: Begin in Wall Caterpillar (for a refresher, see "Yinpression: On the Wall," p. 127). Keeping the legs relatively straight and the heels of the feet in contact with the wall, slowly separate the feet away from each other, forming a V-shape with the legs. For greater sensation through the inner legs, widen the V-shape. For less, bring the legs closer together. Allow your heels and legs to rest onto the support of the wall. To moderate inner thigh sensations, place a bolster or block underneath each outer thigh to help hold the weight of the legs. (Yp: *on the wall*; Yp for exploration while you stay: *one-legged, side bend (Fig D), most shoulder-arm binds, inversion*)

Meditative Yinquiry for the Mat

"One Day = 86,400 Opportunities"

Imagine if you had a checking account that received an $86,400 deposit every single morning. The catch? Any dollar you don't use by the end of the day disappears, with nothing carrying over into the next day. We all have this kind of account...it's *time*. Every morning, we receive 86,400 seconds which are ours to spend however we'd like. We can't borrow against it or carry anything over for another day. Each day delivers 86,400 seconds to live and love wholeheartedly, to awaken to each moment, fully present for ourselves and those around us. Each time you practice coming home to your body on the mat, coming home to each breath and to each moment, you build your ability to stay present for all of life, every word, every person, every smile, every choice.

Eye of the Needle

Physical Focus

A relatively uncomplicated shape to shed layers of tension through the outer hip, relieves tightness in glutes and IT band area and potentially the hamstrings.

Qi Charting

Kidney-Urinary Bladder
Liver-Gall Bladder

FINDING your Expression of the shape

Setting Up: Place a single-folded blanket on the mat for your seat. Place two blocks, a bolster, and a blanket near the middle of your mat off to the side within reach.

Easing In: Sit on the folded blanket on your mat and extend your legs in front of you. Begin by establishing a slight anterior tilt in the pelvis (for a refresher, see "Yinpression: Seated Forward Bend," p. 109). Place two blocks at the lowest height against the back of each hip. To assist your spine in staying upright, place one hand on each block behind you and point your fingertips in the direction most comfortable for your wrists. If the mat is within reasonable reach, slide the blocks to the side and gently press hands on the earth to lengthen the arms and support your spinal column upright. To create **Eye of Needle**, roll your right thigh and knee outward, dialing the right toes about forty-five degrees to the right to find an easeful external rotation of the thigh at the hip. Curl your right toes lightly back toward your shin to support the knee joint, then bend the right knee. Rest the outside of your right ankle on your upper left thigh.

Fig. A Eye of the Needle

Bend your left leg and place your left foot on the floor in front of you. To find mild sensations in the focus areas of the hips, glutes, and hamstrings, inch the left foot slowly toward or away from your left sit-bone (Fig A). Generally, the closer the foot is to your seat, the greater the sensations, and vice-versa. Stay mindful to not overtax the hips or the knees. Play with adjusting the location of your right outer ankle by moving it slightly higher, lower, or toward the inside or outside of your right thigh until the sensations feel OK. As you explore, also check in with the lower back. There can be a tendency to inadvertently roll back onto the sacrum while making adjustments. If you feel that happening, further elevate your seat with a prop and/or slide the left foot a bit further away from your seat. (Yp: *hip-leg work, seated forward bend*)

⦿ **YINPRESSIONS FOR EXPLORATION While You Stay**: *shoulder-arm bind* (Sky Gazing), *supine + twist* (Supine Twisted Needle)

Sky Gazing: You might also experiment with this chest, shoulders, and wrist opener. From seated Eye of the Needle with your palms on the mat behind you, lift your hands enough to rotate your fingertips out toward the sides of the mat and then to point backward to a degree that resonates with your wrists. When you've found what feels right, press your palms on the mat once again. To open the upper body a little more, maintain straight arms but slide your hands a bit further behind you. Keep your heartspace lifting slightly forward and upward to avoid sinking through the chest and rolling back onto the sacrum. Stay aware of any shoulder strain. If the neck allows, you could carefully let your head drop behind you to a place of extension that is agreeable for your neck, opening the front of your throat. Take extra care to not let your head tip too far backward, given the sensitivities of compressing the back of the neck. To return to the upright position, slowly tip your head forward so your neck returns to neutral. With palms on the floor, slide your hands back toward your body.

Supine Twisted Needle: Before proceeding, keep in mind Supine Twisted Needle is a relatively deep twist, so general twisting precautions apply, including for lower back/SI joint issues. Place a single-folded blanket on the back of your mat to serve as a cushion for your head once you've reclined. Place a bolster and a blanket near the middle of your mat off to the left side within reach. Lie on your back with the back of your head settled on the blanket. Place both of your feet to the floor hip-width distance apart with your knees stacked over your ankles, then extend your right leg overhead. Turn your right toes out to.the right a bit, then curl them toward your right shin as a support for that knee. Bend your right knee and place the outer right ankle anywhere on the left thigh that works well for your lower body. To create the twist, keep your upper body on the mat and maintain the shape of the legs as you begin to lower them to the left as a package toward the floor.

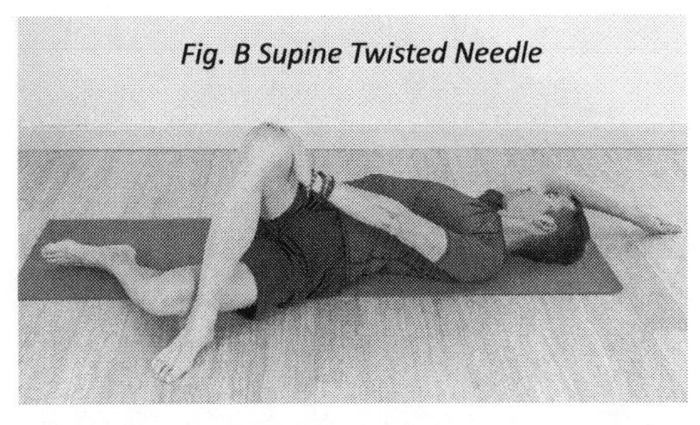
Fig. B Supine Twisted Needle

Rest your outer left leg, the outer edge of your left foot, and the sole of the right foot on the floor. If this is too intense, slide a bolster under your left leg and right foot to soften the twist. You could play with shifting your legs a bit below the navel line to help you find the sensation that feels stay-able and reaches the desired locations in your body. Keep your chest open and facing the sky. If you wish, lift your arm(s) overhead and lower them behind you onto the mat. If your body invites, look to the right to expand the twist into your neck (Fig B). To emerge from this twist, lower your arm(s) and return your neck to neutral. Activate your core muscles and use your hands to assist your legs up and to the center. Place the sole of your left foot on the mat, then slowly straighten your left leg down your mat. Uncross your right leg and extend it beside the left. When you're ready, switch sides.

Easing Out: From the seated Eye of the Needle position, slide your left foot away from you as you unbend the left leg and then uncross the right leg and extend it down your mat. When the time is right, give the second side a go.

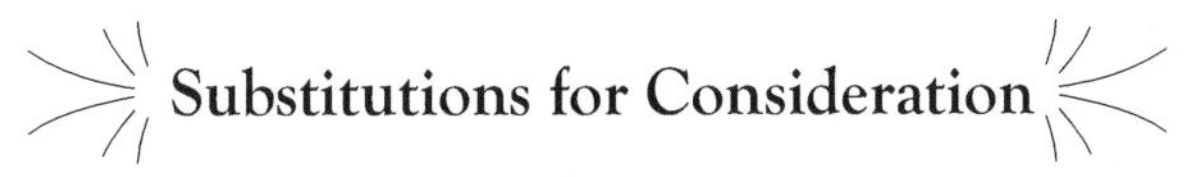

Substitutions for Consideration

Supine Eye of the Needle (below), Wall Eye of the Needle (below)

Try these variations any time you'd like the bonus benefit of a more supported hip opener.

Supine Eye of the Needle: Place a single-folded blanket on the back of your mat to serve as a cushion for your head once you've reclined. Place a bolster and a blanket near the middle of your mat off to the left side within reach. Lie on your back with the back of your head settled on the blanket. Place both of your feet to the floor hip-width distance apart with your knees stacked over your ankles. Extend your right leg overhead and turn your right toes out to the right a bit. Curl your right toes toward your right shin as a support for that knee and bend your right leg. Place the right outer ankle anywhere on the left thigh.

Fig. C Supine Eye of the Needle

Stay with this phase of the pose, or, if you need to turn up the volume of sensation, lift both of your legs as a unit and bring them closer to your chest. Slip your right arm through the triangle space of your legs and wrap your left arm around the left outer thigh. Interlace your fingers behind the left thigh to support the weight of the legs (Fig C). If holding the thigh feels out of reach or causes your shoulders to come off the mat, place a strap between your hands, separating the hands on the strap far enough apart to allow the backs of your shoulders to relax on the earth. Guide your legs closer to your chest to give rise to more sensation or, to tone it down, do the reverse. If holding your legs up with your arm strength becomes tedious, place a bolster or block underneath the left foot. Let your arms rest by your sides or perhaps place them overhead on the mat behind you. As you hold this shape, feel for sensations through the right glute/IT band and/or hamstrings areas and a sense of release in the lower spine.

This supine position offers the added perk of opening the left side of the hamstrings if you desire. Simply unbend your left leg so the sole of the left foot is facing the ceiling. If within reach, hold the back of your left thigh with your interlaced fingers. Otherwise, bridge the gap between your hands with a strap. Hold for a minute or so. To exit this shape, re-bend your left leg, if straightened. Keep your legs crossed and lower your left foot to the floor. Uncross your right leg and place the right foot to the floor hip-width distance from the left. When you're ready, go to the other side. (Yp: *supine, hip-leg work;* Yp for exploration while you stay: *shoulder arm binds: overhead binding*)

Fig. D Wall Eye of the Needle

Wall Eye of the Needle: Begin in Wall Caterpillar (for refresher, see "Yinpression: On the Wall," p. 127). Turn your right toes outward to the right a bit. Curl the right toes toward your right shin as a support for that knee and bend your right leg. Place your right outer ankle anywhere on the left thigh that works well for your lower body. Bend your left knee and slide your left foot down the wall until you feel appropriate sensation in the outer right hip, buttocks, and/or hamstrings (Fig D). To ease out, unbend the left knee slowly and slide your left foot back up the wall, stretching out the leg and resting the heel on the wall. Uncross the right leg and stretch it up the wall, returning to Wall Caterpillar. Rest a moment, then try the other side. (Yp: *on the wall, hip-leg work;* Yp for exploration while you stay: *shoulder arm binds: overhead binding, inversion*)

Meditative Yinquiry for the Mat

"What Time is It?"

While on retreat with Thich Nhat Hanh, I wandered through the rain one afternoon to the monastery's bookstore. On the counter was a display of a new Plum Village wristwatch design. This "watch of the present moment" featured the word *It's* written in Thich Nhat Hanh's recognizable calligraphy at the center. Around the edges where the hour numbers would typically be was simply the word *NOW* repeated over and over again, so that anytime you lifted your wrist to see what time it was, you'd be grounded in the only time it ever is: *Now.* When you follow your breath and the quality of sensations arising in the body, you strengthen the muscles of your awareness and dedicate your attention to what you're experiencing. This concentration restabilizes the mind and steadies the heart. The present time is the perfect time to invite the sensations in your physical tissues to be your anchor, mind alert and awake in this place where *here* meets *now* on the mat.

Fish

Physical Focus

Reconnect with spaciousness of heart, feeling tensions evaporate through chest, middle/upper back, neck, and intercostals. This back-lying pose builds breathing room as it settles the body, soothes the mind, and softens the heart.

Qi Charting

Kidney-Urinary Bladder
Lung-Large Intestine
Heart-Small Intestine
Pericardium-Triple Burner

FINDING your Expression of the shape

Setting Up: Create a sloped support for the upper body by placing a firm bolster lengthwise on your mat with a block at the lowest height under the bolster's back edge. Place a double-folded blanket on the elevated back of the bolster to serve as a pillow for the head. Place a single-folded blanket in front of the bolster for your seat. Place two blocks beside your seat within reach.

Easing In: To begin exploring the phases of **Fish**, sit on the blanket just in front of the sloped bolster. Bend your knees and place your feet on the floor a comfortable distance in front of you. Bring your knees into an X-shape by walking each foot toward the outer edge of the mat and allowing your knees to drop together so the inner knees touch. Place a block the narrow way between the inner upper thighs. With your hands to the earth on either side of you, begin to lower your upper body onto the bolster. Land your head on the blanket as you rest into **Gentle Fish.** If neck sensitivity or a low back injury exists, be cautious and keep your neck in line with the rest of your spine. If you experience difficulty relaxing in this phase of the pose, consider a substitute posture such as Floating Fish (See Substitutions). If in Gentle Fish and you need a bit more sensation through the lower back, straighten your legs in front of you one at a time. If the knees feel strained, try placing a blanket underneath them as support (Fig A).

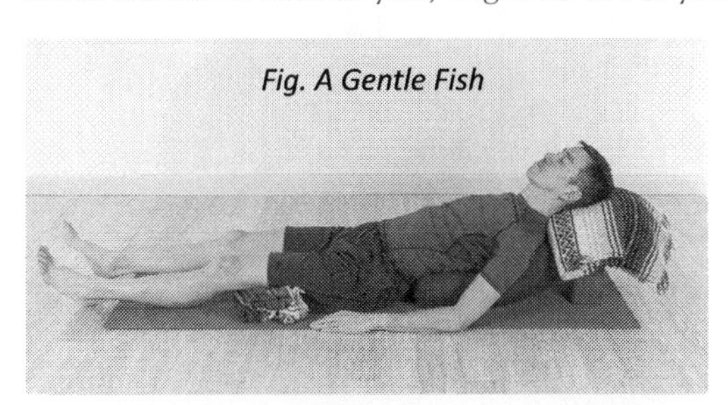
Fig. A Gentle Fish

Fig. B Angel Fish with X-shape legs

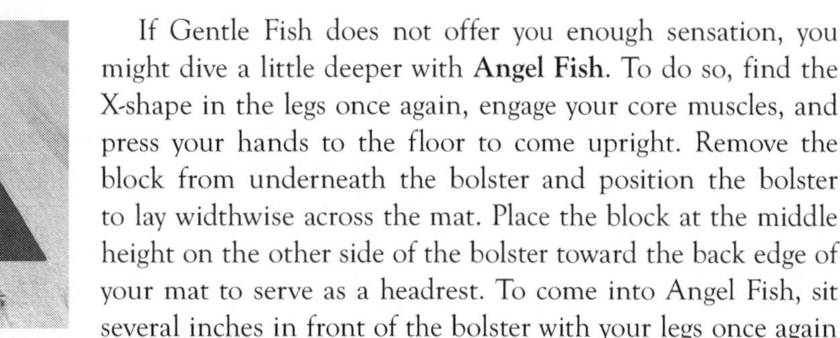

If Gentle Fish does not offer you enough sensation, you might dive a little deeper with **Angel Fish**. To do so, find the X-shape in the legs once again, engage your core muscles, and press your hands to the floor to come upright. Remove the block from underneath the bolster and position the bolster to lay widthwise across the mat. Place the block at the middle height on the other side of the bolster toward the back edge of your mat to serve as a headrest. To come into Angel Fish, sit several inches in front of the bolster with your legs once again in the X-shape. Place your hands on the bolster behind you and bend your elbows to lower onto your forearms. Continue to recline over the bolster so that your mid and upper back drape onto the bolster. Situate the bolster to rest more under the upper back rather than under the belly. Reach back with your hands and position the block at a comfortable height under the head for support (Fig B). The middle and highest block positions are generally easiest on the neck here, so play to find just what you need, ensuring the block is underneath the head and not touching the neck.

Fig. C Angel Fish

While reclined in this posture, keep from turning your head to safeguard your neck. To emphasize lower back sensation, extend your legs in front of you (Fig C). To open the neck more, lower the height of the block or remove it so your head rests directly on the mat. Whenever extending the neck by dropping the head back, be watchful for lightheadedness and dizziness, as you may be compressing one of the major arteries flowing through that area. Should you experience anything inappropriate, bring the neck back to a neutral position or come out of the pose if it doesn't resolve.

⦿ **YINPRESSIONS FOR EXPLORATION While You Stay:** *hip-leg work, shoulder-arm binds: overhead binding*

Both Gentle Fish and Angel Fish offer the opportunity to open the inner thigh/groin area with the added benefit of stimulating the Qi that flows through all the inner leg Qi channels. From X-shaped legs, let the knees fall out toward the sides of the mat and bring the soles of the feet together to form Butterfly-legs (Fig D). Stay here or explore Sukhasana-legs by crossing your right ankle in front of the left and bringing the feet in closer to your seat. If you need more hip/leg stimulation, try Square-legs: keep the ankles crossed, move the feet away from you to a comfortable distance, and slide the feet away from one another and toward opposite knees. Curl the toes gently toward their respective shins. Whatever variation you've chosen, notice if a block is needed for support under the outer knees or thighs. Don't forget to save time to switch the cross of the ankles if in Sukhasana-legs or Square-legs.

Fig. D Angel Fish with butterfly-legs

As you flow into your expression of Fish, explore various placements and angles of the arms to enhance or diminish sensations through the upper body. For example, raise your arms overhead and cradle your head with interlaced fingers or let the arms rest freely by your sides. You could also place one hand on the belly and the other over the heart for a grounding effect, calling the mind home to the body. (Yp: *supine, backbend, hip-leg work*)

Easing Out: To mindfully ease out of your Fish variation, rest your arms at your sides. If enjoying any of the hip and leg variations, return your feet to the floor and hip-width distance apart. Roll gently onto your favored side, then scoot the bolster out of the way as you ease yourself onto the mat. Lie comfortably on your side with your arm as a cushion for your head.

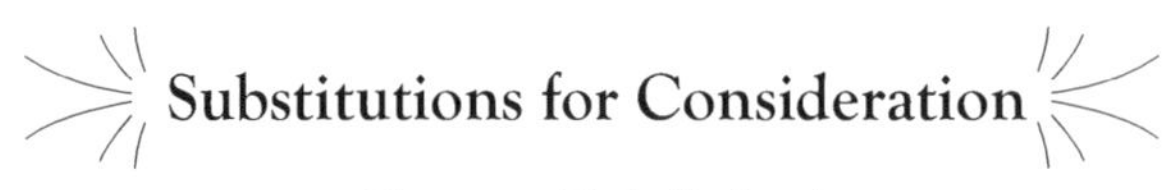

Substitutions for Consideration

Floating Fish (below)

This substitute offers a more assistive approach than the deeper Fish versions. By using the props to hold the body in a relatively straight line, Floating Fish lightens the pressure on the lumbar spine while still offering a soothing opening for the chest and upper back.

Floating Fish: To set up, place your bolster lengthwise at the center of your mat. Position one block at the middle height toward the back edge of your mat about ten to twelve inches from the top edge of the bolster. This will serve as a support for your head. Place two additional blocks also at the middle height side by side at the front edge of the mat. These blocks will serve as pedestals for your heels once you're atop the bolster. Sit on the bottom portion of your bolster, bend your knees, and place your feet on the floor at a comfortable distance in front of you. To use a bind to help the legs relax, loop a strap around both of your mid-upper thighs and draw the strap relatively taut.

With your hands on the floor beside you, bend your elbows to lower your torso onto the bolster so that the top edge of your shoulders aligns with the top edge of your bolster. Reach back with your hands to carefully position the block underneath the head, ensuring it's not resting anywhere under the neck. Lift your legs and extend them down the mat, placing your heels onto the blocks (Fig E). If necessary, re-tighten the strap to ensure your legs feel supported and held. Find an arm position that promotes mild sensations through the upper body, as desired. When ready, ease out by bending your knees to place your feet onto the mat. Loosen the strap a bit. Engage your core muscles and use your hands for support to gingerly roll off the bolster toward your favored side, resting there for a few moments. (Yp: *supine, backbend;* Yp for exploration while you stay: *shoulder-arm binds: overhead binding*)

Meditative Yinquiry for the Mat

"Nurturing the Beautiful Gardens of our Mind and Heart"

Each moment, we water seeds with what we're doing, seeing, saying, thinking, and believing. Within all of us lie seeds of love, seeds of anger, seeds of judgment, and seeds of joy. Thich Nhat Hahn encourages us to be a conscious gardener, actively deciding which seeds of the mind we will choose to water. Will it be a seed or a weed? Our mat offers a supportive space to practice training our attention on this moment, to water the seeds of slowing, feeling, and compassionate awareness.

While you're staying in this pose, you could inquire: *What seeds am I watering? Am I nurturing the seed of listening to my body? Am I watering the seed of kindness as I respond to what's happening inside of me?* Your attention and your approach are always watering a seed, and you get to consciously choose which seeds receive your attention and care. The seeds of permission and self-love are within you right now – how might you water them? As you nurture the seeds of compassion and understanding in yourself, notice how this affects your body, what happens in the mind, and what grows in the space of the heart. Ask yourself: *How will I continue to grow a beautiful garden inside me?*

Foot Cradle

Physical Focus

Wakes up the feet, clears tightness in the plantar fascia by gently spreading soles of feet, and extends ankles

Qi Charting

Kidney-Urinary Bladder
Liver-Gall Bladder
Spleen-Stomach

FINDING your Expression of the shape

Setting Up: Place a single-folded blanket on the middle of your mat to serve as padding for your knees and shins. Place a block at the tallest height on either side of the blanket within reach.

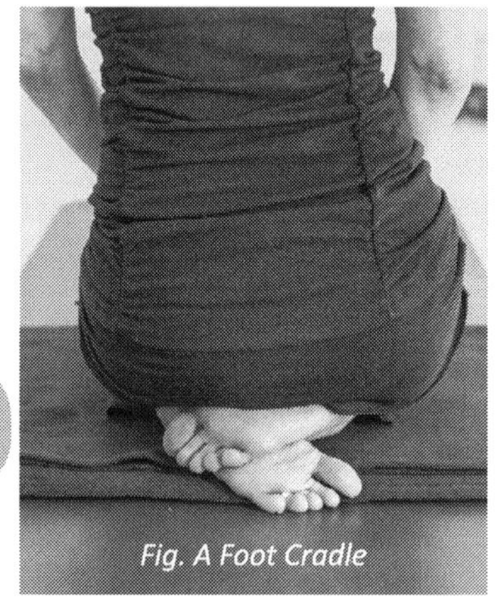
Fig. A Foot Cradle

Easing In: Kneel on the blanket with hips over knees. Rest the tops of feet onto the blanket with toes pointed comfortably backward. Cross your feet so the top of the right foot nestles into the cradle of the sole of the left foot. Place your hands to the blocks on either side of your outer hips. Begin to lower your sit-bones, staying cautious of strain arising within the knees, feet, or ankles as you move into this Seiza position. If any of these areas feel compromised anywhere along the descent, skip this posture for now and try one of the substitutions. Otherwise, rest the sit-bones lightly on your crossed feet (Fig A). Press your hands into the blocks as much as you need to. Use your shoulder strength to lift some of your upper body weight off the feet if the sensations are too strong. If sensations are too weak, release the hands from the blocks and rest them in your lap, allowing the full weight of the upper body to settle into the feet. Hold the top foot in one spot, or after thirty seconds or so, reposition the top foot slightly higher, lower, or side-to-side along the bottom foot to help focus the release of plantar fascial tension where you most need it. Play with this a couple of times, holding each position for thirty to forty-five seconds for a total of two or three minutes before exiting.

Your feet will thank you! (Yp: *hip-leg work*)

⊙ **YINPRESSIONS FOR EXPLORATION While You Stay:** *most shoulder-arm binds*

Easing Out: To mindfully ease out of this posture, release your arms slowly if you're exploring a shoulder-arm bind. If holding the blocks for support, press into them as you lift the hips. Rise so that your shoulders are positioned over your hips and your hips are over your knees. Switch the cross of the feet for the other side.

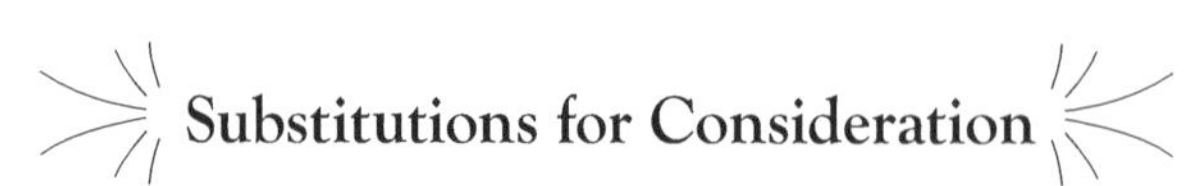
Substitutions for Consideration

Toe-Weaving & Massage (p. 174), Toes Up the Wall (p. 174)

These substitutions target release in the feet and toes with fewer or no demands on hips and knees.

FROG

PHYSICAL FOCUS

Deep hip maintenance pose to support lower body moveability and strength, including hip adductor muscles and upper/inner-thigh. Option to extend nurturing into upper body for suppleness of shoulders.

QI CHARTING

Kidney-Urinary Bladder
Liver-Gall Bladder
Spleen-Stomach

FINDING your Expression of the shape

Setting Up: Fold a blanket into a rectangular shape and place it widthwise across the back third of the mat so its edges extend onto the floor to serve as padding for your knees and shins. Place a bolster widthwise on your mat directly in front of the blanket. Place two blocks near the front of your mat off to the side within reach. Place a small, rolled-up blanket beside the blocks to be used for your ankles as necessary.

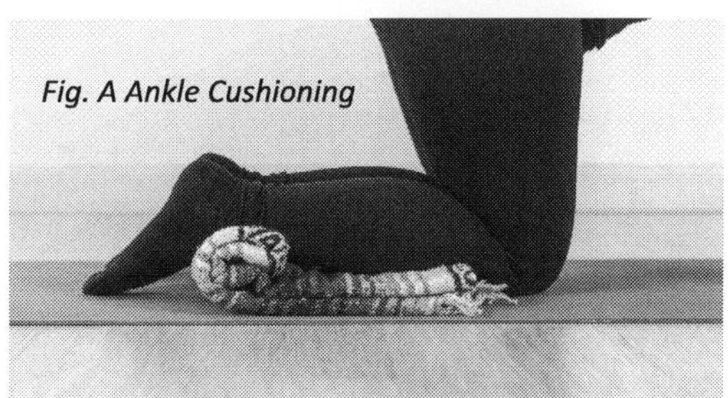

Fig. A Ankle Cushioning

Fig. B Tadpole

Fig. C Frog with bolster

Easing In: Kneel onto the blanket in Tabletop position with your shoulders positioned over your wrists and your hips over your knees. Separate your knees a comfortable distance toward the edges of your mat and bring your big toes together behind you. If you experience strain in the tops of the ankles, place the small, rolled-up blanket underneath them to reduce the angle of extension and soothe any painful compression where the ankles meet the mat (Fig A). As you proceed into these phases of this pose, take precaution with any knee, low back, shoulder, or neck sensitivities. If your hips at any time are above your heart and head, this becomes a mild inversion.

Keeping hips over the ankles and big toes together, place your forearms onto the bolster in front of you to come into **Tadpole**. Keep the forearms on the bolster, or if the floor is within reasonable reach, rest them directly onto the mat. From here, be watchful that the hips stay level (Fig B).

To generate more sensations through the hips, groin, and inner thighs, you might choose to ease into **Frog** by slowly sliding the feet further away from each other toward the sides of the mat. Point your toes in the direction that feels best in the knee joints. If you need more stimulation in the focus areas, gently slide the knees further away from each other, allowing the hips to lower until you feel mild sensation. For some, the knees could move beyond the boundaries of the mat and onto the padding of the blanket. Position the bolster or other props underneath the ribcage as necessary for additional support (Fig C). What's right is what resonates best with your body as a whole.

Whether in Tadpole or Frog, if more sensation is needed, lower your chest and head directly onto the bolster, perhaps with folded arms under your head as a cushion. If you wish to increase sensation in the lumbar spine, rest the elbows in front of the bolster and drop your chin into your palms. Be creative with your props to build up as much support under the upper body as needed to moderate sensation levels as you make any shifts. You might also adjust your hips so they're slightly in front of or behind your knees as another way to regulate the intensity felt in the lower half of the body. Continue scanning the body for how the shape feels and use this information to decide to deepen or return to an earlier, gentler phase of the pose.

To increase depth, remove the props from underneath the upper body, fold your forearms onto the floor, and rest your forehead onto the cushion of your arms. If more sensation is still needed through the upper torso and abdomen, perhaps rest your chest and forehead directly onto the floor and reach your arms in front of you. Should the shoulders begin to fall asleep, move the arms further apart or relax the shoulder angles by bending the elbows slightly to see if this resolves it. Keep a mindful attention on the sensations as you hold the pose and make adjustments as needed. To scale back, draw your knees closer together. To increase sensation along the groin and inner thigh line, move your knees further apart. (Yp: *hip-leg work, inversion, backbend*)

⦿ **YINPRESSIONS FOR EXPLORATION While You Stay:** *shoulder-arm binds: single threaded needle*

Easing Out: To mindfully ease out of Tadpole or Frog, activate the muscles of your core. If your arms are threaded, unstitch them and bring the neck to neutral. One at a time, place your hands on the mat directly under the shoulders, then press palms into the floor and straighten the arms to lift the torso a bit. One knee at a time, carefully slide the knees under the hips to form Tabletop.

Substitutions for Consideration

Two-Legged Tipped Dragon (p. 153), Butterfly (p.142)/Supine Butterfly (p. 143), Winged Dragon (for the front hip and leg, p. 151)

These poses provide alternate ways of opening the hips and inner thigh/groin areas without the neck and shoulder demands of Frog. Supine Butterfly can be a gentler back-lying option for the knees if needed.

Lying Crescent Moon

Physical Focus

Liberating supine pose to unlock tension for the whole lateral side of the body. Opens IT band, gently fans out intercostals between the ribs for deeper breathing, stretches abdominal oblique muscles, and stimulates the shoulders.

Qi Charting

Kidney-Urinary Bladder
Liver-Gall Bladder
Lung-Large Intestine
Heart-Small Intestine
Pericardium-Triple Burner

FINDING your Expression of the shape

Setting Up: Place a single-folded blanket on the back of your mat to serve as a cushion for your head once you've reclined. Place a bolster and a blanket near the middle of your mat off to the right side within reach.

Easing In: To prepare for the side bending posture of **Lying Crescent Moon**, lie on your back on the mat. Align the outer right side of your body with the right edge of your mat so you're in a long straight line from head to toes. Raise your arms overhead to an appropriate degree. In this posture, you'll form a curve-like shape with the body, so stay especially attentive with any low back issues. To begin, lift your arms, head, shoulders, and upper back a smidge off your mat. Keep your body parallel with the earth and sky as you move your upper body to the left until there's a gentle pulling sensation along the right side of the torso and a bit of pressure along the left. Lower back down onto the mat in this shape, adjusting the blanket under your head for cushioning. You can also prop the blanket under the shoulders if support is needed to encourage greater muscular relaxation.

Keeping the hips level, scoot the left leg along the mat to the left, followed by the right leg, until you feel mild sensations arise along the outer right hip and IT Band. Feel for a gentle sensation along the length of the back in the *erector spinae* muscles that run vertically on either side of the spinal column. Take a few moments to allow the body to settle into this phase of the posture. Without over-exerting, notice if there's space in the upper or lower body to slide any more deeply into this crescent moon shape.

Fig. A Lying Crescent Moon

To help the leg muscles stay relaxed, consider placing a bolster lengthwise against the outer seam of your right hip and leg as an anchor. If you'd like to play with binding the legs, cross either ankle on top of the other. Rest your arms freely overhead on the mat, or hold your opposite wrists, forearms, or elbows for Overhead Binding (Fig A). Another option is to hold just below your right wrist with your left hand. For this bind, use the left hand to bring a gentle tug through the whole of the right arm and armpit. To expand the sensations into the neck, turn your head to the right. (Yp: *supine, side bend, hip-leg work, shoulder-arm binds*)

Easing Out: Lower your arms and turn your head back to center, if twisted, and untwine your crossed ankles. Lift your head and upper body off the mat just enough to move with ease back to the right side of your mat. Relax your upper body onto the earth. Move your right leg to the right, followed by your left leg, so that your whole body is once again in a long straight line from head to toes. Rest for a few moments, then go to the other side.

YINPRESSIONS FOR EXPLORATION While You Stay: *shoulder-arm binds* (Shoot the Moon)

Shoot the Moon: This phase of Lying Crescent Moon emphasizes stimulation of the shoulders. To set up, create a small loop at one end of your strap and slip it around the right foot just below the ball of the foot. Lie on your back with the right side of your body aligned with the right side of your mat and move into the Lying Crescent Moon shape as described above. Once there, stretch the strap on top of the body and over the left side of your chest and left shoulder. In this pose, you'll create a bow shape with your strap. Cross the right ankle over the left. Raise your right arm overhead and bring it onto the mat behind you. Bend the right elbow so that your right forearm touches the crown of your head. Take the loose end of the strap into your right hand. If the right shoulder feels strained, move your hand closer to the tail end of the strap. If still strained, use a longer strap or skip this variation for now.

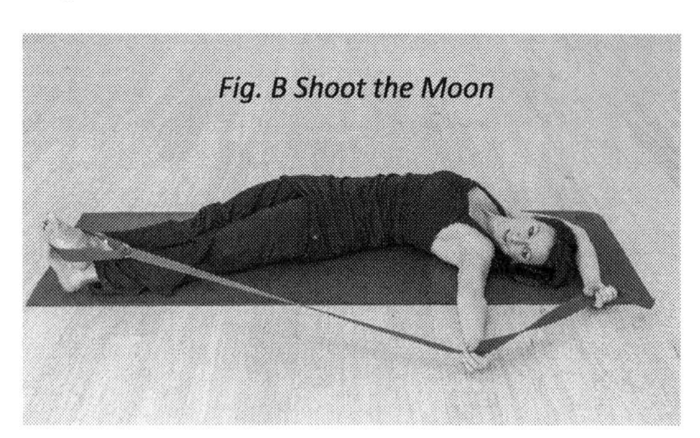
Fig. B Shoot the Moon

To deepen, keep hold of the strap in your right hand and place your left hand on the strap next to your right hand. Slide the left hand down along the strap as you straighten the left arm out to your left side, like an archer. The left arm will form a T-shape with the body. Position your left hand anywhere along the strap to find the most natural opening for your shoulders and the sides of your upper body (Fig B). To come out, let go of the strap, lower your arms, and follow the easing out instructions for Lying Crescent Moon (above).

Substitutions for Consideration

Lingering Crescent Moon (below), Draped Crescent Moon (below),
Sleeping Crescent Moon (below)

While each of these poses are similar in shape to Lying Crescent Moon and still focus on the lateral body, they offer a variety of approaches and prop options which may be more accessible for some bodies and make for interesting alternatives to consider.

Fig. C Lingering Crescent Moon

Lingering Crescent Moon: To set up, sit onto the right hip on the mat with both of your knees comfortably stacked and slightly bent. Place your right hand on the floor under the right shoulder with your fingertips pointed to the right. Create a gentle sensation of tugging along the right line of the upper body and some compression along the left by leaning a bit into the right-side rib cage and right shoulder. Let the torso sink into a crescent shape (Fig C). If you want to deepen, place the sole of the left foot on the mat in front of the right shin. To deepen even more, place the left foot on the mat in front of right thigh, bringing a cross to the legs. Keep your right knee bent or straighten it. Let the left hand rest comfortably onto the left leg. To emerge, uncross the legs if they're crossed. Return your knees to a bent and stacked position, if not already. Engage your core muscles lightly and press into the right hand to raise yourself upright. Switch sides when ready. (Yp: *side bend, hip-leg work, twist*)

Draped Crescent Moon: To set up, place the bolster widthwise on the back third of your mat. Place a single-folded blanket at the back of the mat off to the side within reach. Sit onto your right hip facing sideways on the mat a few inches in front of the bolster with both of your knees comfortably stacked and slightly bent. Place your right hand on the mat on the other side of the bolster and lengthen the right side of your upper body a bit. Bend your right arm and perch your elbow on the mat as you drape the right upper rib cage over the bolster. Reposition

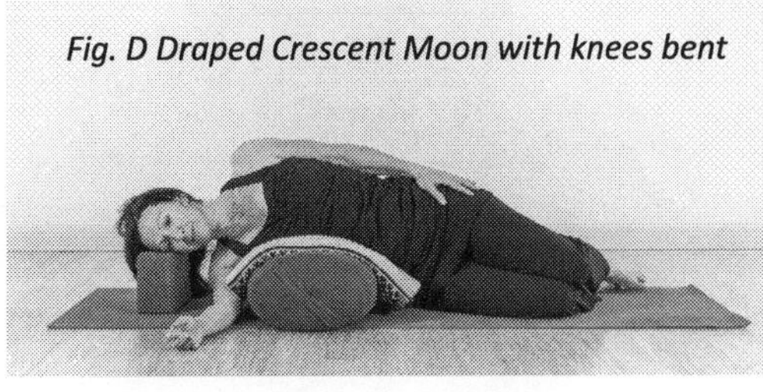
Fig. D Draped Crescent Moon with knees bent

Fig. E Draped Crescent Moon

the bolster under you by moving it slightly up or down to find the best opening for your upper body and shoulders. Rest your head in your right palm or onto a block or folded blanket (Fig D). Stack the left hip directly over the right.

If OK on the low back, you could explore extending the legs down the mat. Stay cautious with your neck. If you happen to need more opening for the neck, you could go deeper by unbending the right elbow and resting the side of your head into the crook of the inner elbow (Fig E). If the angle is too much, wedge the folded blanket between your head and inner arm. For Overhead Binding, lift the left arm above you and then lower it so the left upper arm is gently resting onto the left side of the head. Unbend the right arm and bring the palms together overhead. To go deeper into shoulders and triceps, keeping the hands together, bend both elbows and place your thumbs to rest at the back of your head or neck in Prayerful Hands.

To ease out of Draped Crescent Moon, unbend the elbows. Bend the knees, if not already. Engage your core muscles, place hands to the floor, and straighten your arms to slowly rise. Switch sides when you're ready. (Yp: *side bend, shoulder-arm binds: overhead binding, prayerful hands*)

Sleeping Crescent Moon: For a cozy and grounding version, lie on your belly and follow the instructions for Lying Crescent Moon (above). Soak up the stability and support as you come face to face with the earth that holds you. (Yp: *prone, side bend, hip-leg work*)

Meditative Yinquiry for the Mat

asana

"Steeping in Gratitude"

Spending time steeping in gratitude each day keeps us happier, healthier, and lovingly engaged with those we care about. As you attune to the heart of gratitude residing within you, soften the belly and chest so the breath can flow deeply and fully. Follow the reassuring rhythm of the in-breath and out-breath, noticing the gift of each breath.

In this quiet stillness, you might choose to reflect on any of the blessings in your life. Inquire: *What is something I'm grateful for?* And then: *What's another?* As you inhale, see these things in your mind's eye, receiving them with gratitude...experiences, people who have touched you, the many activities and thoughts and emotions you're capable of. Allow yourself the space to appreciate these gifts and the circumstances and people who have made them possible. As you exhale, imagine sharing these gifts with those around you. Stay with this for as long as you'd like. When you're ready, come back to the simple sensation of your breath for a few moments.

Mayfly

Physical Focus

Fully supported by gravity, drains stress and tensions from tight shoulders, outer arms, upper back, and neck.

Qi Charting

Lung-Large Intestine
Heart-Small Intestine
Pericardium-Triple Burner

FINDING your Expression of the shape

Setting Up: Place a single-folded blanket on the middle of the mat to serve as padding for the hips, helping to avoid any painful compression of the frontal hip bones. Place a block and a blanket at the top of your mat off to the side within reach.

Easing In: To form this prone **Mayfly** shape, kneel on the mat in Tabletop position with your hands on the mat in front of the blanket and knees behind it. Walk your knees backward several inches, then bend your elbows and lower onto your belly. Adjust the blanket as needed under the hips. Reach your arms onto the floor in front of you and your legs out behind you, flying on the mat like the superhero you are!

Lift your chest just slightly to slide your right arm across your upper chest and underneath the left shoulder for the Single Threaded Needle phase. Explore your right palm facing up or down and choose what feels best. Rest your forehead on the mat or slip a blanket underneath your head to raise the neck a bit so it's in line with the rest of your spine. To dampen sensations through the focus areas of the shoulders, arms, and upper back, move the right hand closer to your center and bend the right elbow a bit more. To boost sensations, slide it a little further outward to the left, taking care to keep the sensations in the mild range to prevent pulling the arm from the shoulder joint. If suitable for the neck, create a cervical twist by turning your head to the left, or for a deeper rotation, turn it to the right (Fig A).

Fig. A Mayfly single threaded

asana

The Double Threaded Needle phase of Mayfly pose tends to be slightly deeper for the upper back and shoulders. To proceed, bring your head back to a neutral position, if not already there. Cross your left arm in front of your right arm. This crossed-arm pattern grants access to arms and shoulders simultaneously. Face the palms up or down, depending on what feels best. If the neck needs more support, place a blanket or block underneath your forehead (Fig B). Stay like this, or ease into Hugging Arms by sliding the elbows slightly away from the chest and placing your palms onto the opposite backs of shoulders, giving yourself the giant, warm hug you deserve (Fig C). To further deepen the shoulder and arm work with Twisted Branches, lift your palms and bring your

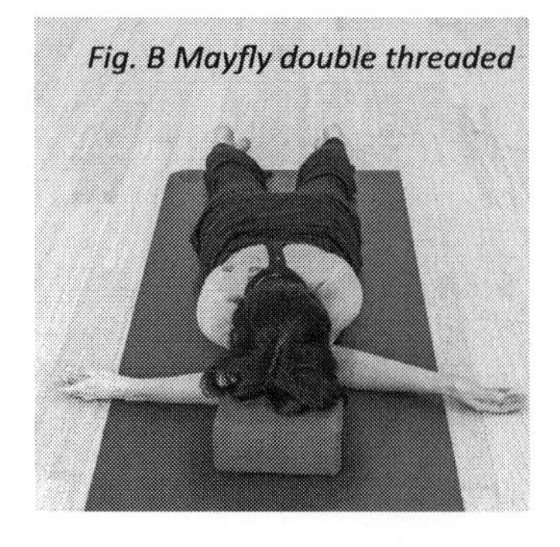
Fig. B Mayfly double threaded

Fig. C Mayfly hugging arms

Fig. D Mayfly twisted branches

hands in front of your face so that the backs of your hands touch each other. If it feels ok, further entwine the wrists so your right fingers hold the left palm (Fig D). To fine-tune sensations, slide the elbows slightly away from or toward you, as needed.

Whichever arm position you've chosen, adjust the neck until it is positioned well without any strain. Lean your forehead into the swaddle of the inner arms, if it feels nurturing. If you'd prefer a cervical twist, rest a cheek into the inner arms, hold for a bit of time, then twist in the opposite direction. In the various phases of this pose, you may also feel sensations of gentle compression within the lumbar spine area stemming from a mild backbend. (Yp: *prone, backbend, shoulder-arm binds*)

⊙ **YINPRESSIONS FOR EXPLORATION While You Stay:** one-legged + hip-leg work (Thigh-High Mayfly)

Thigh-High Mayfly: While holding Mayfly with the Single Threaded Needle bind with the right arm, bring your forehead back onto the mat if the neck was turned. Slip your left knee toward your left-side rib cage with the inner leg line resting on the floor as if you were comfortably lying down. Experiment with moving the left leg above or below the navel line as well as bending or unbending the left knee a bit until you find a relaxing release through the left leg and hip. If the neck requests it, explore a right or left cervical twist. Once you find the position that works well for you, relax your body into stillness. After you've held the pose for the appropriate length of time, switch to the other side.

Easing Out: To mindfully come out of Mayfly, bring your head back to center if your neck was turned. If your leg is bent, straighten it down the mat. Lift your head and chest enough to unravel the arms or unthread your needle, then rest back onto the mat. Let the arms fall freely by your sides with palms face up as you position your head comfortably. When you're ready, do the other side.

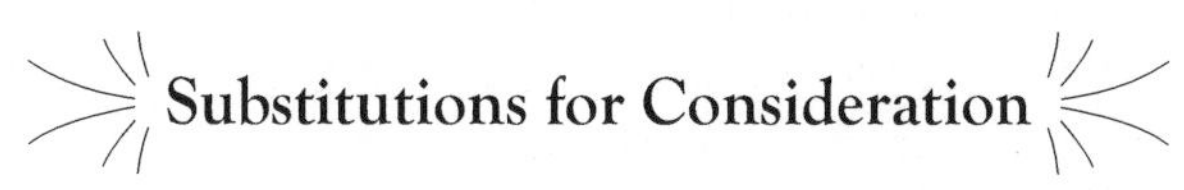

Substitutions for Consideration

Supine Mayfly (below), Perching Mayfly (below)

Practitioners with mild neck or shoulder sensitivities may find these supine and standing versions more viable. They may also be excellent options during later-term pregnancy.

asana

Supine Mayfly: Lie on your back on your mat with a single-folded blanket under your head. Extend your legs comfortably down the mat and rest your arms alongside you with your palms facing the ceiling. For the Single Threaded Needle bind, begin by crossing the right arm in front of your upper chest out to the left. Keep the right arm relatively straight and the right palm facing the floor. Lift your left arm to meet the right forearm, then bend the left elbow to wrap the right forearm into a gentle cradle. Keep the shoulders squared and press the left arm gently toward the body to the degree it feels appropriate for your right shoulder. Maintain the right palm facing the floor, or play with turning it toward the ceiling. Hold for a minute or two. To release the arm bind, unbend the left arm and relax both arms by your sides. When ready, repeat on the other side. (Yp: *supine*; Yp for exploration while you stay *shoulder-arm binds: hugging arms or twisted branches*)

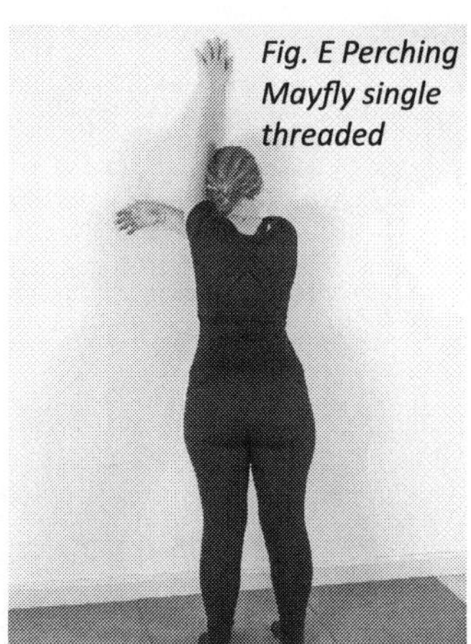

Fig. E Perching Mayfly single threaded

Perching Mayfly: Stand facing the wall a few inches away from it. Place each of your hands on the wall in front of its respective shoulder with your fingers pointing toward the ceiling. Slide your palms up the wall to straighten the arms. Follow the same general instructions for Mayfly (above), only substitute the floor support with wall support (Fig E, F) (Yp: *shoulder-arm binds*)

Fig. F Perching Mayfly twisted branches

Melting Heart

Physical Focus

Kneeling posture that clears congestion and tensions through the whole of the heartspace. Frees the chest, middle/upper back, shoulders, and neck while offering mild stimulation for the lumbar spine. Can become a mild inversion.

Qi Charting

Kidney-Urinary Bladder
Spleen-Stomach
Lung-Large Intestine
Heart-Small Intestine
Pericardium-Triple Burner

FINDING your Expression of the shape

Setting Up: Place a single-folded blanket on the back third of your mat to serve as padding for your knees and shins. Place a bolster widthwise across the front third of your mat. Place two blocks at their lowest height in front of the bolster about a foot apart.

Easing In: To enter, kneel on the blanket with hips over knees in Tabletop position. Place your hands on the bolster shoulder-width distance apart. Either keep the toes pointed behind you or tuck all ten toes under. Notice any effects of these toe positions on your feet and knees and choose what feels best. Keeping your hips over your knees, bend your elbows, rest your forearms onto the bolster, and place your forehead onto folded forearms (Fig A). You'll want to stay watchful of neck and shoulder sensations as you explore the various phases of this posture, remembering that the deeper the phase, the more the upper body weight transfers into these areas. Scan also for sensations in the upper spine, front of chest, and lower back as you ease into the pose and make adjustments.

Fig. A Melting Heart with bolster

Allow for a softening of the heartspace as gravity draws your upper body toward the earth. Let the hips tilt upward slightly to support reasonable and diffuse sensations in the lower spine. Stay in this phase of **Melting Heart** or, if more sensation is needed, slide the bolster to the side, rest your folded forearms directly on the mat, and lower your forehead onto them. If your hips are above your heart and head in whichever phase of the pose you're holding, this becomes a mild inversion. Choose to reemploy the bolster at any point by positioning it under the chest and ribs to provide extra support for the upper body and keep sensations reasonable.

Fig. B Melting Heart with one arm

If you need more sensation, reach one arm forward, placing the palm of that hand to the earth. If staying with a one-armed phase, hold for a bit, then switch arms (Fig B). If the upper body allows, you could explore the two-armed option. Extend both arms in front of you simultaneously. Rest both palms and your forehead on the mat. Experiment with the distance between your arms. If there is a tingly numbness in the shoulders, abducting the arms sometimes alleviates the nerve or blood vessel compression. If not, ease back until the sensations are appropriate. If one

Fig. C Melting Heart with hands on blocks

or both arms are extended and sensations in the focus areas remain too muffled, you might place the outstretched palm(s) onto a block starting at its lowest height with the option of raising the block(s) a level if needed (Fig C). Stay cautious of the upper body pressure on the cervical spine as you make any adjustments to your head position. If it would suit your neck, place a cheek onto the forearms or mat to induce a twist. Resting your attention on your loving, melting heart is a beautiful way to finish any Yin Yoga sequence or to enjoy as a stand-alone posture on a busy day to help release tension and reconnect with blessings in our life. (Yp: *backbend, inversion*)

⦿ **YINPRESSIONS FOR EXPLORATION While You Stay:** *shoulder-arm binds: prayerful hands*

Easing Out: To mindfully rise from Melting Heart, engage your core muscles. If your hands are in Prayerful Hands, unbend the elbows and place the palms to the earth. If your hands are on the blocks or your forearms are on a bolster, move one arm at a time to relocate your palms to the ground. Slide your hands under your shoulders and, keeping your core muscles engaged, push down through the hands to lift your upper body a bit. Straighten each arm to press your upper body back up into Tabletop. If your toes are tucked under, uncurl them slowly and rest the tops of your feet onto the mat with toes pointed behind you. From Tabletop, perhaps you choose to drop the hips back toward the heels for a restful Beetle (p. 137), or you could move the spine through a gentle flow of Cat's Breath (p. 203). If you chose the one-arm option, don't forget to ease back into the Melting Heart shape and do the other side.

Substitutions for Consideration

Standing Rolling Wing/Cactus (below), Standing Prayerful Hands (below), Prone Rolling Wing/Cactus (below), Fish (p. 159)

In the case of neck or lower back sensitivities, these standing versions may be beneficial substitutes for stimulating the shoulders and the *pectoralis major* and *minor* muscles and surrounding fascia through the chest. Without the weight of the upper body pressing into these areas, the standing versions tend to offer a gentler approach. In the case of later-term pregnancy, they are helpful swap-outs for their prone counterparts. The prone variations keep you close to the ground and generally put less pressure on the neck than kneeling in Melting Heart.

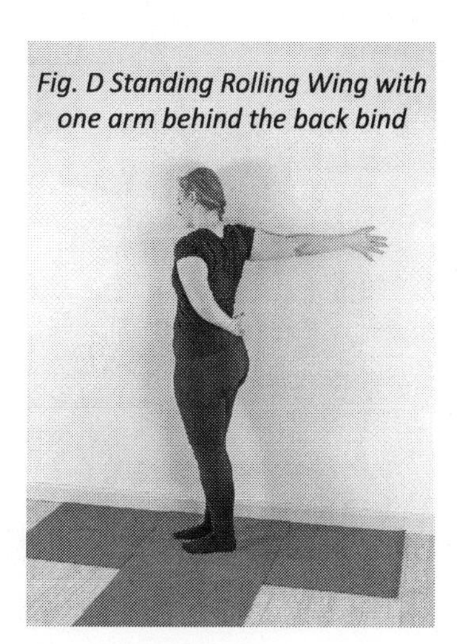
Fig. D Standing Rolling Wing with one arm behind the back bind

Standing Rolling Wing: Stand facing the wall a few inches away from it and reach your arms directly out from your shoulders, forming a T-shape with your body. Place both palms on the wall, bend your left arm, and bring your left palm to press the wall beside your left upper chest. To increase stimulation through the right chest as well as through the front and back of the right shoulder, keep both palms on the wall as anchors, and in small increments, begin to turn the feet to the left away from the wall. The more you turn your feet and rotate your body to the left, the greater the intensity for your chest and shoulders. Stop where it feels best. Lean the right arm and upper body slightly into the wall, if supportive. Explore adjusting the right arm slightly upward to feel how sensations shift. To open the opposite shoulder, choose to add a One Arm Behind the Back Bind (Fig D). To come out, simply turn the feet back so that your toes once again face the wall. Lower both arms, relaxing them alongside the body. When ready, try the other side. (Yp: *shoulder-arm binds)*

Standing Rolling Cactus: This shoulder-opener on the wall is quite like Standing Rolling Wing. Stand facing the wall a few inches away from it and reach your arms directly out from your shoulders to make a T-shape with your body. Place both palms on the wall, then bend your right arm to create a ninety-degree angle between the forearm and upper arm, forming a saguaro cactus shape. Check to see that the right wrist is straight above the right elbow and the right fingers point to the sky. To ease into Standing Rolling Cactus, follow the same basic instructions as for Standing Rolling Wing (above), beginning to turn your feet to the left away from the wall. When you're ready, try the other side. (Yp: *shoulder-arm binds*)

Standing Prayerful Hands: Stand facing the wall a few inches away from it. Place each hand onto the wall in front of its respective shoulder with your fingers pointing toward the ceiling. Slide your palms up the wall to straighten the arms. Turn the palms to face each other and bend both arms, resting your elbows against the wall as you bring the palms together. To the degree the upper body allows, continue to bend the elbows, moving the thumbs toward the back of the head or neck. Thumbs could rest onto the body, or if the palms separate, your hands could settle onto your upper back. A block could also be held widthwise between the palms, which may make this more accessible for some bodies. If useful, explore moving the elbows slightly higher or lower on the wall until the sensations in the triceps and shoulders are just right. If supportive, gently rest your forehead onto the wall. To come out, unbend the arms and extend them back up the wall. Slide your palms down the wall and lower your arms to rest at your sides. (Yp: *shoulder-arm binds*)

Prone Rolling Wing/Cactus: Place two blankets at the front of your mat off to the side within reach. Place a bolster at the back third of your mat off to the right side within reach. Lie in a prone position on the mat and create either a T-shape or cactus-shape with your arms, as in Rolling Wing/Cactus. Turn your head to the left. Place the left palm on the mat beside your left upper chest. Press into your left hand to begin to roll onto the right side, stacking the left side of your body over the right or until you feel mild stimulation in the focus areas of right-side shoulder, upper chest, and upper back. If the lower back is sensitive, bend and stack the knees. You could also hug a folded blanket or bolster to the chest for added stability. If the neck is strained, place a blanket underneath the head so the length of the neck is aligned with the rest of your spine. If the legs are straight and you wish to go deeper, extend the left leg behind you, resting the foot on the floor (Fig E) or the leg on the bolster. To add a deeper twist and hip opener, place the left foot on the floor behind your right and bend the left knee and point it toward the ceiling. If this position feels steady and you wish to go deeper, be mindful of low back, hip, and knee sensitivities as you proceed slowly and carefully. Bend the right leg, lift the right foot, and rest the outer right ankle onto the left inner thigh area.

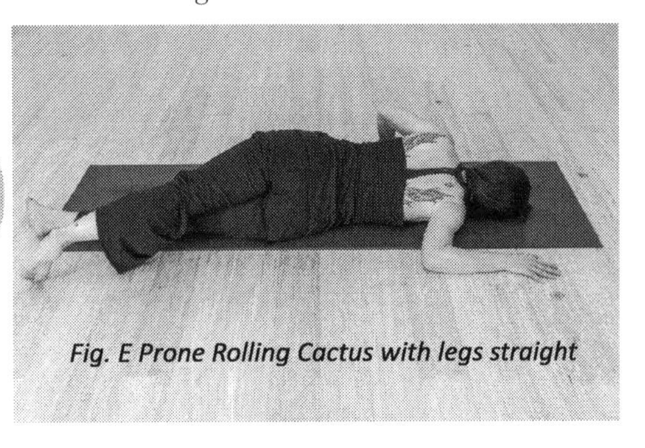
Fig. E Prone Rolling Cactus with legs straight

asana

Whichever phase of the pose you're in, to add a One Arm Behind the Back Bind, reach your left arm straight up so your fingers point in the direction of the ceiling. Turn the left thumb and palm away from you so they face behind you as you gently rotate the upper arm in the same direction, creating an internal rotation in the left shoulder. Reach the left arm behind you and bend the elbow. Wrap the left arm around the lower-mid back area and rest the back of the hand on your lower back (Fig F) To ease out, unwind the top arm, place your left hand on the mat in front of your chest for support, and uncross the legs if bound. Bend and stack both of your knees comfortably, then roll gently onto your belly. Extend your legs behind you. Turn your head in the opposite direction and lower your arms by your sides, palms facing up or down. Repeat for the other side. (Yp: *prone, shoulder-arm binds, twist, hip-leg work*)

Fig. F Prone Rolling Cactus with one arm behind the back bind
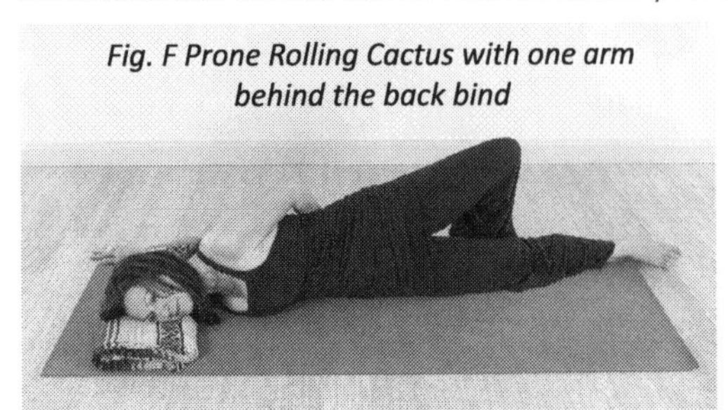

Pixie Toes Squat

Physical Focus

Toes, ankles, fascia of soles of feet

Qi Charting

Kidney-Urinary Bladder
Liver-Gall Bladder
Spleen-Stomach

FINDING your Expression of the shape

Setting Up: Place a single-folded blanket on the middle of the mat as padding for your knees and shins. Place a block at the tallest height on either side of the blanket. Have a third block within reach.

Easing In: Kneel on the blanket in Tabletop position with your shoulders positioned over your wrists and your hips over your knees. Reach behind you and tuck all five toes of both feet under – don't forget the little pinky toes! Press the balls of your feet into the mat rather than balancing on toe tips. Even this beginning phase might feel like enough, and if so, that's OK and it's the place to stay. For more sensation, lift your hands from the mat and rise so that you're kneeling upright with your shoulders positioned over your hips and your hips are over your knees.

Fig. A Pixie Toes Squat with block

If more sensation is desired, place a block widthwise on your heels as a pedestal for your hips and slowly begin to lower the hips onto the block. If sensations become too intense in your hips or knees during your descent, return to the upright kneeling position. If your body allows, rest the hips onto the block (Fig A). If seated on the block and you need to moderate the sensations in the feet and toes, press your hands into the blocks positioned on either side of your outer hips to lift some of your upper body weight slightly off the feet and toes. Notice if this yang-like muscular engagement of the upper body helps to mitigate the sensation enough for it to be reasonable. If it doesn't, ease yourself back up.

Fig. B Pixie Toes Squat

To increase stimulation, remove the block and sit directly onto the heels (Fig B). If the ankles and knees allow, you might scoot the feet closer to one another. If the hands are free and your body is stable, this is an opportunity to integrate some shoulder-arm work to bring sensations to the shoulder joints and upper body and also gain access to the Qi tracing through these areas. If you're feeling sensations in the toes and shoulders, you're activating all six Qi channel pairs while simultaneously helping to strengthen and balance the energy flowing through them to the Organ Systems. (Yp: *hip-leg work*)

⦿ **YINPRESSIONS FOR EXPLORATION While You Stay:** *most shoulder-arm binds (Fig C)*

Fig. C Pixie Toes Squat with twisted branches

Easing Out: To mindfully ease out, slowly unravel any shoulder-arm binds or release your hands from the blocks. Rise upright so that your shoulders are positioned over your hips and your hips are over your knees. Gently uncurl the toes so that the tops of your ankles and toes rest on the mat, toes pointing behind you. Place your hands on the mat in front of you and return to Tabletop. Rest in stillness here and feel the energy as it flows.

Substitutions for Consideration

Toe Weaving & Massage (below), Toes Up the Wall (below)

These substitutions help open access to the feet and toes without the demands of kneeling.

Toe Weaving & Massage: Come to a comfortable seated position on your mat. Massage each foot with your hands one at a time, then weave the fingers of one hand between the toes. The closer you slide the fingers to base of the toes, the greater the sensations will likely be. With your fingers between the toes, gently flex and extend the toes slowly back and forth, curling them in and out. Lift or prop the leg off the floor to create a little room to move the ankle in a circle several times in one direction and then the other. Release your fingers and massage the sole of your foot with hands or elbow, then switch sides. You might also explore Toe Weaving in Butterfly pose. Simply place the pinky toes side by side and then alternating side to side, weave the toes of one foot into the other.

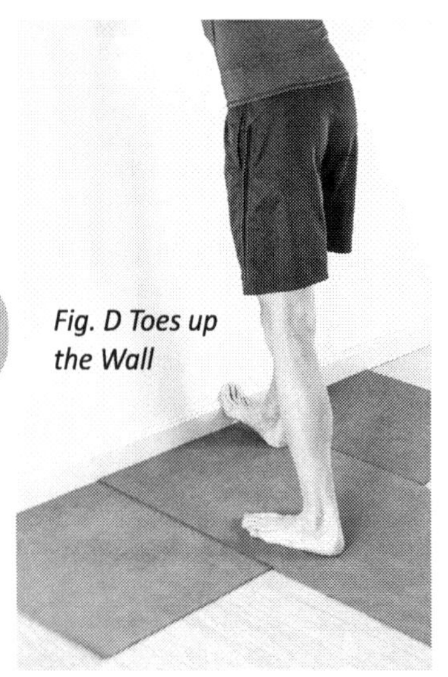
Fig. D Toes up the Wall

Toes Up the Wall: If the knees complain in a seated position, take this toe exercise to the wall. Stand facing the wall about one foot away from it. Place your palms on the wall in front of your upper chest. Position your right foot at an angle to the wall so that the heel is on the floor and the ball and toes of the foot press gently against the wall (Fig D). Play with keeping the right knee straight to open the calf tissue, or bend it a bit which might accentuate sensations in the ankle. If it would feel supportive, lean your folded forearms onto the wall and rest your head on them. If necessary, adjust the angle of your foot to the wall to find mild sensation through the ankle, toes, and fascia of the sole of the foot. Hold a minute or two, then switch sides.

Saddle

Physical Focus

All-around posture with the potential to tend to many regions of the body simultaneously. Gives plenty of chances to play with props to help unstick any stuck areas. Stimulates SI joints, opens front of hips/thighs, ankles, and upper body.

Qi Charting

Kidney-Urinary Bladder
Liver-Gall Bladder
Spleen-Stomach
Lung-Large Intestine
Heart-Small Intestine
Pericardium-Triple Burner

FINDING your Expression of the shape

Setting Up: Create a sloped support for the torso by placing a firm bolster lengthwise on your mat with a block at the lowest height under the bolster's back edge. Place a double-folded blanket on the elevated back of the bolster to serve as a pillow for the head. Place a single-folded blanket in front of the bolster for your seat. Place two blocks, a blanket, and a strap beside your seat within reach.

Easing In: Begin by easing first into **Lingering Windshield Wipers**, a gentle hip-opening twist. Sit on the folded blanket positioned in front of your sloped bolster and extend your legs in front of you. Bend both knees and place the feet on either side of the mat at a comfortable distance from you. Place your hands on the floor behind you for support. Lower your bent knees to the right. If the knees are tender, add a blanket or block under the outer thigh and/or inner knee. This phase might be just right, or as the body allows, recline your upper body onto the sloped bolster behind you and rest your head on the blanket (Fig A). If you need more sensation and would like to try **One-Legged Saddle**, press back to upright.

Fig. A Lingering Windshield Wipers with bolster

As the left knee and ankle permit, explore bringing your left heel toward your left outer hip. It's not important that the heel and hip touch, just find the placement that offers reasonable sensation for your lower body from the left-side hip down to the left toes. Typically, the left knee is happiest if toes point backward rather than out to the side, but discover what's best for you and your bones. If the top of the left ankle is over-stressed, notice what happens if you reduce the angle of extension by tucking a small rolled-up blanket underneath it. You could also move the left knee slightly inward or outward from your midline, knowing that sometimes the slightest adjustment can make the difference. If the bent left knee lifts off the floor, extra pressure is likely to go into the top of the left ankle. That's not a problem as long as it feels OK, generating gentle diffuse sensation only and nothing sharp, localized, or pointed. If in doubt, opt to go softer. If the knees are painful and adjustments don't provide relief, you'll need to ease out a bit or return to Lingering Windshield Wipers.

You might straighten your right leg in front of you. If the hips become unlevel in any phase, use an additional blanket under the lower sit-bone so they return to parallel. Experiment once again with the distance between your legs if needed, which may impact sensations through the lower half of the body. Scan for sensations through the lower body and lower back. Feel for gentle pulling along your front left thigh/hip and diffuse pressure through the lower back and sacrum and make sure everything feels appropriate. To intensify sensa-

Fig. B One-Legged Saddle with bolster

tions, place your hands behind you and ease yourself down onto the sloped bolster, resting your head back on the cushion of the blanket (Fig B).

If there's still not enough sensation in the desired areas of exercise, try adjusting or removing the bolster, being sure to engage your core muscles as you rise to upright. Roll to your outer right hip to unbend your left knee, then choose to position the bolster either lengthwise or widthwise flat on the mat or remove it altogether. Any of the following options will generally increase sensations in the focus areas:

Position the bolster lengthwise and flat on the mat. Sit on the folded blanket a few inches in front of the bolster and follow the instructions above for easing into Lingering Windshield Wipers. Place your hands on the floor to help you recline gently backward to rest your upper body and head on the bolster.

Position the bolster widthwise and flat on the mat. Sit on the folded blanket about 12 inches in front of the bolster and follow the instructions above for Lingering Windshield Wipers. From that position, place your hands on the bolster behind you, bend your elbows, and lower your forearms to rest on the bolster. Slowly recline so that your middle/upper back drapes over the bolster. Reach behind you and place the block underneath your head, making sure it isn't compressing your neck. If your neck allows for extension, you have the option to lower the block a level or rest your head directly on the mat. Given the sensitivities of compressing the back of the neck, go slowly and take extra care to not let your head tip too far backward. Stay watchful for any feelings of lightheadedness or discomfort.

Remove the bolster. Sit on the folded blanket and follow the instructions above for Lingering Windshield Wipers, only without using the bolster and blocks under your upper body. From that position, place your hands on the floor behind you, bend your elbows, and slowly lower your forearms to rest on the floor. This might be enough, or if the body allows, continue to lower your upper body and head directly onto the floor, observing the sensations along the way.

Whichever phase of One-Legged Saddle you've chosen, there are some additional interesting options to explore as you hold the pose. Bend your right knee and place the right foot on the ground. Stay with this, or if arms are free, bring your right thigh toward your right-side chest and hug it close to you, interlacing your fingers around your shin. If your right leg is out of reach, sling a strap around the shin and hold its tails in your right hand while keeping the upper body relaxed. Hold this shape, or add a Butterfly-leg. To do so, release your right leg, return the right foot to the floor, and let the bent right knee fall outward toward the right side of your mat, externally rotating and abducting the right leg at the hip (Fig C). Keep your right knee bent, or to morph into Dragonfly-leg, unbend your right knee so that the right leg stretches diagonally to the right. If you'd like to work into your shoulders, raise your arms overhead and rest them behind you or cradle your head with the hands. Alternately, rest your arms by your sides. Placing your palms to your chest and belly is another comfortable and comforting position.

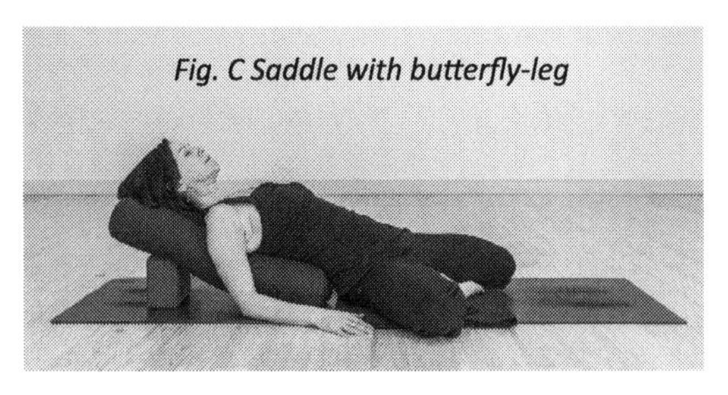
Fig. C Saddle with butterfly-leg

The two-legged **Saddle** version is generally deeper than One-Legged Saddle phases. If in One-Legged Saddle, exit the pose before attempting a two-legged version. One good way to find out if the two-legged option might work for you is to kneel on the folded blanket in front of a sloped bolster. Situate a block lengthwise on the mat between the inner ankles. Begin to ease your sit-bones toward the block, stopping if the knees or ankles feel strained anywhere along the journey. If this starting position isn't working, forego the two-legged version for now and stay with One-Legged Saddle or an alternate pose. If seated on the block comfortably and your knees feel steady, stay here, or slide the block to the side and see if sitting directly on the heels feels OK. For more in-

Fig. D Saddle with bolster

Fig. E Saddle

ternally rotated hips, there is also the option of sitting between the heels. Choose what's best for your body. To deepen, lower your upper body on the sloped bolster behind you (Fig D).

If you need more sensation, you might try positioning the bolster flat on the mat lengthwise or widthwise as indicated above, exiting the pose first. If an even deeper variation is needed, remove the bolster and recline directly onto the mat, easing yourself back down using your hands and forearms as supports (Fig E).

Whatever phase of Saddle you've chosen, remember there's no one ideal shape. Our goal is simply to find stay-able sensations. (Yp: *hip-leg work, twist, supine, backbend, one-legged, shoulder-arm binds*)

⊙ **YINPRESSIONS FOR EXPLORATION While You Stay:** *twist, side bend + twist, or seated forward bend* (Straddle Saddle)

Fig. F Straddle Saddle with side bend

Fig. G Straddle Saddle with forward bend

Straddle Saddle: If you find One-Legged Saddle to be reasonable for your body, you might also enjoy checking out Straddle Saddle options. Begin in an upright One-Legged Saddle. Separate your legs into a V-shape until you feel mild sensation through your inner leg line. This Straddle Saddle is a foundation for a side bend over the outstretched leg (Fig F). Alternately, you could try an open or closed upright twist or a seated forward bend. Before forward bending, remember to first create a slight anterior tilt of the pelvis (for a refresher, see "Yinpression: Seated Forward Bend," p. 109). Keep your legs wide and fold either between the legs, or over the straight leg (Fig G), or you could choose to bring your legs closer together to fold over them both. Remember to take into consideration the total amount of time you spend in each variation of the pose to be sure to stay within reasonable limits of stimulation. Switch the legs of your One-Legged Saddle to repeat on the other side.

Easing Out: To dismount from your version of Saddle, lower your arms, if raised. If in Lingering Windshield Wipers, activate your core muscles, lift your bent knees back to center, and place the soles of your feet on the floor. If reclined, recruit your core muscles and shoulder strength as you press your hands to floor and lift yourself upright. From the upright Saddle position, extend your legs straight down the mat one at a time, rocking to the side a bit, as helpful. Unless you've been enjoying two-legged Saddle, go to the other side and see which variation works best for it.

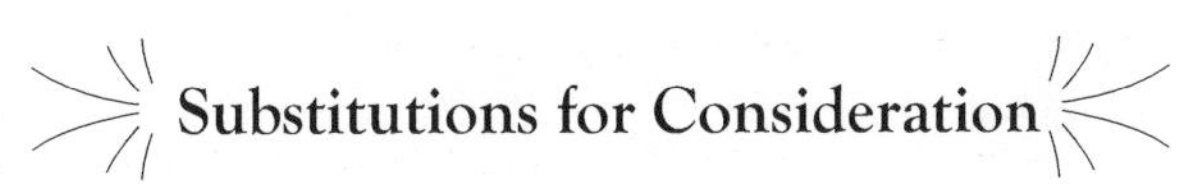

Substitutions for Consideration

Supine Lingering Windshield Wipers (below)

Because Saddle works so many different parts of the Yin body, many substitutions abound. Consider the area(s) you wish to exercise in concert with the needs of your body, conscious of any areas of contraindication. Here are just a few additional examples to consider: Sphinx-Seal (for a backbend, p. 188), Dragon (for hip extension in back leg p. 150), Drawbridge (for a backbend and the front of torso, p. 140), and Deer (for an internal rotation in back hip, p. 148).

Fig. H Supine Lingering Windshield Wipers with blocks & overhead binding

Supine Lingering Windshield Wipers: This supine twisting posture continues to offer internal and external rotation for the hips while typically being gentler on the knees than the Saddle variations discussed above. Place a single-folded blanket on the back of your mat to serve as a cushion for your head once you've reclined. Place two blocks and a blanket near the middle of your mat off to the side within reach. Lie on your back with the blanket under your head. Bend both of your knees and place your feet on the floor mat-width distance apart with your knees stacked over your ankles. Lower your bent knees to the right. For extra support, add a blanket or block underneath the outer knee and/or inner thigh areas and play with the placement of your feet by moving them closer to or further from the body and/or one another. To stimulate your shoulder joints, raise your arms overhead and rest them on the mat behind you. For an overhead bind, clasp the right forearm with your left hand to create a gentle tug down through the right armpit and ribcage. To bring a twist to your neck, look to the left (Fig H). To ease out, lower your arms and unwind the neck. Activate your core muscles and lift bent knees back to center, placing the soles of your feet on the floor. When ready, switch sides by letting your knees fall in the opposite direction. (Yp: *supine, hip-leg work, twist*; Yp for exploration while you stay: *shoulder-arm binds-overhead binding*)

MEDITATIVE YINQUIRY FOR THE MAT

"Mountain Solid"

Thich Nhat Hanh noted, "A mountain cannot be swayed by the wind." If, as you practice, you feel the winds of distraction or strong emotions blow, bring to mind the image of a snow-capped mountain. See it clearly in your mind's eye and how solid it sits, ageless and towering over the landscape. Weather systems pass by it, countless summers and winters cycling over and over, yet still the majestic mountain remains, essentially unchanged. Trees sprout, grow, and pass away, while generation after generation of animals and birds roam its sides. The stable mountain just keeps being there as everything around it shifts. We, too, have within us this fundamental stability, even as the circumstances of life shift constantly around us.

As you breathe in and out, feel yourself stable and solid like a mountain, not swayed by the winds that blow. Find the solid places within you, the bones, the organs, the muscles, and connective tissues. Feel for the places your body touches the earth and root there, down, down, grounded like a great stone, silent and still for hundreds and thousands of years as the world passes by.

Savasana

Physical Focus

Savasana is sacred space as the practice journey comes to a close, a time of rest and restoration for our physical tissues from head to toe where we can integrate all aspects of ourselves...mind, body, energy, and heart. Savasana is a time of balance, as important to our practice as the sensation-ful poses themselves. This shape is also useful as a reliable counterpose to rest between postures.

Qi Charting

Deep relaxation throughout the body supports harmonious flow through all energy channels

FINDING your Expression of the shape

Setting Up: To prepare your mat space, fold a blanket in half lengthwise and spread it across the entire mat to serve as cushioning for your whole body. It's time to get cozy, so gather your props! A bolster, blankets, blocks, and an eye pillow or kerchief are all wonderful Savasana supports to help you soak in the stillness as comfortably as possible.

At a minimum, I would suggest that the length of your Savasana be the longest length of time that you held any single pose, but ideally, it would be at least double that time. Depending on your intention and if you're integrating an enhanced Yoga Nidra-inspired experience, it could be up to thirty minutes or more.

As you settle into Savasana, thoughts may rise and fall. If you find yourself distracted, that's OK, simply come back to this place of relaxation and release. Resting isn't always easy, but with practice, it's something we can get better at. Give yourself permission to enjoy a more complete release of *doing* for this period of time.

Easing in: You may want to dim the lights or draw window shades as you prepare for your **Savasana**. For this closing pose, let yourself be as comfortable as possible. The shape you choose for your class-closing Savasana journey into rest depends on what feels most nurturing for your body and spirit in that moment. Be creative as you consider different set-up options and remember that each time you practice, your body's needs might be different. Whichever posture you pick, what matters most is that you feel snug, relaxed, and able to breathe well.

Fig. A Savasana

To start exploring your Savasana position, lie on your back with your legs extended down the mat. Position the feet a little greater than hip-width distance apart to give space for the hips and low back to release more completely onto the earth (Fig A). Take a peek down the mat to align the length of your spine. Adjust your hips and legs so they're able to relax, finding the position that feels most solid and balanced. Let your toes roll in or out, whatever feels most natural when all the leg muscles let go. Your arms can reach overhead and onto the mat behind you for **Starfish**.

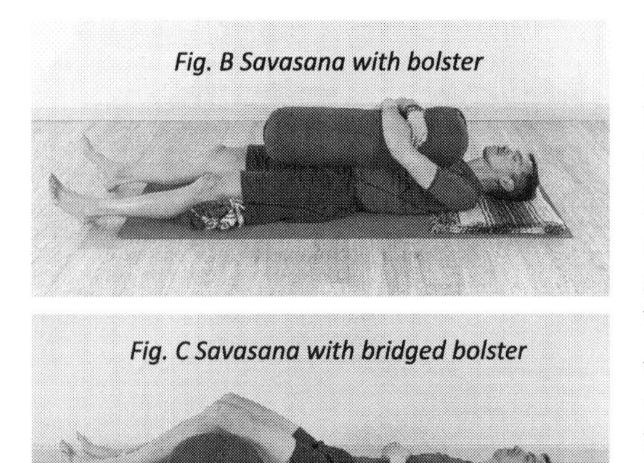

Fig. B Savasana with bolster

Fig. C Savasana with bridged bolster

A block at the lowest height or a small, rolled-up blanket under the lower legs/knees typically aids the release of the lower back and hip flexors, specifically the *psoas*. This sends a signal to the central nervous system that all is well and engages the relaxation response to encourage deeper rest. For some, a bolster or folded blanket on the chest or belly feels grounding; just be sure it's not too heavy to allow the breath to flow well (Fig B). You could also bridge a bolster for your legs by placing it lengthwise onto two blocks at the low or middle height (Fig C). Drape the lower legs over it, supporting your heels if they dangle with blocks to bring greater ease to the leg muscles. If lying flat on your back doesn't feel right, try an alternate position offered in the substitutions.

Whichever position you choose, your destination is total relaxation, so build the amount of support that feels like complete relief. You could nestle a small, rolled-up blanket under your neck to support the natural curve of the cervical spine. Spread a thin blanket or towel under the back of your head as an additional cushion if more softness is needed. Keep your chin slightly tucked down rather than allowing it to tip higher than your forehead to help you relax more completely. The body typically cools as relaxation deepens, so you may want to cover yourself with a light blanket to ensure you stay comfortably warm.

Let your shoulder blades sink toward the earth, dropping easefully down and away from your ears. Allow your arms to be very comfortable, whether down by your sides with palms toward the earth or opening up to the sky or lying on the mat overhead. One hand on the belly and the other over the heart may also feel restful. Make any final adjustments to your clothing, hair, and props until you feel yourself become so at ease that you prefer to be still rather than move.

Find the familiar internal breeze of your breath as you let your physical body sink more completely onto the floor. Take a deep breath in, then sigh it completely out. Here you are, right here, just where you are meant to be. Now is your time to let everything go and fully relax into this time and place...stillness more satisfying than movement, all of you calm and relaxed. Inhabit effortlessness in this moment and enjoy the grace of this space where the body and spirit are one.

Rest in Savasana with your eyes open or closed, whatever feels most soothing and supports a natural, inward-turning awareness. If your eyes are closed, perhaps you'd like to cover them with a light eye pillow or kerchief.

If any form of discomfort arises during Savasana, try to watch it, offering it a little space. If it persists, you're always welcome to open your eyes, shift your position, call to mind someone or something that is safe and reassuring, or exit the pose. This is your practice.

Find an evenness along the places where the body rests onto the floor so that the weight between the left and right sides is balanced and stable. Here you are with your heart open and settled for this spacious encounter with the universe around and inside you, held safe and close to the earth. Allow your whole body to lean into the support beneath you: earth holding your whole body, breath flowing with ease, no effort required. Watch with warmth and welcome in these moments, your naturally loving heart a curious and compassionate observer.

As a way to enter into the deep rest of Savasana, you're invited to use your breath and your awareness to help you experience complete relaxation and peace.

Let the breath and attention go to each part as you breathe quietly and easefully through the nose. There's no need to move the body itself. Simply move your breath through the body by focusing your attention on each part. Inhale and exhale as though directly into and out of the parts of the body, letting any stress or tension pour slowly out with exhalation.

Bring your attention to the crown of your head. Let your breath move itself to the crown of your head as well. Breathe gently in. As you exhale, notice how tension in the top of the head dissolves.

Bring your awareness now to the forehead, the eyes, the mouth, the chin. Inhale, becoming aware of any tension. As you exhale, let softness flow through the forehead, eyes, mouth, and jaw. Let softness flow, too, through the mind, allowing any thoughts or mental tensions to flow effortlessly through you and away from you, out of your body, out of your mind.

Go slowly with your attention and send your breath down the neck into the shoulders, the chest, the back. Quietly breathe in and out from the upper torso. Feel any tightness vanishing away with each exhale.

Let your awareness slide down the arms, feeling the breath move into each part of the arms. Breathe in and out, letting the breath go through the upper arm, elbow, lower arm, hands, and the tips of the fingers. Allow the breath to be natural. Feel it carrying away all tension.

Mentally move your attention now into the abdomen. Inhale and exhale from within the lower torso. Allow any tensions to flow away from this place. Again inhale, and as you slowly exhale, feel the belly softening even more.

With your mind, go now to the hips and legs. Inhale and exhale from the hips, thighs, and lower legs. Inhale fully, then exhale fully, breath flowing through the entire length of the legs. One more time, inhale, then exhale. Feel the breath relaxing, releasing, and clearing the lower half of the body.

Next, move your attention to the feet. Breathe in and out of the feet and toes, inhaling and exhaling, tensions releasing.

Now glide your awareness upward to the chest space and begin to breathe into the heart center. As you exhale, allow the feeling of relaxation to flow through this place, all concerns drifting away on the breeze of the breath. Soothing and easeful, each movement of the breath fills the chest and then empties from the chest. Continue to breathe effortlessly, the natural breath coming in and going out from the center of the heart.

Feeling the whole body become relaxed...the whole body calm...the whole body free of any tension or cares, your full awareness residing in the center of the chest in the heartspace. Allow your awareness to utterly empty of words, thoughts, pictures, and memories. With your awareness deep in silence and stillness, rest fully in the boundless space of your heart. All of your awareness is relaxing into this place completely, everything else falling away...only deep stillness, deep silence, there in the middle of the heart, the space of your spirit. (Yp: *supine*)

Easing Out: When it's time to awaken from your Savasana rest, begin to bring your awareness back to your body. Become aware of your physical body lying on the floor...aware of your head, your trunk, your arms and legs. Take some moments to feel your body lying supported on the earth, scanning slowly from toes to head to orient yourself in the place of the present moment. Slowly bring your attention to the space around you, remembering you are here in this room. Allow the external environment to arrive gently into your awareness, the soft and supportive earth under you, the air all around you, and sounds both near and far.

Take some moments to notice and feel your breath as it flows effortlessly. Sense it come in and go out. Become aware of your whole body and aware you are breathing...your whole body, your whole mind, here totally relaxed. Gradually begin to move your body, just little movements at first in the fingers and toes. Maybe then you would like to stretch your arms and legs. Slowly, tenderly stretch your whole body. There's no hurry.

Draw your knees toward your chest, roll onto your right side, and curl softly into a little ball. Form a pillow under your head with your arm as you pause a few moments in the stillness. Lie quietly for a few moments here with your eyes closed, sensing your body, mind, and heart, reflecting on anything you've experienced during your rest. Offer yourself these gentle moments to soak in the benefits of your time on the mat, confident the gifts of your practice will go with you when you leave this place and carry themselves into all the lives around you. Take your time in this transition. When you're ready, use your bottom hand to slowly press yourself upright and come to a seated position to take some moments to seal your practice.

⦿ **YINPRESSIONS FOR EXPLORATION While You Stay**: Savasana is an opportune time to enhance the relaxation experience with guided relaxation meditations, visualizations, or even a complete Yoga Nidra journey to blissfully rest in your true nature. See "Yoga Nidra-Inspired Methods" (p. 240) for a sampling of techniques.

Substitutions for Consideration

Sleeping Fish (for a light upper body opening, below), Side-Lying Savasana (below), Resting Crocodile (for a belly-lying alternative, p. 188)

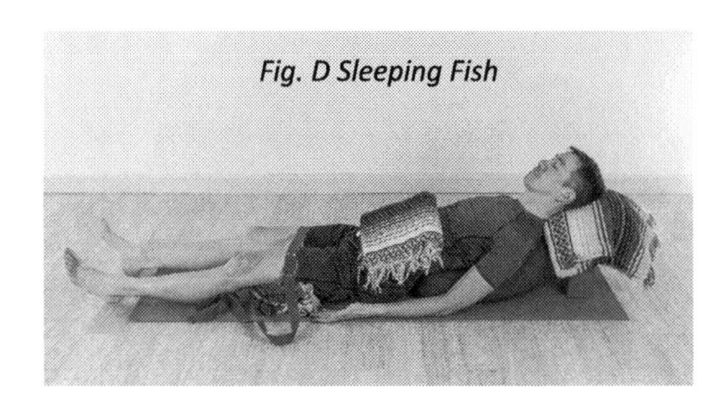

Fig. D Sleeping Fish

Sleeping Fish: For this supported Fish variation, create a sloped bolster with a blanket along its back edge as a cushion for your head. Sit in front of the bolster with your knees bent and feet to the floor. If you'd like, loop a strap around the mid thighs for the legs to relax more into a bind. Recline onto the bolster with your head on the blanket and extend the legs in front of you. If it would feel nurturing, place a blanket over the belly (Fig D). (Yp: *supine*)

Fig. E Side-Lying Savasana

Side-Lying Savasana: For those times when the supine option of Savasana isn't the best choice, or if you'd just like to try out different positioning, create an equally restorative side-lying option. Lie on your side and bring one or both of your knees toward your body. Place a blanket, block, or bolster between or underneath the leg(s) if supportive. Use your bottom arm as a cushion for your head or place a blanket underneath for support to help the neck stay in comfortable alignment with the rest of your spine. Hugging the bolster into your chest like a giant pillow might be the perfect complement (Fig E). For an extra sense of stability, nestle a blanket along back of your shoulders and upper back. Take time to make any other adjustments to your body and props to find whatever helps you feel most relaxed and held. (Yp: *one-legged*)

Shoelace

Physical Focus

Maintains wellbeing of the hips, including glutes and IT band with additional possibility of spreading happiness through the hamstrings and fascia of the back thigh.

Qi Charting

Kidney-Urinary Bladder
Liver-Gall Bladder

FINDING your Expression of the shape

Setting Up: Place a single-folded blanket on the mat for your seat. Place two blocks, a bolster, a blanket, and a strap near the middle of your mat off to the side within reach.

Easing In: Sit on the folded blanket on your mat and extend your legs in front of you. Begin by establishing your neutral pelvis position (for a refresher, see "Establishing a Neutral Pelvis in Seated Postures," p. 68). Curl the right toes gently toward your shin, then bend your right leg to place your right outer knee on top of the left thigh. If the right knee feels strained or your right leg muscles are unable to relax, nestle a blanket between the legs for support. If there's too much pulling on the hamstrings of the straight left leg or the knee is strained, try placing a rolled blanket under the left thigh/knee. This is **One-Legged Shoelace**. This shape might be a good option for tighter hips and sensitive knees that can sometimes prevent access to the two-legged cross. This version of the pose offers the bonus benefit of stimulating the hamstrings of the bottom leg while still working the top leg's outer hip and thigh. Stay and explore this one-legged phase, or if the body allows and you wish to deepen sensations through the glutes/IT band on both sides simultaneously, try **Shoelace.** To morph into this two-legged Shoelace, curl your left toes toward the shin and lean a bit toward the outer left hip. This creates some space to bend the left leg and wrap it underneath the right leg. Move the knees toward stacking on top of one another, just be sure not to force the shape (Fig A). Play with slight adjustments of each heel relative to the opposite hip, moving the heels slightly further away from or closer to the hips to possibly affect the sensations. Both phases of this pose provide a great foundation from which to add a variety of shoulder-arm binds as well as a chance to integrate many of the other Yinpressions as you like. (Yp: *hip-leg work, one-legged*)

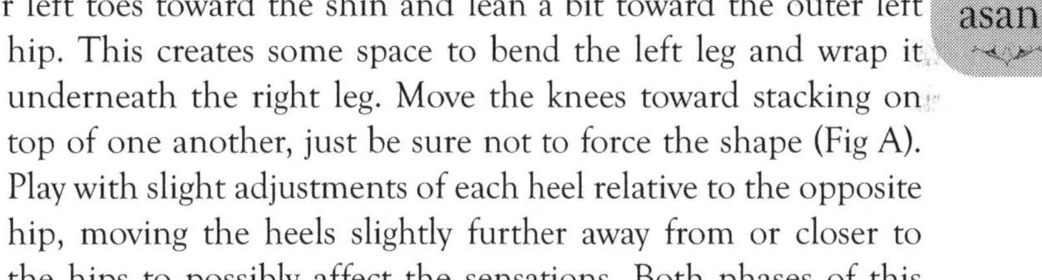

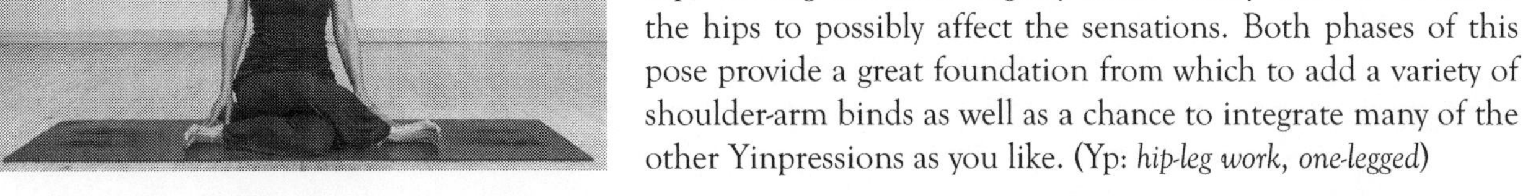

Fig. A Shoelace

⦿ **YINPRESSIONS FOR EXPLORATION While You Stay**: *seated forward bend, one-legged + twist (Fig B), side bend (Fig C), most shoulder-arm binds (Fig D, E)*

Fig. B One-Legged Shoelace with twist

Fig. C Shoelace with side bend

Fig. D Shoelace with cow-faced arms

Fig. E Shoelace with forward bend & cow-faced arms

Easing Out: Place your hands on the floor behind you, lean back, and slowly unfold the top leg and the bottom leg if folded, extending both legs straight down the mat. When ready, go to the other side.

Substitutions for Consideration

Supine Shoelace (below), Leaning Swan (p. 194)

Supine Shoelace is similar in shape to Shoelace, but reclining releases the work of the spine which becomes fully supported by the earth. Leaning Swan is an alternative to access the outer hip region with the benefit of perhaps being a bit easier on the knees.

Fig. F Supine Shoelace

Supine Shoelace: Place a single-folded blanket on the back of your mat to serve as a cushion for your head once you've reclined. Place a blanket and a strap near the middle of your mat off to the side within reach. Lie on the mat on your back. Bring both of your knees into your chest, forming Tipped Beetle. Keeping the knees bent, cross the right leg over the left leg so that the knees stack as if you're sitting politely in a chair. Curl your toes gently toward the shins and hold the tops of your stacked knees or the backs of your thighs with your hands. If your arms don't reach, no problem, simply wrap a strap around the back of the left thigh and hold a tail of the strap in each hand. To go deeper into the Supine Shoelace shape, slide your hands down your shins and hold anywhere within reach. You could also hold the outer feet with your hands, if within reach (Fig F). Before settling into stillness, play a bit with sending your heels closer or further from the outer hips to find the sensation that feels best. If necessary, place an additional blanket under the head and/or lengthen the strap in your hands to help relax the backs of your shoulders and head on the earth. To experiment with a one-legged version, simply unbend the left leg and extend it straight overhead while holding onto the strap or the back of the left thigh with your interlaced fingers. Gently draw the straight left leg toward the left side chest to increase sensations as needed. If within reach, slide your hands to hold the left calf to deepen sensations further. To ease out, bend the left leg if straight and uncross your knees back into the Tipped Beetle shape and then switch sides. (Yp: *supine, hip-leg work*; Yp for exploration while you stay: *one-legged*)

Snail

Physical Focus

Inversion that unburdens tight muscles and fascia through the whole back and decompresses the span of the spinal column while massaging organs in the abdomen. The fullest forward bend in the Yin Yoga series, calling us to Yinternalize our awareness.

Qi Charting

Kidney-Urinary Bladder
Stomach-Spleen

FINDING your Expression of the shape

Setting Up: Place a single-folded blanket on the back third of your mat. Place a bolster widthwise on the floor along the back edge of your mat to serve as a pedestal for your feet once inverted. Be sure to remove any ponytails, barrettes, scarves, or hoods located at the back of your head or neck before entering this posture.

Easing In: The most vigorous inversion in Yin Yoga, **Snail** also offers the fullest spinal flexion and decompression, so it's essential to be mindful that all the same inversion benefits and precautions apply. Be aware of back conditions that may be exacerbated when rounding the spine. If inverted postures don't work for you at this time, there are a variety of alternate poses offered in the Substitutions you can explore, depending on your desired area of exercise.

If you're newer to inversions, starting with the added stability of the wall support in Wall Arch (see the Substitutions below) can build confidence in going upside down. Trialing a softer inversion such as Waterfall pose (p. 200) is another relatively accessible way to get acquainted with the feeling of being inverted. Given the depth of forward bending in Snail, we can benefit from first opening the spine with a milder forward folding shape like its seated complement Caterpillar (p. 146) and/or Beetle variations (p. 137).

Sit several inches in front of your blanket and lie down so your head is on the mat and the top of your shoulders are aligned with back edge of the blanket. Be sure the space behind your neck is clear to allow plenty of room for the natural curvature of the cervical spine. Bend your knees and place your feet to the floor hip-width distance apart with knees over ankles. Engage your core muscles and draw both knees together and in toward your chest. From this point forward in the pose, any neck rotation can be injurious, so you must not turn your head.

To ease into **Snail**, place your finger pads to the floor on either side of your outer hips. Engage your core muscles and press into your finger pads to slowly lift your hips and bent legs off the mat and up overhead, keeping your lower back rounded. Place your hands onto your lower back for support. Check in here with the neck, shoulders, and low back as you move. If any area feels compromised, gently roll your spine back down onto the mat, place your feet to the floor, and opt for a substitute posture.

Stay here, or to deepen your Snail, continue to raise the hips in order to move the legs overhead and behind you to the degree that generates a mild sensation of opening along the spinal column without having to force at all. The pressure from your lower body shouldn't land on your neck but rather spread diffusely through your shoulders and back, so make subtle adjustments to help with this. For example, shimmy your shoulder blades a smidge underneath you if there's space to do so without cramming, or slowly unroll out of the shape a little. Continue to hold your back with your hands for added stability, which may also take some pressure out of the neck. Scan the whole length of your spine for sensations and choose what's most supportive. If the body invites, bring your legs further behind you and rest your feet either on the bolster or the floor if within reasonable reach.

Fig. A Snail with straight legs & bolster

Maintain bent legs, or to go deeper into the hamstring tissues, experiment with unbending your legs until you feel a mild tugging along the backs of the legs. If your feet are dangling in the air, it's OK if it feels OK. If within reach, you might rest them on the bolster for support (Fig A). Lowering your feet to the floor will likely generate more sensation. You might straighten your arms down the mat with the palms flat, or you could interlace the fingers, which may alter the intensity of sensations in the shoulders and neck. As you make adjustments, stay attentive to the neck to ensure sharp or painful sensations do not arise and that you can continue to breathe well. If you can't, back out of the shape as necessary.

For a deeper phase of Snail, return the hands to your low back for support. Bend your legs and let your inner knees drift down by the ears (Fig B). If you feel secure and the spine allows, you could release your hands from your back once again and extend your arms down the mat, interlacing your fingers. Stay with this, or you could circle your arms around your outer calves to bind your lower legs. Use your thumbs to gently seal the ears to withdraw the attention further inward. Breathing intentionally and lightly engaging the core muscles throughout the posture will add a bit of support for the lower back and help keep sensations appropriate. (Yp: *supine, inversion, hip-leg work, shoulder-arm binds*)

Fig. B Snail with knees bent & hands on back

⦿ **YINPRESSIONS FOR EXPLORATION While You Stay:** *n/a*

Easing Out: If not already, loosely bend your legs and place your hands to your lower back for support. As you slowly roll out of Snail, you have the option of pausing at various places along the spine for intervals of thirty to forty-five seconds. Stay aware of the total time you're in the pose to avoid overstressing the spinal column. Otherwise, gently roll out in one slow, smooth motion, allowing the spine/neck to follow its natural curves as your feet come toward the mat. Eventually, let go of your back and place your feet on the mat hip-width distance apart, stacking your knees over your ankles. Take some time to rest in a reclined counterpose, such as Constructive Rest (p. 204) or Savasana (p. 179). Coming up to a seated position too quickly after inverting can sometimes cause dizziness, so stay patient and watchful in your transition.

Substitutions for Consideration

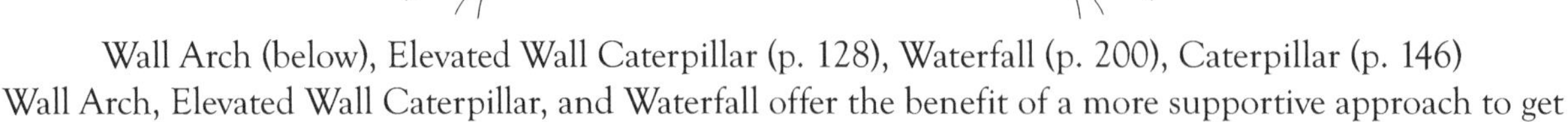

Wall Arch (below), Elevated Wall Caterpillar (p. 128), Waterfall (p. 200), Caterpillar (p. 146)
Wall Arch, Elevated Wall Caterpillar, and Waterfall offer the benefit of a more supportive approach to get acquainted with inverting. Caterpillar focuses on the spine and hamstrings without the need to invert.

Fig. C Wall Arch

Wall Arch: Begin in Wall Caterpillar (for a refresher, see "Yinpression: On the Wall," p. 127). Slowly bend your knees and slide your feet down the wall about twelve inches so your knees form a ninety-degree angle. Press the soles of your feet onto the wall, engage your core muscles, and begin to lift your hips off the floor, placing your hands on the lower back for support. Before settling in, you might move your feet a touch up or down the wall, depending on what feels most steady for you. If there's space, tuck your shoulder blades a little more underneath you. Check in with your neck and shoulders. If all is well, choose to hold here in Wall Arch (Fig C). To deepen, you could ease into Snail. Get started by gently kicking one leg into the air overhead and behind you to see how this movement

Fig. D One-Legged Wall Arch

feels (Fig D). Return the foot to the wall, then try the other leg. Once you're steady, kick one leg overhead and behind you and then the other, resting your feet on the bolster if within reasonable reach. If the bolster is too far from your toes, allow your legs to hang suspended in the air overhead and behind you, if it feels OK. To ease out, place your hands on the lower back if they're not there already and bring each foot back to the wall one at a time, returning to Wall Arch. Once your feet are on the wall, slowly lower your hips back down to the earth, releasing your hands from your lower back. Straighten your legs to return to Wall Caterpillar. (Yp: *on the wall, inversion*)

Meditative Yinquiry for the Mat

"Fear Falls Away, Courage Takes its Place"

The energy of the Kidneys asks us: Is there something in life that we'd like to do? Perhaps there's a decision we've delayed or a step we've intended to take in a new direction. It can be tempting to be distracted or even derailed by the notion that we're not good enough or ready enough to take steps in our life toward those things we know will support a happier, healthier us. Maybe we feel that we need to wait until our perfect self shows up, or until all fear disappears.

As you stimulate the Qi channels nourishing the Kidney energy, you might take a few moments to acknowledge challenges you've already faced, both small and large. Recall in detail the brave and spirited steps you took and how it felt to overcome those difficulties. Remind yourself you have all the strength and inner know-how you need to make the next right move. You were made for happiness, wired with power and wisdom, and fully capable just as you are right now to follow your spirit's intention.

Sphinx

Physical Focus

Invigorating backbend to support a supple spine, serving sacrum and lumbar area. Spreads open the front of the chest and creates space for abdominal organs in the belly.

Qi Charting

Kidney-Urinary Bladder
Spleen-Stomach

FINDING your Expression of the shape

Setting Up: Place a single-folded blanket on the middle of your mat to serve as padding for the hips, helping to avoid any painful compression of the frontal hip bones. Place two blocks, a bolster, and a blanket at the front of the mat off to the side within reach.

Easing In: The primary focus in this pose is to bring compression to the lumbar and sacral spine, so take precaution with low back conditions. In the case of lower back sciatica caused by a disc issue, the McKenzie physical therapy method suggests a regular mindful practice of gentle backbends like Sphinx may help open space along the frontal spine and its interverbal discs, allowing the gelatinous fluid pressing against the spinal cord to be reabsorbed and alleviating painful pressure. Should lying directly on the belly in this prone posture not feel right for any reason, there are a couple of delightful alternatives offered in the Substitutions.

Fig. A Resting Crocodile

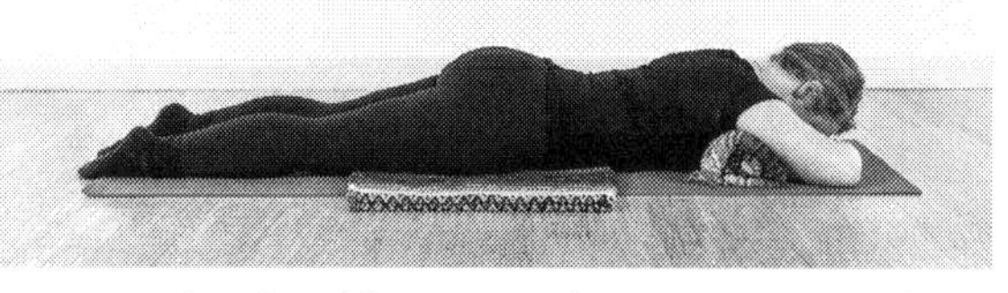
Fig. B Resting Crocodile with blanket

To begin, kneel on the blanket in Tabletop position with your shoulders over your wrists and your hips over your knees. Walk your knees behind you a several inches, slowly bend your elbows, and lower to a belly-lying position. Check to see that the full length of your spine and neck are in a straight line. Reach your arms in front of you and your legs behind you to bring a stretch to the whole body, then let the stretch go, releasing the weight of your bones to the earth. Bend your elbows and stack your hands on top of each other, with palms facing down. Rest your forehead on the backs of your hands and separate your feet a comfortable distance apart. Allow your heels to roll in or out, whichever feels most natural as you relax your legs in this gentle backbend, **Resting Crocodile** (Fig A). If there's strain in the shoulders or neck, try propping the upper body with a small, rolled blanket underneath the shoulders, arms, and head to release the extra pressure (Fig B).

Fig. C Sphinx

If sensations through the lower back and base of spine are sufficient, stay in this phase for now. If sensations are absent or negligible, raise your head and upper chest enough to slide your folded forearms closer toward you. Prop yourself onto your forearms to transition into **Sphinx** (Fig C). Before settling into stillness, play a bit with positioning your forearms a little further away from or closer to you until you feel a mild sensation of diffuse pressure arising through the lower back. Be sure your elbows stay under or in front of your shoulders to avoid joint irritation or injury. Choose to keep your arms folded as they are or open them to be parallel to each other.

If your shoulders begin to fall asleep in this propped upright position, broadening the distance between your arms could help clear nerve or blood vessel compression, which is often the root of the tingly numbness. You could also slip a bolster underneath your armpits, resting your chest and shoulders onto its support to help alleviate any unhelpful pressure in the shoulder girdle. Position your head on your forearms or props (Fig D) so it's comfortable.

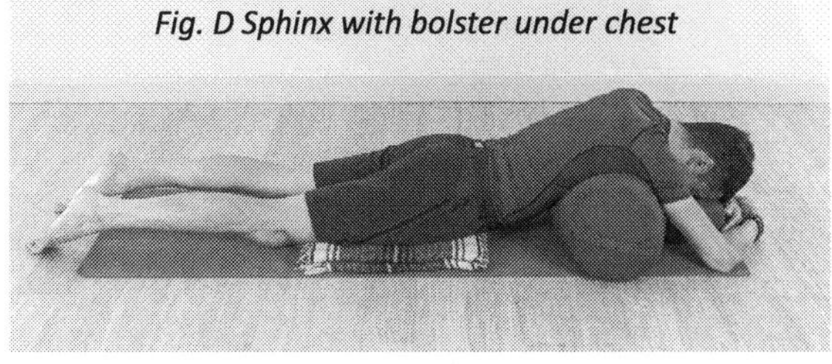
Fig. D Sphinx with bolster under chest

If your lower back is requesting more stimulation, place your forearms on the bolster or blocks to increase the angle of spinal extension. Keep sensations gentle and diffusely spread from the base of the spine and throughout the lower back, avoiding anything that feels localized, sharp, stingy, or zappy. If questionable, opt for a softer phase of this backbend or return to Resting Crocodile. Feel also for a light sense of opening through the belly and front of chest. Keep your head upright or lower it onto a high stack of blocks in front of the bolster, if that feels better on the neck. Take time to find the stay-able position for your body.

If Sphinx still offers too little sensation, clear your props from the front of the mat. Place your hands directly on the mat about shoulder-width distance apart and keep your frontal hips on the ground. Straighten both of your arms and lift your chest higher to rise into **Seal**. Once again, position your hands further away from or closer to your body, depending on the level of sensation you're experiencing. Just take care not to slide them behind your shoulders. Widen or shorten the distance between your hands to find what suits your shoulders best. Maintain intentional breathing and a mindful awareness of the sensations that are arising. If you sense a resistance to relaxation in the areas of sensation, for example muscular clenching in the belly or buttocks, attempt to consciously release them and notice your body's response. If you're not able to intentionally release the muscles or the sensations become too great, your body is likely signaling you've gone too far, and you'll want to ease off a bit. If your breath is labored, soften your posture and see if that helps. If you find you're unconsciously holding your breath, you could try a mindful breathing exercise to free it.

Whatever phase of the backbend you've chosen, experiment a bit with the positioning of your legs, bringing them closer together or further apart. There's also the option to bend your knees and lift your feet off the floor. If your knees are bent, bring your feet together, float them over the ankles, or let them fall a bit outward toward the sides of the mat. As you adjust, remain watchful for shifts in sensations. From either Sphinx or Seal, you could elevate your shoulders toward your ears to stimulate your shoulder joints, hold a handful of breaths, then gently depress the shoulders down and away from the ears. Hold this a few moments, then allow your shoulders to relax. While in Seal, if you want to bring more stimulation to your neck, reach your crown toward the sky, then let your head drop slowly forward to flex your neck. Hold for a few breaths before bringing your neck back to neutral. You also have the option of neck extension in Seal. Whenever extending the neck by dropping the head back, be watchful for lightheadedness and dizziness, as you may be compressing one of the major arteries flowing through that area. Should you experience anything inappropriate, bring the neck back to a neutral position or come out of the pose if it doesn't resolve. (Yp: *backbend, prone*)

⊙ YINPRESSIONS FOR EXPLORATION While You Stay: *shoulder-arm binds: wrist press- extension*

Fig. E Seal with wrist press- extension

If your wrists allow, you might choose to integrate wrist extension into your Seal shape. Exercise one wrist at a time or both together, maintaining contact between the palms and the mat as you hold. To begin, lift your right hand a touch off the mat, slowly rotate your right fingertips clockwise to a point that feels sensible, then lower your palm onto the mat. To exercise the left wrist, lift left hand a bit, turn your left fingertips counterclockwise to a point that feels appropriate for the left wrist, then return your left palm to the mat (Fig E). In the deepest phase, your fingers point toward you. Hold each or both wrists for about a minute.

Easing Out: Bring your head back to neutral, if not already. If holding Wrist Press, turn your fingertips to point forward and press your hands onto the mat. Unbend your legs if your knees are bent. To mindfully ease out of either Sphinx or Seal pose, take a long, full breath in, then as you exhale, slowly lower your upper body to the floor, moving any props to the side. Fold your arms under your forehead as a cushion or rest them down by your sides with palms facing up, with your head comfortably positioned on the mat or a blanket.

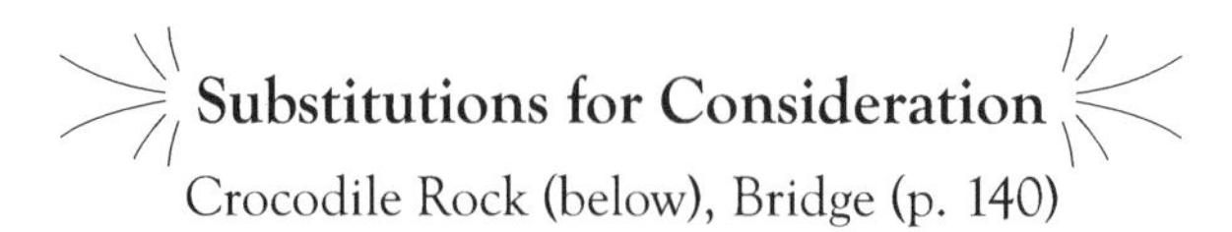

Substitutions for Consideration

Crocodile Rock (below), Bridge (p. 140)

Should lying directly on the belly not feel good, crank up some Elton John and enjoy Crocodile Rock! A favorite alternative for many, Crocodile Rock also offers pregnant practitioners some comforting space for a growing belly and welcome relief for the lower back.

Anytime you prefer going supine, swap Sphinx with a back bending Bridge.

Crocodile Rock: Place two blocks and a blanket at the front of the mat off to the side within reach. Position one full-sized bolster widthwise across the front third of the mat and another bolster of the same size widthwise across the back third of the mat to serve as pedestals for your chest and hips. Kneel just behind the back bolster with the front of your thighs against it. Reach forward to place your hands on the front bolster, then lower onto your forearms. Once steady, move your hips toward the front of the mat, allowing the tops of your thighs to rest on the back bolster and your upper chest on the front bolster. Place your elbows on the mat ahead of the front bolster and your chin into your palms as you allow the belly to rest freely in the space between the two bolsters. The front bolster may be positioned underneath your chest or armpits, whatever best suits you. Keep your chin in your palms, or use your arms or props to support your head in the way that feels most supportive for your neck (Fig F). Keep the tops of your feet on the mat or tuck your toes, if that feels more supportive. To ease out, place your hands on the front bolster, engage your core muscles, and use your shoulder and arm strength to press yourself up as you rock the hips gently back to return to Tabletop. (Yp: *backbend, prone*)

Fig. F Crocodile Rock

Square

Physical Focus

Opening for the hips. Relief for the often-tight glute/IT band area. Offers many options for leg shapes to find what works for you, as well as the chance to bring exercise to the upper body while you stay.

Qi Charting

Kidney-Urinary Bladder
Liver-Gall Bladder
Spleen-Stomach

FINDING your Expression of the shape

Setting Up: Place a single-folded blanket on the mat for your seat. Place two blocks, a bolster, a blanket, and a strap near the middle of your mat off to the side within reach.

Fig. A Sukhasana

Easing In: Sit on the folded blanket on your mat and extend your legs in front of you. Begin by establishing your neutral pelvis position (for a refresher, see "Establishing a Neutral Pelvis in Seated Postures," p. 68). Turn the toes and thighbones outward to create a slight external rotation of the thighs at both hips. Curl both sets of toes gently toward the shins for a little extra knee support as you cross your legs in front of you, right leg in front of left. Bend the knees and bring your feet toward your seat (Fig A). To support sensitive knees in this **Sukhasana** shape, place a block or blanket underneath the outer thighs/ knees. If your knees still balk, try a substitute pose.

Fig. B Square

If you're not feeling much sensation in the hips, you could explore **Square** pose. Keeping the ankles crossed, begin to move the feet away from your seat until your ankles line up with your knees. Slowly slide the feet further apart and toward their opposite knees to create Square (Fig B). If the body allows, stack the knees directly above the opposite ankles. Staying mindful of your hips and knees, if this phase of the shape still feels too soft, lift your right shin with your hands and place it atop the left shin so that the right ankle sits above the left knee and the left ankle is below the right knee, forming **Firelog** pose (Fig C). As necessary, blocks or blankets can be placed in any space between the top knee/shin area and bottom ankle in Firelog for support. If you find that one variation causes too much sensation and the other not quite enough, you are welcome to take the Goldilocks approach of meeting somewhere in the middle. A hybrid version somewhere between Square and Firelog might turn out

Fig. C Firelog

to be just right, so you could try placing the right shin on a rolled blanket or bolster directly in front of the left shin, bringing the shins relatively level with one another. (Yp: *hip-leg work*)

Fig. D Square with forward bend

Fig. E Square with forward bend & side bend

⦿ **YINPRESSIONS FOR EXPLORATION While You Stay:** *seated forward bend (Fig D), seated forward bend + side bend (Fig E), side bend, twist, most shoulder-arm binds*

Easing Out: To mindfully exit from the upright position of each of these three shapes, slowly unbend the right leg and then the left leg, extending each in front of you. When ready, do the other side.

Substitutions for Consideration

Supine Sukhasana/Square (below), Wall Sukhasana/ Square (below)

Fortunately, hip-focused postures are plentiful in Yin Yoga, so there are many possibilities to consider. Here are a couple of options highlighted for their ability to target the hip and leg area with the added support of the floor or the wall, which may soften pressure on the knees while releasing some of the requirements on the back.

Supine Sukhasana/Square: Place a single-folded blanket on the back of your mat to serve as a cushion for your head once you've reclined. Place two blocks and a blanket near the middle of your mat off to the side within reach. Lie on your back with the folded blanket under your head. Follow the same guidance as Sukhasana/ Square to form a back-lying version. Use props as needed to support the knees and moderate the sensation levels in the hips and inner legs. To come out of the pose, release the arms if exploring shoulder-arm binds and extend the legs in front of you one a time. When ready, go to the other side. (Yp: *supine, hip-leg work*; Yp for exploration while you stay: *side bend, shoulder-arm binds)*

Wall Sukhasana/Square: Begin in Wall Caterpillar (for a refresher, see "Yinpression: On the Wall," p. 127). Bend the knees and slide the feet down the wall, crossing the right leg in front of the left to create Sukhasana-legs resting against the wall. If this feels suitable, stay here in Wall Sukhasana with the ankles crossed. If you need to increase sensations in the hips and legs, Wall Square is an alternate option. To create this shape, slide the feet away from the pelvic floor until your ankles line up with your knees. As it feels appropriate, slowly slide the feet further apart and toward their opposite knees as you create Wall Square (Fig F). Once again, allow the legs to lean into the support of the wall. To come out of the pose, free the arms if they're bound. Unbend the knees one at a time and extend your legs up the wall to return to Wall Caterpillar. When you're ready, do the other side. (Yp: *on the wall, hip-leg work*; Yp for exploration while you stay: *side bend, shoulder-arm binds, inversion)*

Fig. F Wall Square

Swan

Physical Focus

Grounding hip-focused posture to nurture hips and glute/IT band area. Loosens tensions through inner thigh/groin, lower back, hip flexors, and quads of the back leg. Potential to bring release to the piriformis muscle deep in the buttock.

Qi Charting

Kidney-Urinary Bladder
Liver-Gall Bladder
Spleen-Stomach
Lung-Large Intestine
Heart- Small Intestine
Pericardium-Triple Burner

FINDING your Expression of the shape

Setting Up: Place a single-folded blanket on the back third of your mat to serve as padding for your knees and shins. Place two blocks, a bolster, a blanket, and a strap at the front of your mat off to the side within reach.

Easing In: Kneel on the blanket and come onto your hands and knees to form Tabletop. Stay keenly aware of knee sensitivities as you ease into **Swan**. Should the lower body oppose anywhere along the way, consider exploring Leaning Swan or another posture offered in the Substitutions. Slide your right knee forward toward your right thumb. Keeping hands on the mat to support your lower body, extend the left leg behind you with the front of the thigh facing the mat and the left toes pointed back.

Toe-heel the right foot toward the left edge of mat until you feel mild sensation through the right hip and leg, allowing the right inner leg line to turn to face the sky. Lightly pull the right toes back toward the right shin to help stabilize the knee joint. If more sensation is needed, nudge the right knee further outward to the right, noticing any shifts as you play. Stay mindful of the right hip, leg, and knee as you move into a place that feels appropriate. If the right hip lifts off the mat, you might slide a prop(s) underneath it to keep the hips level, support release of the muscles, and allow you to relax more fully into the shape. If a deeper opening is needed for the front of the left thigh, slide the leg backward a little further.

Fig. A Proud Swan

Shift your attention to the lumbar spine, noticing any sensations there. To bring focus to this area, press your hands to the floor to lengthen the spine. To deepen the spinal extension of this backbend, slide the hands closer to you, staying mindful that the hands don't go behind the shoulders. Heart confident and open, enjoy this **Proud Swan** (Fig A). You also have the option of neck extension in Proud Swan if the body allows. Find length in the neck and, taking extra care to not let the head tip too far backward given the sensitivities of compressing the back of the neck, allow the head to drop back a bit for a couple of breaths before bringing the neck back to neutral. If the hips are steady and don't require the support of your upper body strength to keep you stabilized, you could incorporate the Double Arm Behind the Back Bind (p. 123). To amplify sensations through the left leg's front hip and thigh, another more yang-like option is **Trumpeting Swan**. To enter, shift your weight slightly forward of the back knee, then bend it, foot floating skyward. Stay with hands pressing to the floor for stability, or if you feel steady, take hold of the floating left foot with the left hand. If the foot is out of reach, lasso it with a strap and hold the tails in your left hand (Fig B).

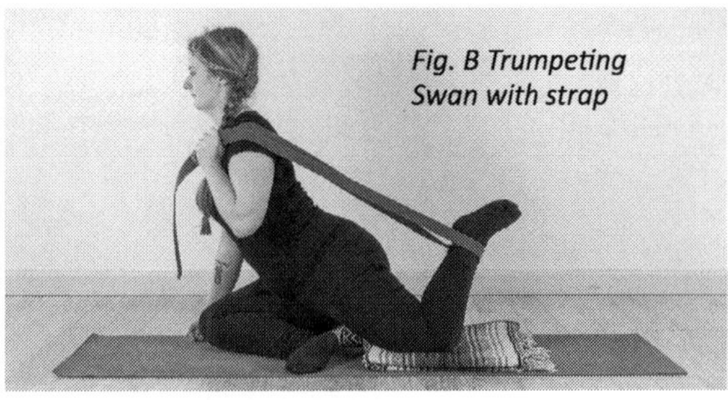
Fig. B Trumpeting Swan with strap

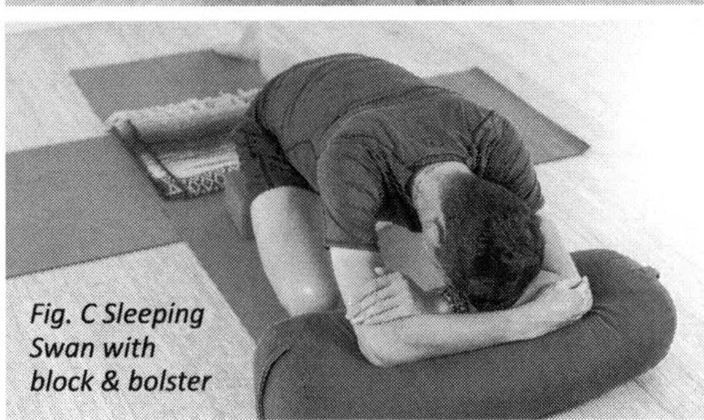
Fig. C Sleeping Swan with block & bolster

When you're ready, gently release the foot and place your hand on the mat, returning to Proud Swan.

To move into the **Sleeping Swan** phase, lengthen the spine and slowly fold your upper body forward and down. If the upper body doesn't reach the floor, place folded forearms, a bolster, or blocks underneath you as needed to meet your body partway (Fig C). Notice the effects as you fold, staying aware of sensations along the right side through the knee, hip, and lower back, adjusting if necessary. If you experience painful groin compression at the frontal right hip, shift your upper body to the left a bit. If this doesn't remedy the painful sensations, lift the torso slightly. Once sensations are steady, linger in Sleeping Swan. (Yp: *hip-leg work, backbend*)

⊙ **YINPRESSIONS FOR EXPLORATION While You Stay:** In Sleeping Swan, you might enjoy integrating some of these Yinpressions: *side bend, shoulder-arm binds: threaded needles (Fig D), one arm behind the back bind*

Fig. D Sleeping Swan with threaded needle

Easing Out: To mindfully emerge from Sleeping Swan, slowly unwind the arms if they're bound and place the hands on the floor once again. Slide both hands closer to you and press into the earth to lift the upper body, returning momentarily to Proud Swan. Remove any props from underneath the right hip. Tuck the left toes under, activate your core muscles, and press into your hands to lift the upper body enough to return the right knee under the right hip to return to Tabletop. When ready, enjoy the other side.

Substitutions for Consideration

Leaning Swan/Sleeping Leaning Swan (below), Supine Eye of the Needle (p. 157), Supine Shoelace (p. 184)
These hip-openers tend to be relatively gentler options for the knees while offering similar access to the hips and legs as Sleeping Swan. These are just a few of the many hip-ful poses to explore.

Leaning Swan/Sleeping Leaning Swan: Kneel on the blanket and come onto your hands and knees to form Tabletop. Slide your right knee forward toward your right thumb. Keeping your hands on the mat, gently lower yourself onto your right sit-bone. Make certain to maintain this essential seal between the right sit-bone and the floor for all phases of **Leaning Swan** to avoid over-straining the right hip and knee. Toe-heel the right foot toward the left edge of the mat any amount to cultivate mild sensation through the outside hip and leg. Play with the position of the back leg, turning the front of the thigh to face down or outward to the left. Depending on what feels best for your body, the back knee can bend or straighten. Make your adjustments in small investigative increments before settling into stillness to gain access to various corners of the hips and legs. If your knees or any other part of the body complains, select an alternate pose. Remain in Leaning Swan with

Fig. E Sleeping Leaning Swan with bolster

an upright spine, or move into **Sleeping Leaning Swan** by folding over the leg with a prop underneath the torso, if supportive (Fig E). To emerge, slide the hands under the shoulders while keeping the right sit-bone to the floor. Press your spine upright, then slowly sweep the left leg out to the left and around to the front of your mat. Give yourself some moments of rest before moving to the other side. (Yp: *hip-leg work;* Yp for exploration while you stay: *side bend, shoulder-arm binds: threaded needles, one arm behind the back bind)*

Meditative Yinquiry for the Mat

"Feel Before You Follow"

We're reminded in our Yin Yoga & Meditation practice that we don't have to be ruled by unconscious tendencies. The brain is a brilliant instrument that equips every response with a mindful, magic quarter-second pause. As we train in inhabiting this pause between a stimulus and our reaction, we remember that our response is ours to select. In any given moment, we have the choice to feel before we follow.

Practice allowing whatever is here with you in this moment to naturally manifest itself. If there's an urge to move, flee, or to reflexively resist in any way, try feeling before you follow it. Inquire: *Is there space to stay instead? Does this pause open up possibility for me to create more peace and less struggle?* Inquiring with interest and curiosity before following, we open ourselves to receive the wisdom the pause offers.

Twig Twists

Physical Focus

Supine twists to unravel tightness through the whole of the spine and back, including the deep back muscles and encasing fascia of the vertebral column. Opens the chest and the side seam of the body, working out lines of tension from shoulders down through intercostals, side obliques, and outer leg/IT band area.

Qi Charting

Kidney-Urinary Bladder
Liver-Gall Bladder
Spleen-Stomach
Lung-Large Intestine
Heart-Small Intestine
Pericardium-Triple Burner

FINDING your Expression of the shape

Setting Up: Place a single-folded blanket on the back of your mat to serve as a cushion for your head once you've reclined. Place two blocks, a bolster, a blanket, and a strap near the middle of your mat off to the left side within reach.

Easing In: Lie on your back and align your spine in a straight line from top to bottom. As with any twist, remain mindful of the low back and any SI joint concerns as you approach this posture. To move into **Two Twig Twist**, bend both knees and gather them toward your chest, coming into the Tipped Beetle shape. Slip a block the narrow way between the inner upper thighs. Stretch your arms straight out to your sides with palms facing the sky, then bend the elbows to a ninety-degree angle to form cactus arms. Soften the backs of both of your shoulders onto the mat and slowly drop your knees to the left as one unit.

Keep the chest open and facing the ceiling. If the back of the right shoulder lifts a bit off the mat, slide a blanket underneath to see if it helps the shoulder joint relax more. If the block between the knees is uncomfortable, trade it for a folded blanket or a bolster positioned between or under the knees. To create a deeper twist, remove the prop from the legs.

Fig. A Two Twig Twist

Use the navel as an orientation point, keeping the knees even with it or perhaps a bit above or below to find what feels best. For added stability in these supine twists, you could position a bolster against the backline of the body as an anchor of support. Arrange the arms at various angles beside you or overhead onto the mat behind you until you find sensations that suit your shoulders and upper chest. Turn the head to the right to bring a twist to the neck, if desired (Fig A). (Yp: *twist, supine, hip-leg work*)

Fig. B One Twig Twist

One Twig Twist is generally a deeper supine twist option than Two Twig Twist. To ease in, lie on your back and align your spine in a straight line from top to bottom, then cradle your right knee into your chest. Take your left hand to the outside of your right knee, and keeping the backs of shoulders on the mat and the front of the chest level with the ceiling, use your hand to guide the right leg across the body to your left (Fig B). If the right leg doesn't reach the mat and this creates strain, position a prop underneath the leg/knee area to moderate the sensations and allow your muscles to relax more fully. Once in the twist, you can deepen the sensation through the right glute area and lateral leg by keeping the top thigh where it is and unbending the right knee to bring the leg perpendicular to the body. You have the option to bind the right big toe with the left fingers, or if the foot is beyond reach, loop a strap over the foot and hold its tails in your left hand. For a cervical twist, turn your head to the right.

If you'd prefer to place more emphasis on the thoracic spine and go a bit easier on the lower back/sacrum, explore an alternate entry position for both One and Two Twig Twists. Start lying on your left side with the shoulders and hips aligned in a straight line and your knees bent and comfortably stacked on top of one another. While keeping the knees in this position and the outer left leg still on the mat, begin to twist your upper body to the right and rest the back of both of your shoulders and head on the mat. Stay in this Two Twig Twist, or move into One Twig Twist by simply extending the bottom left leg straight down the mat. Use props under the legs, if supportive. Position your arms where it feels best for your shoulders. (Yp: *twist, supine, hip-leg work, one-legged)*

Fig. C Twined Twigs Twist, closed

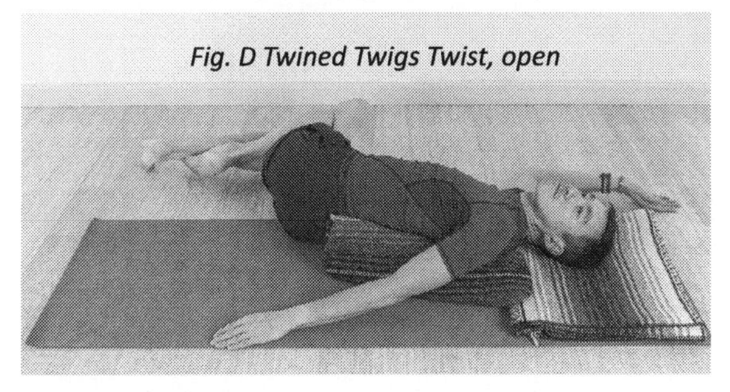
Fig. D Twined Twigs Twist, open

For **Twined Twigs Twist**, we add an internal rotation of the hips by twining the legs, which may cultivate greater sensations through the outer glute/IT band area than the other Twig Twists. To ease in, lie on your back, align your spine in a straight line from top to bottom, then bring both knees into the chest. Cross the bent right knee over the bent left knee, like you're sitting politely in a chair. If the knees, hips, and ankle joints allow, further entwine the legs by wrapping the right lower leg and foot around the left calf/ankle. Lower the twined twigs of your legs slowly to the left (Fig C). If they're lifted off the floor, slide a block or blanket under them, as long as it feels supportive for you. A bonus option in this shape is an open twist to emphasize a release through the front of left hip/thigh and the waist circle. To explore an open twist, engage your core muscles, bring your legs up to center, then drop your still-braided legs to the opposite side (Fig D). (Yp: *twist, supine, hip-leg work*)

⦿ **YINPRESSIONS FOR EXPLORATION While You Stay:** *shoulder-arm binds: overhead binding*

Easing Out: To unwind from your Twig Twist, lower the arms if they're lifted, turn the gaze back to the sky, and with the support of the core muscles, lift the knee(s) up to center. Before going to the other side, check to see that the spine is in a straight line. If not, lift the hips and realign before proceeding.

Substitutions for Consideration

If lower back/SI joint concerns prevent twisting, skip the twists and replace with another shape. Otherwise, generally speaking, a One Twig Twist is gentler than Twined Twigs Twist, and the Two Twig Twist is softer than the One Twig Twist. Try that for a tongue twister!

Walrus

Physical Focus

Attend to hips, inner legs, and tops of ankles with the opportunity to refresh and revive tired wrists

Qi Charting

Kidney-Urinary Bladder
Liver-Gall Bladder
Spleen-Stomach

FINDING your Expression of the shape

Setting Up: Place a single-folded blanket on the middle of your mat to serve as padding for your knees and shins. Place a block near the front of the mat off to the side within reach.

Easing In: To move into **Walrus**, kneel on the blanket and place your hands on the floor to come into Tabletop position, stacking the shoulders over the wrists and the hips over the knees. While moving into this hip-opening posture, be aware of any strain in the hips, knees, or ankles. Separate the knees toward the outside edges of your mat until you feel a light sensation through the inner legs. Bring your big toes together and slowly lower hips toward heels, if your body allows. If hips, knees, or ankles complain during the descent, try placing a block widthwise between the feet at the lowest level to serve as your seat and to see if that brings more ease. If this is still disruptive, substitute with another hip-opening posture of choice. To deepen into Walrus, walk your hands along the floor toward you and slowly press yourself upright so that your shoulders stack over your hips and your sit-bones rest down onto your feet or the block. (Yp: *hip-leg work*)

⊙ **YINPRESSIONS FOR EXPLORATION While You Stay:** *shoulder-arm binds: wrist press*

Fig. A Walrus with wrist press (extension)

From Walrus, you could add Wrist Press to stimulate the Lung-Large Intestine, Heart-Small Intestine, and Pericardium-Triple Burner Qi Channels. Given the relatively small size and more delicate structure of the wrist joints compared to larger joints like the hips, remember you'll want to take extra care that sensations in the wrists remain mild to ensure you're working safely with them. To begin, reach arms forward in front of you with your palms facing the sky. Bend the elbows and bring them toward the sides of your rib cage. Lower the hands until the tips of middle fingers lightly touch the ground between the inner knees and your palms face away from you. As the wrists allow, gently lower the heels of your hands forward and down toward the floor, stopping at the point of mild sensation through the wrists, hands, and fingers (Fig A). This means the heels of your hands may or may not be hovering above the floor. As you extend the wrist joints, avoid forcing. Just find a sensation that feels stay-able and stop there. For greater intensity, slide the hands a little further away from the body and lean forward a bit more. For less sensation, keep hands closer to you and lift the heels of the hands away from the floor, as necessary. Hold relatively still for just a minute or so, then slowly lift the hands off the floor. Rest your wrists on your thighs for a few moments in recovery.

For wrist flexion, reach your arms forward in front of you with the palms facing the mat. Bend the elbows and bring them toward the sides of the rib cage. Lower the hands until the tips of the middle fingers lightly touch the mat between the inner knees, and your palms face toward you. As the wrists allow, gently rock the wrists forward over the fingers so that the backs of fingernails and hands move slowly toward the mat. Lower only

Fig. B Walrus with wrist press (flexion)

until you feel a diffuse sensation within the wrists, hands, and fingers (Fig B). If you're not feeling enough sensation, try sliding the hands a little further away from the body. For less, keep the hands closer to you and lift the backs of hands away from the floor, as necessary. Hold in stillness for a minute or so. To release, gently peel the hands slowly away from the earth and bring them to rest on your lap as you take in the effects of the wrist work.

Easing Out: If in Wrist Press, slowly lift the hands from the earth and rest the wrists on the lap for a few moments. As a refreshing counterbalance, you might try the gentle movements of Pinwheel Hands Cp (p. 205). To mindfully ease out of Walrus, place your hands on the mat in front of you, lift your hips, and walk the hands forward to bring yourself back into Tabletop.

Substitutions for Consideration

Butterfly (p. 142), Deer (for internal rotation of the back leg, p. 148), Sukhasana (p. 191)
These are just a few of the many seated hip-opening possibilities. To incorporate Wrist Press, select one that allows you to comfortably reach your hands to the floor beside or directly in front of you.

WATERFALL

PHYSICAL FOCUS

A mild inversion to soothe the reactive stress system, inducing tranquility in body and mind. Drains fatigue from tired legs and feet due to long periods of sitting or standing and leverages gravity to aid the return of lymphatic fluids and offer rest for the heart.

QI CHARTING

Kidney-Urinary Bladder

FINDING your Expression of the shape

Setting Up: Place a single-folded blanket on the back of your mat to serve as a cushion for your head once you've reclined. Place a bolster near the middle of your mat off to right side within reach.

Easing In: Waterfall is a relatively accessible, rejuvenating inversion which carries many of the same benefits as other more physically demanding inversions, but keep in mind that the same inversion contraindications still apply. To enter **Waterfall**, lie on your back with the blanket under your head, then bend your knees and place your feet hip-width distance apart on the mat, with your knees stacked over your ankles. Be mindful not to turn your head once you're inverted, as this could be harmful to your neck. Press your feet into the mat to lift your hips just high enough to slide the bolster widthwise beneath them. Lower your hips onto the bolster. Lift your feet off the ground to bring your knees to stack over your hips, then unbend your knees to a degree that feels appropriate for the backs of your legs. If the legs are relatively straight, the soles of the feet will face the ceiling. Float your ankles over your hips rather than letting your toes drift over your nose (Fig A).

Fig. A Waterfall

While keeping ankles, legs, and hips in a relatively straight line, bend your knees a small amount if you find the backs of your legs feel strained or if the core muscles are working harder than you'd prefer. Resting the hands on the front of the thighs is another way to ease the effort of the core muscles. Otherwise, allow the arms to go where they naturally want to go, falling along your sides, overhead on the mat behind you, or perhaps place one hand on the belly and the other on the heart.

From Waterfall pose, there is an option of hovering in **Diving Dragonfly** by allowing the legs to slowly fall away from one another into a "V-shape" until you feel a light sensation of tugging through the inner leg lines. The wider the V-shape, the greater the angles of hip abduction and, typically, the more intense the tug will be on the groin and inner thigh area, and vice-versa. To soften sensations, support the outer thighs with your hands using some shoulder strength to prevent the legs from falling out too far. If you need more stimulation, try pressing the hands lightly on the inner thighs to apply a touch of outward pressure. To return to Waterfall, place hands to outer thighs and assist the legs back together. (Yp: *supine, inversion, hip-leg work*)

⊙ **YINPRESSIONS FOR EXPLORATION While You Stay:** *shoulder-arm binds: hugging arms, twisted branches, single threaded needle, overhead binding*

Easing Out: To emerge from Waterfall, bend the knees and place the feet on the mat hip-width distance apart with your knees stacked over your ankles. Activate the core muscles and press down through the feet to lift your hips off the bolster just enough to be able to slide the prop to the side. Lower your hips slowly onto the floor to rest.

Substitutions for Consideration

Wall Caterpillar (p. 127)/Elevated Wall Caterpillar (p. 128)

Wall Caterpillar opens the backs of legs while benefiting from the support of the wall. Remember there is also the choice of Elevated Wall Caterpillar created by adding a bolster under the hips in this posture to migrate into a mild inversion.

Meditative Yinquiry for the Mat

"Flower Fresh"

Thich Nhat Hanh taught that we as human beings are born as flowers, graceful and fresh, here to shine our beauty into the world. With mindful attention, we can refresh ourselves. He said when we breathe in deeply, "We make every cell in our body turn into a flower." When we smile to someone, we offer them the flowers of our eyes and mouth. When we reach out to others in caring and love, we offer them the flowers of our hands. When we speak compassionate truth, we send the flowers of our words to all who hear us. When we walk on the earth with respect and cherish all of its gifts, we plant flowers in every footprint. Every interaction is a chance to offer a flower to others and even to ourselves. How might you offer your body and your spirit a flower right now?

Counterposes for Balance, Rest, and Recovery

Suggestions for Integration

With a variety of counterposes available to mix and match between the poses in our Yin asana flows, we have a lot of freedom to explore ways to blend rest and recovery into our practice. There's no absolute right or wrong way to incorporate counterposes. We use them to help create balance, and many factors shift what balance looks and feels like. When selecting counterposes, here are a few things to consider:

How do you select which counterposes to incorporate?

Take note of the focus areas of the Yin Yoga poses in your flows. Foster balance and bring relief by choosing counterposes that either rest the part of the body that has just been stimulated or that gently move the joint(s) in the opposite direction. Sometimes full body relief is just right, and the simplicity of a Savasana counterpose generally makes for a wonderful go-to resting posture to integrate throughout any practice.

How much time do you spend in a counterpose?

Counterpose hold time recommendations typically fall somewhere between one and three minutes each, but they could run longer or shorter depending on your intention as well as the average length of hold time of your primary poses. When the poses are held longer, consider lengthening the counterpose rest period as well. In addition to supporting physical recovery, counterposes offer multiple mental, energetic, and emotional benefits. Lengthier counterposes typically create a quieter, more nurturing effect. Staying longer also gives you a chance to practice a variety of complementary meditative methods, deepen internal observation, or provide the simple enjoyment of pure rest.

How often should we counterpose?

There's no concrete rule about frequency. Consider what will bring balance based on the bigger picture of your Yin Yoga sequence as well as your moment-to-moment needs. If you're not certain, inserting a resting counterpose before continuing into the next pose can be beneficial, especially if the next pose focuses on the same general area of the body. Some postures string nicely together one right after the other without the need for a counterpose between them, for example, Shoelace into Sleeping Swan. We access different directions of movement as well as different areas of the hips and legs in those postures, so threading them together without a counterpose in between them could still deliver balance and rest. You might find you enjoy doing a short string of poses on one side, resting in a counterpose, then doing the same series on the other side.

To move or not to move?

You may choose to counterpose in stillness, counterpose with movement, or try a little bit of both. The choice is yours depending on your intention in the practice. Select relatively still counterposes like Savasana to add a more meditative, yin-like quality to a practice. Choosing gently moving counterposes adds a touch of yang. When you do chose moving counterposes, move slowly and mindfully while the tissues recover from the stresses of the postures. Be sure to go especially easy with any counterposes that call for weight bearing.

Practitioner's Tip: In addition to serving as recovery poses between postures, several of the below counterposes can make great class starter options. Their simplicity and supported nature can help settle the body and mind into the space of the practice and they require uncomplicated guidance. There are nearly endless possibilities for effectively and creatively using these essential and beneficial rest patterns in your practice.

Counterposes (Cp)

Here are some counterpose options to explore. I've alphabetized them for easy reference.

Bear Rolls Cp...*to bring space through sides of ribcage and spine*

1. Begin in Tabletop (below).
2. Slowly roll your ribs to the right, then transition to arching your upper back toward the sky.
3. To continue this smooth, circular roll, shift your ribs over to the left, then drop your belly toward the earth to return to the starting position.
4. Let your movement be fluid and slow as you repeat this spinal roll several times, perhaps playing with increasing the bend in the elbows to deepen the spinal opening where you most need it.
5. When you feel ready, roll the ribcage in the opposite direction, enjoying the space it brings.
6. When you're done, pause in the stillness to feel the liveliness of your spine and the Qi flowing through it.

Beetle Cp...*to bring rest to the hips and the spine, available in a variety of restful counterposing shapes* (p. 137)

Cat's Breath Cp...*to open the spine and the energetic channels running through and beside it*

1. Begin in Tabletop (For instructions, see Tabletop Cp below).
2. As you take a slow inhale, tip your tailbone up while simultaneously lowering the belly to deepen the curve in the back (Fig A).

Fig. A Cat's Breath

3. Pause and lift your head to a degree that works for your neck.
4. Press into your finger pads and palms lightly as you exhale, rounding your lower back toward the sky as you tip your tailbone slightly down and sink your chin toward your chest (Fig B).

Fig. B Cat's Breath

5. No need to force, just enjoy the smooth, easy movement as you repeat this cycle a few times, following the flow of your breath.
6. Feel free to linger in any position along the way.

Practitioner's Tip: Consider interspersing Cat's Breath with some Bear Rolls.

Constructive Rest Cp...*a restorative posture that relinquishes the whole of the body to the earth, relaxes the low back, and gives the hard-working iliopsoas a nurturing break, inviting neither lengthening nor contraction*

1. Lie on your back, bend your knees, and place your feet on the floor hip-width distance apart. Stack your knees over your ankles.
2. With your knees bent, walk your feet outward to the edges of the mat and allow the inner knees to fall together, placing a block the narrow way between inner upper thighs if desired (Fig C). This relaxed position encourages the femur bones to rest gently into the hip sockets and releases the *iliopsoas* hip-flexors. Releasing tension in this major muscle can bring balance to the central nervous system and soothe the reactive stress response.

Fig. C Constructive Rest with block

3. To come out of the pose, slip the block out of the way, toe-heel the feet toward the center of the mat to hip-width distance apart, and stack knees over ankles.

Practitioner's Tip: Consider lengthening the amount of time you hold Constructive Rest to encourage deeper observation and insight. This Cp can accommodate almost any meditative method of choice.

Down Dog Cp...*an inversion to open the spine and whole back seam of legs*

This yang-like posture is an inversion, so all the typical inversion benefits and precautions apply.

1. From Tabletop (below), walk your knees behind you a few inches and then tuck all ten toes under.
2. Press into your palms and finger pads, lifting your hips up and back to create a lengthened, inverted V-shape with your body.
3. Start with your feet about hip-width distance apart. Adjust the distance between your feet and hands to complement the opening of the backs of legs and the spine. With your finger pads and palms, press the floor away from you.
4. Hold here in stillness, keeping a slight bend in your knees. If you'd like to walk your dog, bend one knee as you press the opposite heel toward the floor, then alternate with the other side.
5. To deepen, gently swing one leg into the air for a moment or two, then return your foot to the floor. Switch legs and repeat.
6. From Down Dog, slowly lower the knees to the floor, untuck the toes, and return to Tabletop.

Practitioner's Tip: As we know, a dog's heart is boundless, able to make friends with creatures of all kinds, so Down Dog pairs nicely with Cat's Breath.

Heart Beacon Cp...*to gently open the chest and keep shining the light of the heart with ease*

1. From a seated position with your legs extended in front of you, place your palms comfortably behind you on the mat with your wrists under your shoulders.
2. Straighten your arms and, keeping sit-bones on the mat, tip your frontal hips slightly forward.
3. Lift and open the heartspace and, if it works for your neck, slowly let the head drop back just a bit. Take extra care to not let the head tip too far backward, given the sensitivities of compressing the back of the neck (Fig D).

Fig. D Heart Beacon

4. Bring relaxation to your face by moving the jaw around, opening and closing the mouth, and playing with tensing and releasing all the muscles through your cheeks and forehead.
5. Squeeze your eyes closed, then let them open. When you're ready, return to an upright position.

Leg Reviver Cp...*to free the circulation of energy and blood through the legs and hips*

1. Sit on a folded blanket and extend your legs in front of you.
2. With your hands, massage the length of your legs lightly, including front and back of thighs, shins, calves, and all the way to the feet, if they're within easy reach.
3. Reverse and massage your way back up your legs toward your hips, repeating the cycle several times.
4. Once finished, bounce your legs lightly onto the earth, shaking and loosening the whole of the legs.
5. Swish the thighbones in their hip sockets, gently turning your legs and feet inward toward the midline of your body while very lightly tapping the inner big toes together. Repeat a few times.

Lying Full Body Stretch Cp...*for a full-body release, from toes to crown*

1. Lie flat on your back in a straight line and interlace your fingers in front of your chest.
2. Turn your palms to face the sky. Straighten your arms into the air above your chest as you reach out through the palms.
3. Stretch through your arms as you carry them over and behind you, resting them on the mat.
4. At the same time, stretch both legs by curling your toes towards your shins and pressing lightly out through the heels.
5. Enjoy this whole-body stretch as you take a few deep, full breaths.
6. When you're ready, use a long exhale to relax the entire body completely, releasing the stretch and all muscular tension.

Pinwheel Hands Cp...*to invigorate the wrists and stimulate Qi flow through the hands*

1. Bring your palms together to form Anjali mudra prayer position in front of your chest. Slowly pinwheel your prayer hands by turning your fingers to point away from you, palms still pressing.
2. Continue rotating your fingertips away from you and down toward the earth.
3. Here, release your palms and switch to the backs of your hands touching, then pinwheel them back up to center. Trace your fingertips along your sternum on their way back to upright prayer hands, palms pressing once again.

4. As you repeat this pinwheel, maintain contact by keeping a light pressure between your hands all the way through the rotation. Flow slowly and remain attentive to the sensations in your hands, fingers, and wrists.
5. Pause after a few pinwheel cycles, then reverse the direction. Turn fingers first towards the chest, rotate downward, release the palms for the backs of the hands to touch, then return to palms touching to complete the pinwheel. Let the movement be organic and fluid. Repeat a few more cycles.
6. When complete, rest your hands on your thighs.

Prone Penguin Cp...*to open the chest and bring gentle compression to the middle and upper back; offers relief for upper back and chest, and gentle adduction for tense shoulders*

1. Lie on your belly.
2. Position a block underneath each shoulder at the lowest height, then let your arms rest comfortably at your sides with the backs of your hands on the floor.
3. Rest your forehead on the mat, or use a blanket as a cushion for your head and to support your neck (Fig E).

Fig. E Prone Penguin

Qi Tapping Cp...*to activate and invigorate the yin and yang Qi channels*
These simple techniques revitalize our internal energetic architecture and integrate well as counterposes done while standing or comfortably seated with legs extended in front of you. For instructions, see "Qi Tapping & Massage to Clear and Revive the Energetic System" technique (p. 258).

Reverse Tabletop/Slide Cp...*to unfurl the frontline of the body using core and shoulder strength*

1. Start seated with the soles of your feet on the mat in front of you about hip-width distance apart with your knees over your ankles.
2. To begin, place your hands on the mat behind you with your wrists under their respective shoulders. Depending on what best accommodates your wrists, point your fingers forward toward your feet, outward to the edges of the mat, or behind you.
3. Engage your core muscles, and as you inhale, press into your hands and feet to lift your hips and chest in a straight line, forming Reverse Tabletop (Fig F).

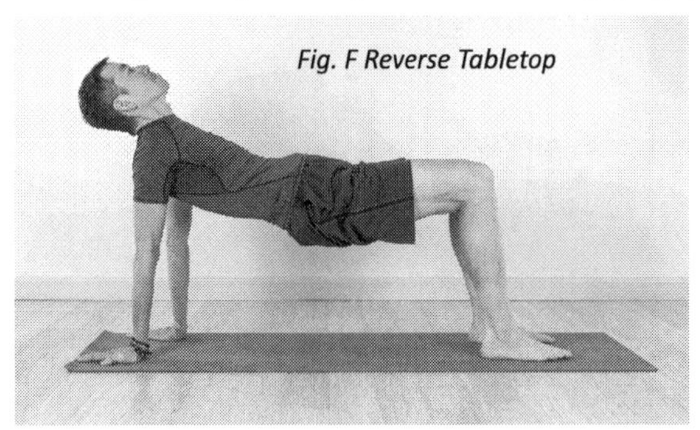
Fig. F Reverse Tabletop

4. Keep your chin tucked slightly toward your chest, or if the neck allows, carefully let it relax back in line with the rest of your spine.
5. Pause a moment or two, then on the exhale, lower your hips back to the floor. Again, enjoy a momentary pause.
6. Repeat this a few times, harmonizing the movement with your slow and steady breath.
7. To increase the challenge for your shoulders and core, repeat as above but with your legs extended in front of you in the more yang-like Slide variation. Keep the heels of your feet pressing to the floor as you lift (Fig G).

Fig. G Slide

Savasana Shapes Cp...*for a restful interlude between the Yin Yoga postures as well as at the end of a session before transitioning off the mat*
For instructions, see Savasana Yin Asana Spotlight (p. 179) and its suggested substitutions.

Shoulder Lifts and Rolls Cp...*to relieve tightness and stress through the neck and shoulders*

1. From any seated position, inhale as you lift your shoulders toward your ears.
2. Hold a moment, then as you exhale, gently let them lower.
3. Repeat this several times in rhythm with your breath. Continue breathing with awareness and intention, inhale...up, exhale...down.
4. As you inhale, roll the shoulders forward and then up toward the ears. On your exhale, slide them backward and down. Keep these movements easeful and flowing.
5. Continue this loop in harmony with your inhale and exhale. Pause some moments, then go in the reverse direction.

Stargazer Cp...*offers a slightly more yang flavor, using core and shoulder strength to bring a heavenly opening to the side and front lines of the body with a potential of a backbend and a twist*

1. Sit on a single-folded blanket, extend your legs in front of you, and separate your feet about twelve inches or so away from each other.
2. Bend your right knee and slide your right foot toward your inner left thigh for an easygoing One-Legged Dragonfly.
3. Place your right hand on the floor behind your right hip with your fingertips pointing in the direction that best agrees with your wrist.
4. Press into your right hand to straighten your arm, and using your core muscles and shoulder strength, lift both of your hips off the floor to a height that feels right.
5. Roll gently onto your right shin and wedge your left heel into the earth as an anchor.
6. Place your left hand into your left hip crease, or go deeper by sweeping your left arm in a big circle in front of your chest and across your face so that your bicep lines up with your left ear.
7. With your core muscles still engaged, stay here some moments, breathing and feeling freedom through the long line extending from your left foot to your left fingers.
8. Continue holding here, opening the chest-space toward the stars in a slight arching backbend. Keep your neck in line with your spine as you gaze toward the sky and make a wish!

9. To come out, circle your left arm back around and down as you lower your hips to the ground, arriving back to your starting position facing forward.
10. Rest a moment, then enjoy this full-body stretch on the other side.

Stay a While Crocodile Cp... *to aid the release of tension in the hips, legs, and lower spine*

1. Lie on your mat in a comfortable prone position. Bend your right knee and slide it up to waist height, keeping the inner knee and leg resting on the floor. Depending on how this leg position feels, play with bringing the knee slightly above or below waist level. You might also bend your right knee a little more or less to find what feels best for your lower body.
2. Keep your forehead on your forearms, or for a mild cervical twist, turn your head to look toward your bent knee. For a deeper neck twist, turn your head in the opposite direction of your bent knee and rest your cheek on your hands (Fig H).

Fig. H Stay a While Crocodile

3. Stay a while, crocodile, then half-way through the rest period, return your neck to neutral if it's twisted. Slide your right leg down the mat, straightening it out behind you, then switch sides to bring balance to your hips and cervical spine.

Supine Calf-Hamstring Opener Cp...*dual purpose shape to bring focus to the hamstrings or keep the sensations extra-soft to help bring relief through the back of the leg especially after postures working hips and legs*
For instructions, see Caterpillar Yin Asana Spotlight (p. 146).

Tabletop Cp...*for a simple, neutral counterpose that also serves as the foundation for several other counterposes as well as an entry point for several Yin Yoga poses; also known as Hands & Knees pose*

1. Spread a single-folded blanket across the middle of the mat to serve as padding for your knees and shins. Kneel on the blanket and place your hands on the mat with your wrists under their respective shoulders and your knees positioned directly under their respective hips.
2. If you find the wrists are sensitive, try placing a single-folded blanket underneath them as padding to soften the pressure.
3. Find the natural curves of your spine, starting with a neutral pelvis position (for a refresher, see "Acquainting with the Orientations of the Pelvis," p. 67).
4. Lengthen your neck so that the crown of your head is level with the tip of your tailbone.
5. Press lightly into your finger pads and palms to lighten any pressure on your wrists.

Tiger Stretch Cp...*to lengthen the spine and build a strong core*

1. Begin in Tabletop Cp with your spine in its neutral position.
2. Gaze down and just slightly forward of your thumbs so that your neck is in line with your spine. Press your palms and finger pads onto the earth to support your wrists.

3. Engage your core muscles to protect your lower spine and support your balance.
4. Lift your right knee and straighten your right leg behind you, hovering the front of your right thigh over the mat at the height of your hip.
5. To intensify the core work, lift your left palm and reach your left arm forward as you press back through your right heel, curling your right toes gently toward your right shin.
6. Keep your hips level as you reach from end to end, stretching from the left fingers through your right leg as if being pulled gently in both directions at once (Fig I).

Fig. I Tiger Stretch with leg & arm lifted

7. Return your left palm to the mat underneath your left shoulder.
8. To stimulate the side of the rib cage, gently swing your right leg across the centerline of your mat to the left and over your bent left leg, tucking the right toes under so that the ball of your foot presses to the floor.
9. Push back a bit through your right heel to open the backline of the leg through the calf and hamstring tissues.
10. If your neck allows, look over your left shoulder to bring a twist to your cervical spine.
11. For a deeper variation, lower your forearms onto the mat.
12. To emerge, if you're lowered onto forearms, push back up to place your palms on the mat. Keep your core muscles engaged as you slowly swing your right leg across your midline and behind you to line up with your right hip.
13. Bend your right knee and place it under your right hip, returning to Tabletop.
14. Repeat on the other side.

Wall Caterpillar Cp...*provides a restful, rebalancing pause between your supine wall shapes as needed*
For instructions, see "Yinpression: On the Wall" (p. 127).

Windshield Wipers Cp...*to bring balance and freedom to the hips using mindful movements*

1. Begin in an upright seated position on top of a single-folded blanket with your hands pressing comfortably on the earth behind you for support.
2. Place the soles of your feet to the floor mat-width distance apart in front of you with your knees bent.
3. Inhale, then on the exhale, slowly drop your bent knees down to the right. Allow your left hip to lift to a degree that feels good. Pause there a few breaths.
4. On the inhale, lift your bent knees back up to center. On the exhale, drop your knees to the left. Again, it's OK to let the opposite hip lift.
5. Repeat this side-to-side movement several times, freeing up circulation of blood and Qi through the hips and legs as you cycle between internal and external rotations of the hip joints.
6. To twist a bit more through the waist, shift your feet closer together, then repeat as above.
7. Move mindfully with your breath, there's no need to rush. You have no destination but smooth flowing movement, any sensations happening where they feel right.
8. If you wish to deepen a little, lean backward and rest your forearms on the mat and continue.
9. To explore **Supine Windshield Wipers**, simply lie on your back and follow these same movements.

Chapter 11

Meditative Methods for Presence, Possibility, and Wellbeing

Guided Techniques and Complementary Aids

A primary experiential element of our Mandala Map, meditative methods contain guided techniques grounded in the root traditions of Yin Yoga & Meditation. They are crafted as applied opportunities to explore the many ways these ancient philosophies, teachings, and principles can serve us as we continue to travel the pathways of presence, possibility, and wellbeing on and off the mat.

The techniques are grouped into four primary meditative methods to provide an easy-to-navigate, consolidated framework:

- Breath Inquiry and Directed Breathing Methods
- Mindfulness-Inspired Concentration Methods
- Yoga Nidra-Inspired Methods
- Taoist-Inspired Energy Cultivation Methods

Within the methods, you'll also find several complementary aids available to enhance your meditative experience.

Complementary Aids

- Mantras: Phrases or verses that state intention (such as a Sankalpa), train the attention to gather energy, or share blessings
- Visualization: The power of the inner eye that couples the creative capabilities of the conscious mind with the manifestation power of the subconscious mind
- Healing Sounds: Sound vibrations used to harmonize and strengthen our energetic architecture while relaxing and refreshing the body, mind, and heart
- Internal Scans: Deliberate and systematic exploration of all layers of being
- Illustrations for Illumination: Stories that engage symbols, illuminate meaning, and deepen our sense of shared humanity
- Mudras: Gestures made with hands/fingers to direct energy and intention, bridging the physical body and a larger cosmic energy
- Journaling: Written contemplations reflecting on our experience and needs. Think intention, insight, and inspiration!

How we practice is as important as what we practice. To help keep our approach and attitude yin-like, these exercises prompt us to embrace our internal yin qualities and call upon the yin guardians as companions to accompany us on our journey. Within many of the techniques, you'll encounter the jewels of encouragement acting as touchstones. The yin and yang wings of natural presence and complementary aids are integrated throughout the exercises to foster continued present moment awareness.

Guiding Yourself or Others in the Techniques

Each group of meditative methods begins with a brief introduction discussing its potential benefits and is followed by a sampling of guided techniques, which include:

- Suggested Time: Recommended length of time to practice
- Suggested Use: Ideas for integrating the technique into your Yin Yoga & Meditation sessions or throughout the day
- Instructions: Step-by-step guidance

To get started, choose the guided technique you'd like to explore. Prior to trying the technique, read through the introduction and ready-to-use instructions to become acquainted with it. If you're leading yourself through the technique, you could follow along as you read, where possible, or pre-record the exercise by reading it into your phone or other recording device. As you become more familiar with the technique, you'll likely become more able to lead yourself mentally through the exercises. If you're leading others in the technique, you can choose to bring these written scripts to class as guides, where helpful.

Informed by our Yin Yoga & Meditation practice principles, here are some suggested guidelines for leading yourself or others safely and effectively through any of these techniques:

- Start short and small. If you're newer to any of the techniques, perhaps begin on the shorter side of the recommended timeframe and extend the length gradually. When you're incorporating the techniques into a Yin Yoga posture, the length will also depend on the nature of the pose and its duration.
- Whenever the instructions call for selecting a posture for a seated meditation technique, consider positions that are relatively comfortable and help you remain alert and relaxed, such as Sukhasana (for a refresher, see "Establishing a Neutral Pelvis in Seated Postures," p. 68). If a seated position doesn't feel right, Gentle Fish (p. 159) or Constructive Rest (p. 204) are good back-lying options to try.
- Be aware that mindful attention and intentional breathing could occasionally induce a bit of anxiety, fleeting sensations of slight dizziness, or a brief spike in heart rate. If you notice any of these occurring, watch it for a couple of moments to see if it resolves. If it persists, take a break from the technique.
- It's natural to occasionally encounter challenging emotions. If this happens, you could place your hand on your heart and send compassion there. You might also bring to mind someone who nurtures and loves you dearly, or perhaps a spiritual figure who brings you comfort. Stopping the technique is also always an option.
- Within the guided techniques, you'll see more specific information to assist you as you work with whatever emotions are presenting themselves. If something is persistent or especially upsetting, reaffirm the option and value of seeking professional support as needed. As teachers, we invite, inform, inspire, and guide, but students remain in charge of their experience.
- If doing these exercises within the Yin Yoga poses and your attention drifts from the physical experience of the posture, stop the technique until your attention refocuses and stabilizes. If practicing any of these techniques off the mat, be sure do so in a safe environment in which you can internalize your attention and comfortably close your eyes, if desired. Always avoid engaging in them while driving or operating heavy machinery.
- Remember to relax the musculature, as muscles may unconsciously tense while concentrating. Providing regular relaxation reminders supports us in staying both aware and at ease.
- Offer yourself some space for reflection to feel the effects the guided technique has had. Just a few quiet moments of curious observation and acknowledgment of what we've gained can encourage us to put the progress of our practice to use in daily life.
- Keep in mind that it's your practice and you know what serves you best. Choose to honor your needs, and know it's OK to set aside the rest.
- If you're just getting familiar with these exercises or find any of them challenging, trust that your skill will build with time and dedication. The more we travel this path, the more readily the path opens itself to us. Remain patient and kind with yourself.

Many adaptations and variations exist for each of the methods, so all are malleable and yours to experiment with. Try them as they're written or use them as a springboard to create your own version, adapting them to fit your needs or those of your students. For those of us who are teachers, pre-recording a technique gives us another chance to hear our voice and continue honing our delivery.

To receive the gifts of these techniques, we need to experience them first-hand, so I hope you're feeling inspired to give them a try! Whether a practitioner or teacher, take your time with them as you discover which work well for you and what you might want to adapt or expand. I've found them to be treasured companions in my own practice and life journey, and I hope they'll serve your practice and teaching, too.

Breath Inquiry and Directed Breathing Methods

An ever-present yin guardian and teacher, the breath is the empowering tool we'll be exploring within this section of the meditative methods element of the Mandala Map. With practice, we become better listeners to the wisdom and insight the breath contains, and we grow our ability to use it in support of our wellbeing.

Offered here is a collection of guided directed breathing and breath inquiry techniques that can help build our capacity to relax and connect to the wonders of the present moment. All are excellent options to help us settle into our body at various points in our Yin Yoga & Meditation practice. If you're newer to any of them and they at first feel challenging, there's no need to judge the natural process of learning. Give yourself time to get acquainted with them. Keep at it and trust that they'll become easier the more you practice them. I encourage you to take them off the mat, too, and experiment with ways they help develop and maintain a relaxed and mindful presence throughout the day.

Breath Inquiry as a Pathway to Inner Wisdom

Simple breath inquiry brings our awareness into the body as it sits on the earth, releasing the rest of the day and allowing us to arrive fully to our practice. When we listen, the breath has much to tell us about the state of our mind, body, and heart.

Guided Technique 1

Suggested Time: Moments to minutes

Suggested Use: This guiding inquiry helps illuminate our interior experience whether during sitting meditation, a pose, or our daily activities.

Instructions:

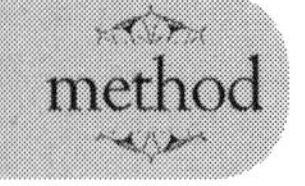

Turn your awareness to your breath, your wind-horse, the flow of life always coming in and going out. Allow the breath to be natural. Allow it to be the wise communicator and teacher it is with no need to fix or manage it.

Inquire: How are you finding your breath right now? How would you describe it in a word or two?

Observe the character of your in-breath at this moment. Is it short or long? Deep and full or shallow? How do you experience its texture? Is it smooth or jagged? Pay close attention to how it moves – does it feel effortless or forced?

Notice, too, the nature of your out-breath. Is it slow or fast, labored or easeful?

As you follow the out-breath, take its temperature and its pulse. Meet it as if you were meeting a friend. Ask, "How are you?" and it will tell you.

Do you sense any ways your breath is reflecting the current state of your body? Your mind? Your heart? Continuously communicating, each breath offers a pathway to clearer insight and understanding when we take the time to inquire and to listen.

Guided Technique 2

Suggested Time: Moments to minutes

Suggested Use: This guiding inquiry helps illuminate our interior experience while in any Yin Yoga pose.

INSTRUCTIONS:

In a Yin pose, just as in life, if we unconsciously go beyond the body's natural limits, the breath, our good friend, will communicate this to us. With a sense of wonder and appreciation for all the ways it helps us, observe how your breath is flowing in this present time.

What do you notice when you look to your breath as a gauge, a personal Yindicator, of the intensity and quality of sensations you're experiencing right now?

Are you able to breathe freely, fully, and easefully while in the Yin Yoga postures? If not, are there any adjustments you'd like to make to your props, body position, or your mental or emotional approach to ensure you're not striving in the pose?

Continue to reflect: Is it unnecessary for me to do anything I'm doing right now? Am I trying to be something else or get to somewhere else? If so, why? What am I growing in awareness of as I watch and feel the breath?

GUIDED TECHNIQUE 3

Suggested Time: Moments to minutes

Suggested Use: Chin mudra generates a grounding energy, whether used during a sitting meditation, at the start of a Yin Yoga & Meditation practice, or anytime in your day it would feel beneficial.

INSTRUCTIONS:

Come into a seated meditative posture of choice. Feel yourself stable and centered.

To form the Chin mudra, make a gentle fist with each of your hands, thumbs on the outside of your fingers. Touch the tips of the left and right index fingers to their respective thumbs so that each forms a circle. No need to squeeze forcefully, just allow your finger and thumb to connect, then loosely spread the middle, ring, and pinkie fingers open.

Place your palms face down comfortably on your legs, maintaining the finger-thumb circles you've created.

Breathe deeply and naturally through your nose with only a slight separation between inhalation and exhalation. Feel your muscles gently engaged but easeful with each breath, just like the attention. Be alert but remain relaxed.

As your index finger and thumb rest against one another with palms resting on the legs, notice any sensations or feelings evoked by this mudra.

While maintaining your attention on the rooting energy of Chin mudra, find yourself increasingly relaxing into the present moment, enjoying the sense of being grounded on the earth.

POST-PRACTICE REFLECTIONS:

- Consider a time when your breath was a source of wisdom. Remind yourself of the details of that experience and what your breath taught you.
- How does your breath communicate with you when you're feeling stressed? How about when you're feeling content, relaxed...irritated...or inspired?
- Observe the state of your breath before, during, and then after your Yin Yoga & Meditation practice. What changes did you perceive? What information did you receive at each point?

Warming the Muscles of Respiration for Better Breathing

This brief and uncomplicated breathwork technique stretches and lengthens the muscles of respiration. A fantastic antidote to shallow breathing, whether due to rushing, anxiety, or sitting all day at a desk, this technique can transform how you feel in just a few moments. Expanding the Breath also serves as valuable preparation for directed breathing practices that benefit from opening and warming the interior muscles of respiration.

Guided Technique

Suggested Time: One to three minutes

Suggested Use: Try this technique anytime during your Yin Yoga & Meditation session or day when your breathing feels restricted.

Instructions:

To prepare the lungs, take a full breath in through the nose, then slowly expel the air from the lungs by exhaling through the nose.

Breathe in again through the nose as completely and deeply as possible without over-exerting for a count of five to ten or so.

When you can't bring in any more air, hold the breath for as long as is comfortable. This could be to a count of ten to twenty or so, depending on what feels right and easeful for you.

When it's time, exhale the breath back out through the nose extra slowly until you feel you can't exhale any more.

Take a few moments of rest, breathing naturally.

As it feels appropriate, repeat this exercise three to six times. Be mindful not to force the length of the breath or hold time.

Once completed, allow the breath to return to its natural rhythm once again. Do you sense now an easier breath and more generous lung capacity?

Breathing to Transform Tensions into Ease

Guided breathwork exercises encourage the body to relax, helping us soften more into the Yin Yoga poses. Keeping our muscles loose transfers the stresses deeper into the tissues of exercise, so it's valuable to learn how to direct the breath to relax parts of the body.

Guided Technique

Suggested Time: Moments to minutes

Suggested Use: You could employ this technique when first entering a pose. Because our musculature sometimes re-engages, also play with briefly repeating it at periodic intervals throughout your postures to help ensure the body remain as relaxed as possible.

Instructions:

Body and breath are inextricably interconnected, old friends and trusted companions. Let's work with them together here, sending the breath into parts of the body you sense to be tense or crowded.

Begin by mentally scanning the inner layers of your body slowly from toes to crown to notice any muscles or hidden places of physical tension.

Once you come upon an area of tightness, let your attention linger there.

Experiment with gently breathing from that part of the body.

To do this, feel the in-breath filling and then expanding this area, then sense the out-breath transforming tension into relaxation all the way through the tissues below the skin.

Breathe with intention and invite this place to gently open. Imagine relaxation reaching every cell. See in your mind's eye how the tissues begin to relax.

When you're ready, continue scanning your body slowly with kind attention, looking with fresh eyes for any tensions to relieve.

Pause to breathe from any areas of gripping...the in-breath opening and expanding...the out-breath releasing and relaxing.

If your body happens to resist your intentional invitation to relax, it's likely a signal that you've pressed yourself too far in the pose. Use this heightened awareness to create a softer version of your shape.

As you're ready, repeat the body scan from crown to toes to continue releasing any tissues that have unconsciously retightened.

Blending Breath with Sensations

In the Yin Yoga poses, we will sometimes encounter physical discomfort as we move into places of the body that feel tight or untended. Fortunately, we have two primary avenues of tension relief always at our disposal, our breath and our intentional attention. Consciously fusing the two and sending them toward areas of sensation induces relaxation and allows us to linger in the shape with greater ease.

Guided Technique

Suggested Time: Moments to minutes

Suggested Use: Try this body-breath scan for a minute or two during any pose or counterpose.

Instructions:

As you settle into your pose, guide your attention to the area of the body where you most notice sensations arising.

With your awareness resting there, explore gently breathing from that part of the body, as though the breath is moving in and out from the space of sensation.

With your mind's eye, see each in-breath as a delicate mist filling that part of your body, spreading and expanding.

Envision the out-breath softening and emptying the space completely.

When it feels right for you, continue to slowly scan the physical landscape of your body with careful attention, searching for the next area of sensation.

With each breath, visualize pure mist moving into and out from the sensation.

Feel peace infuse the inner layers of your body, letting any conflicts of tension or holding fall away, leaving only relaxation in its wake.

With awareness, keep loosening each area of stimulation within your body, breath by precious breath, all through the body.

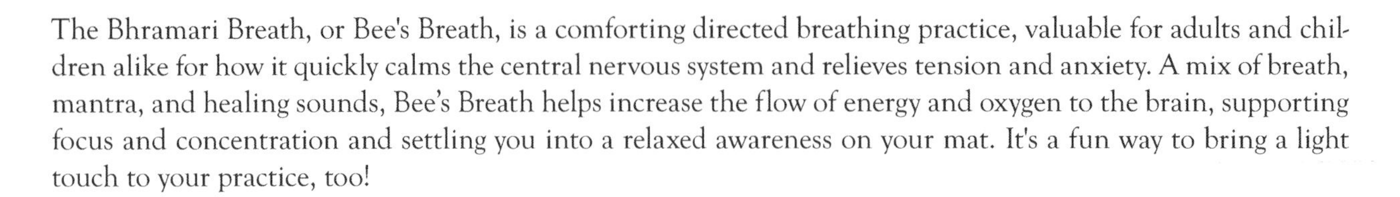

Humming into Harmony with Bhramari Breath

The Bhramari Breath, or Bee's Breath, is a comforting directed breathing practice, valuable for adults and children alike for how it quickly calms the central nervous system and relieves tension and anxiety. A mix of breath, mantra, and healing sounds, Bee's Breath helps increase the flow of energy and oxygen to the brain, supporting focus and concentration and settling you into a relaxed awareness on your mat. It's a fun way to bring a light touch to your practice, too!

Guided Technique

Suggested Time: One to three minutes

Suggested Use: Easily performed as a preparation for sitting meditation or in any hands-free Yin Yoga posture in which your body is steady and stable. Try this out almost anywhere you feel inspired to practice during your day.

Instructions:

The Shanmukhi mudra uses both hands to close the head's six sensory portals and turn the awareness more completely inward during this meditative breath exercise.

To form this mudra, gently place the fingers across each side of the face: the pinky fingers at the center of the chin, ring fingers on the upper lip, middle fingers on either side of the middle of the nose, forefingers over closed eyelids, and thumbs sealing the ears. When in position, your fingers will feel like a mask on your face. You don't have to close your eyes completely if that doesn't feel right, and if the mudra isn't working for you for any reason, simply rest your hands on your thighs with your eyes open or closed. This breathwork is refreshing and relaxing with or without the mudra.

Begin by taking a long and easeful inhale through the nose. Hold the breath for a second or two, then slowly breathe out through the nose, making the extended sound of the letter M (MMMMMM....) along the back of the throat, like the humming sound of a bee's wings.

Repeat this again: inhale slowly through the nose without straining at all. Let it be full and complete. Exhale through the nose, imitating the sound of a happily buzzing bee.

Imagine yourself floating through a field of wildflowers among colorful spring blossoms.

Repeat this in the same way as you fly through the sky in your mind...MMMMMM...

You could substitute MMMMMM....with the sound of OMMMMM......

Experiment with Bee's Breath for five to ten cycles more. When you're ready, place your hands with palms facing up on the thighs and pause to rest with any internal impacts or resonance, returning to your natural breath.

Dirgha Breathing for a Complete Breath

Dirgha Breathing is a complete-breath exercise to help deepen and lengthen the breath while calming the body and mind. This breathing pattern is cultivated by breathing through the nose with nourishing, easeful inhalations and exhalations, first filling the three parts of the torso from bottom to top, then releasing the breath from top to bottom.

Practitioner's Tip: At any time during the exercise, place one hand to the heart and one to the belly to heighten your awareness of the connection between breath and body.

Guided Technique

> Suggested Time: Three to ten minutes, or about a minute in a pose
>
> Suggested Use: This breathwork works well as a sitting meditation. Once learned, it's a great option to use an abbreviated version of this during Yin Yoga postures as a calming, grounding support.

INSTRUCTIONS:

Begin by breathing slowly in through the nose and exhaling very slowly through the mouth.

Inhale again through the nose, exhale through the mouth, and this time at the bottom of the exhale, slightly contract the belly muscles to aid the release of any lingering, stale air from the lungs.

Breathe freely now and notice how your body naturally rises and falls with your breath.

Allow all tension in the face, jaw, neck, and shoulders to release.

To encourage a slightly deeper breath, next we'll slowly fill the torso with air.

Through the nose, breathe in, first filling the lower belly with the breath. Feel it rise as it fills.

Next, let the upper belly fill with the breath, feeling the ribs expand and rise.

Now, fill the space of the chest with air all the way up to the collarbones. Sense their lift as you come to the top of the in-breath.

Pause a moment there, retaining the breath.

Through the nose now, breathe out slowly and seamlessly in the same way back down, first letting the chest soften...next, the upper belly and its ribs...then lastly, the low belly softens.

Pause a moment, letting the body stay empty of the breath, then do this cycle again.

Breathe in – low belly rises, ribs rise, chest rises. Hold the breath a moment.

Breathe out – chest falls, ribs fall, and low belly falls. Hold the breath a moment.

Keep the breath full and long, yet easeful. Let it naturally smoothen out as you continue to breathe intentionally.

Continue on, repeating this cycle.

Keep softening the shoulders, hands, and fingers...soften the gaze.

Once you've created a comfortable and steady pattern, move to the last phase of the exercise. Here you can incorporate counting to naturally lengthen the breath and equalize the duration of the inhalations and exhalations.

Begin by inhaling for four seconds, giving room for a one second hold at the top of the chest and the top of inhale, then exhaling for four seconds, leaving a one second hold at the low belly and bottom of the exhale.

Inhale...four, three, two, one...hold one second...then exhale from the chest first...four, three, two, one... hold for a moment.

Inhale for a count of four, hold.

Exhale for a count of four, hold.

Keep relaxing the space between the eyes.

As the body and breath settle, consider lengthening the duration of the inhales, exhales, and pauses in one-second increments, if it feels comfortable.

Continue this breathwork for a couple more minutes, your deliberate attention supporting softness and ease. Let yourself rest into the calm of this moment.

When it's time, close the practice at the end of your exhale, taking some moments to notice any effects.

Slowing the Brain Waves with the Breezy Breath

Have you heard of psychologist and researcher Les Fehmi? In a series of experiments, he tracked EEG readings on volunteers as he asked them to conjure images of peaceful landscapes, listen to atmospheric music, and inhale certain scents.[1] The readings demonstrated that the subjects' brain waves became synchronous during these activities, moving from the more rapid, erratic beta waves of active daily life to the smooth, flowing alpha waves that dominate relaxed, meditative awareness. Fehmi was fascinated to find that when he asked the participants to imagine the space between their eyes, the alpha waves became especially pronounced. The simple act of resting our attention in the third eye space can literally change our brain waves, transitioning us into an easeful, spacious awareness.

Guided Technique

Suggested Time: One to ten minutes

Suggested Use: Try this third eye center breathwork practice at any time on your mat when your body is stable enough to safely close your eyes and connect with your natural spaciousness of body, mind, and heart.

Instructions:

Bring your awareness to lie in the space between your eyebrows, closing your eyes if you wish.

As you release tension through the forehead and allow your temples to relax, feel the peaceful place between your eyebrows expand. Merely resting your attention on the third eye center in this way helps soothe and smooth the thinking mind, allowing us to feel more at ease and present.

All distractions falling away now, feel the buoyancy of your breath as you breathe attentively.

Begin to imagine that you're breathing from the space between your eyebrows.

Let your breath be natural and unstrained as you breathe in and out through the eyebrow center.

As you breathe in, imagine the airiness of your breath touching the third eye and moving into the space behind your closed eyes.

As you breathe out, feel the breath releasing from this place, expanding and dissolving into the spaciousness around you.

Your breath light like a balmy breeze, your attention relaxed yet steady.

Keep your awareness floating gently in your third eye center, breathing through the space between your eyes.

Should you become distracted, merely return your attention to the peaceful place between your eyes.

Your breezy breath and concentrated attention are actively changing your brain in this moment, paving a pathway to reconnect with the spacious sky within the mind.

When you're ready, let go of directing the breath and allow your undivided awareness to rest solely on this space between the eyebrows.

With relaxed single-pointed concentration, watch with interest for whatever is arising within this space and on the screen behind your closed eyes.

As your awareness lingers here, do you feel a more profound sense of relaxation and ease, helping you to be more present for your experience in this moment?

Allow yourself to be in the peace of this space for as long as you'd like.

Exhalation Extension to Activate the Vagus Nerve

The vagus nerve is like a parasympathetic expressway running from the neck down through torso and diaphragm and into all of our major organs. When soothed during directed breathing practices, such as Exhalation Extension, the vagus nerve signals the brain to engage the parasympathetic nervous system, restoring the body's ability to relax, rest, and heal. Just like tension often snowballs into persistent stress, the act of calming ourselves creates a positive cycle. When we allow our musculature to relax, our mind and heart release as well. Self-repair is our design, and relaxation supports this whole-self healing process.

Guided Technique 1

Suggested Time: Three to ten minutes, or about a minute in a pose

Suggested Use: Experiment with this breathwork exercise at any point during your Yin Yoga & Meditation session or day.

INSTRUCTIONS:

In this exercise, we return to the natural complete breath, the cherished breath that first welcomed you into your precious life.

Begin to tune into your breath. Feel how your breath is flowing in this moment. Become aware of its duration. How many seconds does the in-breath last? How about the out-breath?

Keep an interest in your breath as you breathe naturally through the nose.

Without straining, begin to match the length of your inhales and your exhales. Let both the inhale and exhale be slow, long, and easeful.

Once you've established an equal breathing pattern, begin to slow the exhale down a bit more, extending your exhale to make it slightly longer than your inhale.

Let your breathing muscles stay relaxed as you decelerate the out-breath to stretch out each exhalation. Keep the in-breath full and nurturing as you continue to gently lengthen the out breath.

Over time, you might build up to a two-to-one exhale-to-inhale ratio.

Practitioner's Tip: Keep in mind what matters most is that you feel relaxed and intentional, and that you aren't forcing a thing. Your body will respond if the exhale is even just a touch longer than the inhale.

Guided Technique 2

Suggested Time: Three to ten minutes, or about minute in a pose

Suggested Use: Once you've learned the Exhalation Extension breathwork, consider intermittently employing it while you rest within the Yin Yoga postures. Experiment with this breathwork exercise at any point during your practice session or day.

INSTRUCTIONS:

In this exercise, we'll blend directed breathing with a body, mind, and heart scan.

As you scan the inside of the body for sensations, become aware of any areas of tensions or holding. Is there any gripping of hands or toes? Do you find any clenching in the jaw, the belly, or perhaps in another area of your body?

If so, what happens if you rest your attention on these areas of tension as you extend your exhalations? As you keep the exhales long and easeful, inquire: Does the exhalation extension help to loosen the holding?

Try this for a few moments, letting the in-breath nourish you. Feel the out-breath spread relaxation all through the body.

We can hold tension in our minds too, perhaps from things we tell ourselves that may not be accurate, maybe fears about the future or the rewinding and replaying of old narratives. As you scan the mind, if you notice any mental holding, what happens as you recognize what's there while continuing to lengthen each exhale? Continue with this for a bit. Observe, how does your mind respond?

The heart, too, holds tensions at times. Notice what's happening in the landscape of your heart. As you stay with however it is that you're feeling, maintain your awareness with interested tenderness. Continue to consciously and fully release the out-breath. With each exhale, sense tensions evaporating and a deeper relaxation moving into every cell of your body.

After you complete the internal scan, take one more breath in through the nose and a long, full breath out through the mouth. Know that you can trust your ability to be peaceful, at ease, and in harmony with this moment, reaffirming your sacred nature.

Nadi Shodhana Breathing for Rebalancing the Awareness

The ancient Yogic alternate nostril breathing exercise known as Nadi Shodhana has been used for centuries to clarify the mind, calm the body, and harmonize our energy. In Nadi Shodhana, we slowly breathe through one nostril and then the other, alternating between them during the inhales and exhales. The yin Ida energy channel is located along the spine's left side. When the breath moves through the left nostril, the Ida is activated. When the breath moves through the right nostril, the yang Pingala energy channel on the right side of the spine is activated. In this way, our alternating breath activates and clears one channel and then the other. As these channels become balanced, so do our yin and yang energies.

The benefits of this technique from a Western perspective are equally impressive. As observed by German physician Richard Kayser in the late 1800s, the nose undergoes a natural cycle of side-to-side swelling termed the "nasal cycle," and it impacts how we feel and behave. When one nostril swells, the other becomes the primary passage for airflow. This switch happens every couple of hours. Scientists have discovered that nerve fibers from the sympathetic and parasympathetic nervous systems run through both sides of the body, including the nostrils. Therefore, the nasal cycle is connected to the largest sympathetic-parasympathetic activation cycle in the body. When the sympathetic system dominates on the right side, we're more active and awake, experiencing increased breath and heart rates. Conversely, when the parasympathetic system is dominant on the right side, we're more sedate and relaxed, our breath pattern slows, and we produce fewer stress-response hormones like cortisol and endorphins. In this way, we naturally transition between more yang and more yin states all through the day. As we steadily cycle between left and right nostrils in Nadi Shodhana practice, we balance these extremes, experiencing more calm, ease, and presence. We inhabit a mindful relaxation, an optimized state for your meditation practice.

Practitioner's Tip: Before you begin this technique, be sure your nasal passages are clear. If you have a stuffy nose, you could try resting back onto a reclined bolster to help open the nasal pathways. If the nostrils remain congested, skip this technique for now.

Guided Technique

Suggested Time: Three to ten minutes

Suggested Use: To promote an alert, relaxed awareness, try this breathwork as a brief sitting meditation for arriving to the mat or as a prelude to a longer meditation. It could also be intermittently practiced in a comfortable seated position of choice between the poses or prior to Savasana.

Instructions:

Relax your left hand to the left knee in Chin mudra, with the tips of the thumb and forefinger touching.

Place your right index and middle fingers centered between your eyebrows. Alternating side to side, you'll use the thumb to gently seal the right nostril closed, while the ring finger is used to seal the left nostril. Play with this a few times to get the feel of this switching action. Seal right nostril, open left...seal left nostril, open right.

Be sure to keep a light touch throughout the exercise as you close the nostrils, no need to apply too much pressure.

Avoid overburdening the breath rhythm. Maintain an easy, full flow as you feel the breath move in and out through each nostril. The key is relaxed, intentional breathing.

Begin with both nostrils open. Inhale gently and slowly through them both at the same time. As you breathe in, feel or visualize that you're inhaling all the way into the middle place between the eyebrows, the third eye center.

Retain the breath and attention there for a moment or two before slowly and smoothly exhaling out through the open nostrils.

When the exhale has finished, take a moment of pause.

Now with the thumb, seal the right nostril and inhale smoothly through the left nostril, as if pulling the air toward the third eye center. Observe the nature of the in-flow.

At the top of the inhalation, close the left nostril with your ring finger to retain the breath for a moment or so while keeping both nostrils lightly sealed.

Then, let the thumb lift from the right nostril and exhale slowly through that side.

Keep relaxing the body as you observe the out-flow.

At the end of the out-breath, observe a brief pause.

Inhale steadily and gently through the right nostril up to the space between the eyebrows.

At the top of the in-breath, press the right nostril closed with the thumb and pause, ceasing the breath momentarily, then release the left nostril and breathe slowly and deliberately out through the left side.

You've completed one cycle of Nadi Shodhana breathing.

As you continue with this breathwork, work toward organically regulating the breath, patterning both rhythm and duration so the inhales and exhales become equal in length and quality. Start with a four- to five- second count for the inhale-exhale phases of the breath and one to two second pauses between. As it's comfortable, increase the duration of each of these phases by one-second intervals.

As long as you feel steady, continue to practice for a few minutes more, completing ten to twenty rounds or so, until you feel refreshed, calm, and rebalanced.

Once you've finished, allow your breath to return to its basic rhythm and enjoy a few moments with your natural breath flow. Take a brief survey of the body, mind, heart, and notice with curiosity any effects of the breathwork practice.

Sweeping Away Tensions with the Broom of the Breath

Every time we meet the moment with complete, restful breathing and compassionate attention, we do a bit to soothe the stress response and train our bodies and brains to activate the relaxation response. The following sweeping breath technique uses the breath to invite relaxation into the body to assist the good work of the Yin Yoga exercise.

Guided Technique 1

Suggested Time: Ten to twenty minutes

Suggested Use: This sweeping breath pairs well with the Savasana relaxation journey.

INSTRUCTIONS:

To help release any tension, allow your mind to settle into your breath and your body to settle into stillness.

Now you're invited to use the attention and direction of our breath to sweep through the body,

encouraging calmness and ease to melt into every cell.

Allow the breath to be full and effortless.

Visualize that you're drawing the breath in and up through the bottoms of your feet, up through the legs, torso, neck, head, all the way up to the crown.

Then breathing back down through the crown, sweep the out-breath through the head, neck, torso, legs, and out through the bottoms of the feet.

Inhale again in the same way in through the feet, feeling the breath move with purpose all the way up through your body to the crown.

Exhaling again in the same way from the crown, feeling the breath move all the way down, through head, neck, torso, legs, and out through the soles of the feet.

Use the inhale like a brush, sensing its weight as it sweeps upward through the whole body, sweeping all the way up to the crown.

Then feel its weight, substance, and direction as it sweeps downward with the exhale, sweeping and sweeping into and out through the feet.

Keep inhaling and exhaling in this way a few more times, letting the breath move freely, sweeping through you, clearing the subtle energy pathways as it progresses.

Stay with slow, seamless breathing and brushing.

Sense your breath sweeping through you like a fine energy broom on the inside.

Now perhaps you focus this broom of your breath on only the legs. Feel this energy broom sweeping through the legs, just as they are right now, breath moving its gentle bristles with kind intention through the legs, any tightness, any fatigue, clearing away.

Next, sweep the breath up through the hips where so many things get tucked away. With gentleness, let your breath sweep softly through the hips, giving space, sweeping, sweeping. Feeling more relaxation moving slowly in.

Move all the breath up into the torso now. Breathe in and out, sweeping the broom of the breath through the lower abdomen that holds so much tension...upper abdomen, where breath may be shallow with fatigue and worry. Sweeping through, releasing tensions, expanding space in the depths of the chest, caressing the heart, soothing the lungs.

Sweeping, sweeping, up through the arms as well, your breath taking away tensions in the arms, hands, and fingers, sweeping out any stress in the shoulders.

With awareness, move the breath into the mind, sweeping in your mind, front to back and side to side. Sweeping away stray thoughts, stubborn notions, unhelpful nagging anxieties. Sweeping, sweeping, clearing them all away, just for this bit of time, letting you stay right here with relaxation and ease.

Breath sweeping through the eyes and ears, clearing out painful things you've seen or heard that might be stuck, sweeping, sweeping, clearing anything painful that might be holding.

Breath sweeping through the mouth and throat, clearing out anything that blocks your song of your spirit and expression of your true nature, cleansing and sweeping.

Breath sweeping into the heartspace now, soothing and soft, the broom of your breath moving through the heart, clearing space for forgiveness, healing, and deep love.

Bring your sweeping breath now anywhere else you need it in the directions that feel right...anywhere you might still benefit from clearing the energy channels, the healing brush of your breath sweeping away anything that is stuck...let your inner wisdom guide you.

Now sensing the sweeping motion as your breath moves through the whole body, sweeping out any remaining tightness, moving with tender purpose.

Sense all stress and worries falling away with each in-breath, each out-breath. Feeling all parts of the body letting go, the whole body...the whole body...the whole body sensing greater and greater ease.

When you're ready, release the breathwork, and settle into your natural breath, resting into the open space of this moment, buoyed, light, and free.

Mindfulness-Inspired Concentration Methods

At the foundation of present moment awareness is the simple capacity to concentrate, to place our attention on something and keep it there. As we continue to explore this element of our Mandala Map, let's dive into some Mindfulness concentration practices arising from the Buddhist tradition. Staying attentive in our Yin Yoga practice, we put our ability to concentrate to use as we observe and interpret physical sensations as well as what's arising in our mental, energetic, and emotional landscapes. Concentration exercises build a strong base for an insightful journey into all parts of ourselves as we point a steady, open-hearted spotlight at our internal terrain.

While training in compassionate concentration, we keep the attention stable and collected on a chosen object for a set amount of time. For the duration of the meditation exercise, anything besides that object is designated as a distraction. For example, the object of our attention might be the breath, so we would consider anything that is not the breath a distraction. This technique becomes a chance to get better acquainted with the inclinations and proclivities of the mind as it invariably cycles away from and back toward the selected object of focus. Like a curious puppy playing with its favorite toy, the mind is eager to chase after thoughts as it's teased by emotions, memories, and possible futures. Concentration training is like putting a gentle lead on the brain that helps us whisper over and over, *come back...come back...be here.*

As we've discussed, we're noticing thoughts, not trying to stop them altogether or resist any part of our experience. In a concentration exercise, we maintain a kind and curious but steadfast attention, returning our awareness to our object of focus over and over again with a non-judging attitude. With persistent practice, we discover the mind grows steadier and steadier, like that puppy who's more willing and able to stay.

Any other part of your immediate experience could serve as the object of your focus, for example, the places where the body touches the earth, the flow of thoughts or energetic channels, or a specific emotion are all options. As the mind grows quieter, a wider scope becomes available to us to investigate the fascinating interplay between all layers of being, such as how an emotion impacts sensation or what sensations tell us about energy flow.

Mindfulness of Breathing in Four Phases

The breath is a common object of focus used in Mindfulness concentration practices. To help strengthen our attentional muscles, the Buddha taught many variations of this simple breathing technique called Anapanasati, or Mindfulness of Breathing. Anapanasati uses the sensation of the breath as the object of focus. The primary intention of the exercise is to concentrate on your breath to help cultivate a steady awareness. One common variation includes four progressive breath awareness phases. We begin with the supplemental support of counting the breaths. We then release the counting and put all the focus on just feeling the breath for the remaining phases.

The instructions are simple. Whenever something besides the breath unravels your concentration, simply tag whatever it is that's pulling at your attention with a friendly tone. For example, say *thinking, thinking,* or *sleepy, sleepy,* or *daydreaming, daydreaming.* Just speak its name softly to yourself. Distraction comes...tag it, let it go, and rejoin the breath. Come back to breathing and how it feels in the body. When we invite ourselves back home to the moment with welcome, almost instantaneously we begin to feel a little bit better.

Guided Technique

Suggested Time: Fifteen minutes or more. Distribute the minutes between the stages equally. If time is short, adapt the exercise to include just one or two stages. If you have more time, extend each stage by a couple of minutes as you build up your concentration skills.

Suggested Use: Explore this technique as a sitting meditation when arriving to the mat or at the end of the Yin Yoga & Meditation session to expand on the steady awareness you've cultivated in class.

INSTRUCTIONS:

Find your meditative posture.

Begin to notice your breath. Let yourself breathe naturally. There's no need to direct or guide the breath.

Feel how your body breathes itself without any effort on your part.

Phase 1: Concentrate on and count the exhalations

Feel each exhalation, and to support the breath awareness, count each exhale at its end point. Exhale...then count one. Inhale. Exhale...then count two. Count your exhales like this from one to ten. When you reach ten, or if you get distracted and lose track, simply start again at one. The primary objective isn't so much to successfully reach ten but rather to maintain focus on the breath, so there's no need to judge yourself if your mind wanders. Just begin again with kindness and freshness.

Practitioner's Tip: Allow yourself to relax into the expansiveness of each out-breath. Invite the quality of a relaxed alertness, like the kind of attention you'd have if you were water skiing on your favorite lake one gorgeous summer day, riding the waves with finesse and ease. Not too tight, not too loose.

Phase 2: Concentrate on and count the inhalations

Feel each inhalation as it happens, and to support your sustained concentration, count each inhalation at its top end. Count your inhales from one to ten. Inhale...then count one. Exhale. Inhale...then count two, and so on. When you reach ten, or if you get sidetracked, simply start over at one. Practice tagging and releasing any thoughts or emotions. There will be time later to pick back up with anything that tugged at your attention.

Practitioner's Tip: Remember, we're not trying for an Olympics gold medal in breathing, so there's no need to alter or fix the breath in any way. We're simply using the natural flow of the inhale and exhale to help us stay present.

Phase 3: Concentrate on feeling and following the complete breath cycle without counting

For this next stage, if your mind is relatively stable, let go of the counting and become fully absorbed in the feel of the breath. Bring your awareness to the sensations of each in-breath and out-breath with warmth and fondness. Follow the entire breath cycle: the full in-breath, the full out-breath, and the duration of any pauses in between.

Phase 4: Single-pointed attention on the place of first breath sensation

For the last stage, become aware of the area of your body where you first feel the breath as you inhale. Use a handful of natural breaths to find its location. Maybe you feel it first on the upper lip, the tip of the nose, or inside the nose. Perhaps it's at the back of your throat, in your chest, low belly, or even through the whole body. This place could change with each practice, so find it freshly in this moment. Let your awareness rest tenderly there with interest as you notice what the sensations are like. Is there tingling, vibration, warmth, coolness, stretching, release, or a rise and fall?

Last Minute of Practice:

For the last final sixty seconds, enjoy the expanse of each life-giving breath. Just for this brief time, let your breath be more remarkable than anything else in the whole world. As the Zen adage goes, "Breathe in, breathe out. Breathe in, breathe out. Should we forget this, attaining enlightenment will be the least of our problems."

Post-Practice Reflections:

- Take a moment to reflect on any effects this technique has had on the condition of your body, mind, and heart. Acknowledge your commitment to the practice and the benefits it brings to you and those around you.
- Are there any circumstances off the mat in which the starting-over skill might be particularly helpful?

Acquainting Ourselves with Breath Sensations

A simple approach to training the awareness on the breath is to become aware of the sensations of your in-breath and out-breath. Once you've recaptured the attention by focusing on the breath, you have the ability to redirect it to whatever's happening in the present moment. Like a faithful friend, the breath is always able and willing to walk you home.

Guided Technique 1

> Suggested Time: Moments to minutes
>
> Suggested Use: Briefly integrate this breath inquiry in poses or counterposes. Explore it anytime during the day you need to come home to the moment.

Instructions:

Take these moments to sit with the movements your breath makes.

Follow the in-breath as it happens. Allow it to take its natural course as you track its sensations with your attention. Feel the out-breath as you watch it go.

Observe how your body's movements harmonize with its rhythms. Your most constant companion, this movement is the act of your body keeping itself alive.

Continue to watch how this breath flows without any instruction from you, how it just keeps going in and out, in and out.

If you notice you've become distracted, no worries, you know how to find your breath and follow it home. Trace it back home without judgment. Sense how the breath, your good and trustworthy friend, steadies you in this moment and takes you back to the home base of your body.

Guided Technique 2

> Suggested Time: Five minutes or more
>
> Suggested Use: Explore this technique as a sitting meditation when arriving to the mat, when resting in counterposes, or at the end of a Yin Yoga & Meditation session.

Instructions:

Begin by observing the rise and fall of your chest and belly, the gentle movements in the trunk of the body as the breath goes in and out.

Sense how gravity holds you to the earth in this slice of time and relish the simplicity of this moment, being here right now.

Follow the breath as you feel it coming in and going out without needing to arrange or manage it in any way. Feel how your body welcomes your breath and then allows it to leave.

Let your breathing muscles gently engage, then release.

As you keep a restful yet alert awareness on your breathing, notice if your breath begins to find a slower rhythm of its own accord, in-breath and out-breath extending.

There's no need to fix anything at all, nothing to do.

Notice where you feel the breath happening in your body. Is it in your lower belly, in the chest, in your throat, in your nose? On the skin of your face? Let your awareness touch lightly there, as a dragonfly rests upon a lotus flower. What do you feel there? Is there a transition point between cool and warm, expansion and contraction? What sensations does your breath carry with it?

Allow the breath to be how it is, where it is, as you feel how it flows. Relaxing your body with the breath, sense your relaxed mind and body creating space for the heart to breathe. Continue steadying your attention on the sensations of your breath a bit longer and returning with patience from any distraction.

Breath Mantra for Coming Home

The breath is like an ever-present taxicab leading us home to our body and to this moment. When our awareness rests entirely with our breath, there's no other place we're able to be than right here, right now. Breath mantras are simple aids that concentrate the mind with the support of just a few words spoken either softly aloud or silently to yourself.

Guided Technique

Suggested Time: Moments to minutes

Suggested Use: Try this breath mantra exercise as a brief interlude throughout your Yin Yoga & Meditation session to re-anchor the attention in the body or during sitting meditation at the start or end of class.

Instructions:

Keep your attention on your natural breath as much as possible while all else moves into and through your mind. Follow each breath like a taxicab driving you home to the body in this present time. When we get on board, no matter where we are, we ride it home to this moment, right here, every time.

Whisper to yourself as you breathe these few words:

Breathing in...Here.

Breathing out...Now.

No need to hurry the breath, just let it arrive in its own time.

Breathing in...Here.

Breathing out...Now.

Shorten the mantra even more if you'd like.

In...Here.

Out...Now.

Continue in this way for a few minutes, attention only on breathing in...Here...and breathing out...Now...

Relaxed, alert, Here...Now.

Scanning the Body for Physical Sensations

As we've been learning, Yin Yoga requires that we stay attentive to the body's physical sensations to stay safe and make sure we're getting maximum benefit from our practice. Mentally scanning the body regularly throughout our practice session helps us locate and concentrate on the quality of the sensations we're feeling.

The words we speak carry enormous energy, whether we're speaking to others or just narrating our experience internally. As you work with these guided scans, stay loving in your mental tone while observing and identifying the sensations arising in your body. Unless they're pain, try to simply welcome them in a friendly way. As a refresher on characterizing painful sensations, revisit the "Move Mindfully to Mild Sensation" practice principle at anytime. If you feel tempted to judge what you find or resist what you experience, see instead if you're able to watch with kind eyes and speak with softness.

Guided Technique 1

Suggested Time: Moments to minutes

Suggested Use: Try this technique in any pose or restful counterpose to draw the attention to the physical sensations the shape creates.

Instructions:

If you carry a candle into a dark room, the flame will dance and sway as you walk.

When you stop moving, it will gradually steady and shine in complete stillness.

Let your mind settle like this, a steady shining on the inside space of your body.

Shine the candlelight of your awareness through the interior of your tissues, like a gentle searchlight illuminating the sensations arising within your body.

What are you finding and feeling? One by one, concentrate on each. What is its location? How would you describe its shape or texture? Is it static and stable, or fluid and moving? What about its intensity? Is it bright or subtle? Unless you're sensing painful or warning sign sensations, how does it feel to let things be just as they are?

Keep placing the soft and curious spotlight of your attention on each sensation as it arises. Practice remaining open to whatever you're finding and feeling, resisting any temptation to judge as you watch and feel.

Guided Technique 2

Suggested Time: Moments to minutes

Suggested Use: Explore this exercise in any pose to draw the attention to the physical sensations the shape creates.

Instructions:

Slowly and gently move your awareness through the internal landscape of your body, scanning from top to bottom for any physical sensations.

As you become aware of the area of strongest sensation, allow your attention to rest with it, simply observing what it is. Inquire, is your breath easy and slow? If it's labored in any way, make adjustments to the pose until it settles.

Continue to watch the physical body. As long as the sensations are reasonable, how does it feel to let them be as they are for now? Let the guardian of curiosity accompany you as you watch your body...do you feel any internal space arising?

When ready, move the attention to the next more subtle sensation, staying with feeling this sensation for a time.

Keep tracing your focus deeper inward along the tissues to feel for ever-more subtle sensations as they happen in the body...aware of your sensing self growing more and more perceptive.

Guided Technique 3

Suggested Time: Ten minutes

Suggested Use: This scan builds body awareness and is easily abbreviated or lengthened as needed, making it a good fit for a sitting meditation at the start or end of your Yin Yoga & Meditation session. When inserted at the beginning or end of your mat time, scanning helps attune to the body's ever-changing needs as well as observe the impacts of our practice.

INSTRUCTIONS:

Begin by finding a comfortable meditative posture.

Sensations are the language of the body, so we'll feel for them here, listening on the inside.

As you mentally scan, bring a curious, non-judging awareness to your body. Let your inquisitive attention be friendly and linger several moments with each area to feel any of its physical sensations. Allow your body to communicate any areas of tightness that need release, healing, or extra tending, as well as any areas that feel vibrant, healthy, and open.

Let your attention now move into the feet and ankles. Feel any sensations arising in the feet and toes. Next, notice the ankle joints. How do the ankles feel?

Let the mind move upward into the lower legs, knee joints, and upper thighs. Notice sensations in each part of the legs as your attention glides through them at a pace that allows you to feel each area fully.

Move your awareness into the hip joints. Do you notice any sensations arising inside the hips? Stay curious and be a compassionate observer.

Now traveling into the low belly...are you experiencing any sensations there, or is it neutral? Either way, it's OK, just keep sensing. Feel for what's happening deep in the lower abdomen and into the lower back. Whatever you're noticing, there's no need to solve or improve upon anything.

What about the stomach, the chest, and the heart? Notice, what are you feeling in this moment? Keep letting go of thoughts about anything else, just notice the sensations as they present themselves.

Feel the mid and upper back, observing what's there without adding the burden of any expectations.

Move your mind through the length of the spine from the tailbone to the top of the head. Observe how the spine feels, receiving any information your body offers. No need to judge or resist anything, simply feel it and allow it to be there.

Let the mind travel up into the shoulder joints now, observe how the shoulders feel.

Next, move your awareness down through the bones of the upper arms at each side of the body, into the crooks of the arms, inside the elbow. Feel into the lower arms, wrists, and hands. Glide the attention upward through the arms and into the neck. Are you feeling any sensations in the neck?

From the neck, move the awareness into the face and head. Just focus on observing and feeling, you don't need to do anything about the sensations you're finding.

Now expand your inner perception to encompass your whole body. Feel the sensations of every part of you collectively, resting with them all at once for a few moments, feeling and welcoming the entire body just as it is with your warm affection.

Concentrating on the Waves of the Mind

The brain thinks...thank goodness! Sometimes, though, those thoughts may carry us away from the present moment. In this concentration meditation exercise, we use the image of a boat tied to a dock to help us explore the changing mental landscape within us, bringing the attention to the thoughts constantly flowing through the mind like waves in an ocean. As the steady breath keeps us moored to the present time, we explore observing and allowing the waves of thoughts as they rise and fall within us.

Guided Technique

Suggested Time: Ten minutes or more, or a few moments

Suggested Use: This technique lends itself to sitting meditation and is also useful in an abbreviated format while holding the postures.

Instructions:

Allow your mind to fully inhabit your body. Start by focusing on the breath. Feel each in-breath and out-breath. Feel carefully the pathway each breath follows as it flows. Stay with this for some moments, concentrating on your easy breath.

Imagine now that your awareness is like a boat, bobbing and rocking in the waves while tied to the dock of the present moment by the rope of your breath. Like a boat feels the waves in the water as they come and go but it isn't carried away by them, let your attention be anchored to the here and now by the rope of your breath.

The mind is like an ocean full of waves, thoughts flowing in and thoughts flowing out. As you relax with the breath, watch for waves within the mind.

If a wave of thought arises, observe it. Name it kindly as you watch this thought-wave until it changes into a different thought, or it slowly subsides and dissolves. Whether it is a strategizing thought, a fantasizing thought, a worrying thought, or a happy thought, give each thought a name, then let it go...letting it come, letting it pass. Come back to the rope of your breath, holding you steady to the dock of the present time.

Practitioner's Tip: As you watch the flow of thoughts, remind yourself: *I am not my thoughts. They are just waves flowing through the vast ocean of my mind.*

Post-Practice Reflections:

- As you watched the waves in the ocean of your mind, did you notice any patterns of thinking manifest themselves? Do you see any recurring themes to your thoughts?
- How would you describe the tone you were able to use when tagging the thoughts? Consider, did you find yourself beginning to judge or did you speak sweetly, with kindness?
- How can awareness of thought-waves help you during your week? Is there a situation at home or work where stopping for a few moments and naming thoughts would benefit you or those around you?

Heart Gardening Practices for Unconditional Love and Compassion

These exercises of the heart invite us on a journey of remembering and coming home. We come home to the basic truth that you, me, and everyone who lives shares: we all desire and deserve to be safe, happy, and loved on this earth, and we all share the same capacity for loss and suffering. At times, we might become disconnected from the naturally soft and abundant heart of compassion within each of us. Lovingkindness, or metta, retraces the pathway home.

There are many variations of the traditional meditation technique called the Metta Bhavana, or cultivation of lovingkindness. You can think of it as a form of prayer not contained by any religion. In the Metta Bhavana, we cultivate feelings of metta towards ourselves and extend this same unconditional love, compassion, and empathetic care toward others. These heart-tending techniques cultivate and nurture our innate capacity to open with tenderness and clearer understanding, even in challenging circumstances or toward those with whom we have some difficulty. Honoring our shared experience, we offer unconditional wishes of happiness to all, with no exceptions.

By concentrating on the energy of lovingkindness, we consciously set up the conditions for positive emotions to arise, just as we use soil and water to help seeds grow. Retraining the mind and heart requires patience. We can't force a seed to grow by simply telling it to; we need to create favorable conditions and nurture the seed. Eventually, we notice cumulative changes as we start to make some different choices, one thought, one word, one action at a time. Like the sunflower that just keeps turning its face toward the sun, we continue to turn our faces toward love.

Lovingkindness practice clears pathways to forgiveness and activates the empathy and compassion centers in the brain, curbing self-criticism and judgment of others. This technique may, at times, bring up hurts or other buried emotions. If this happens, try to acknowledge what you're feeling without judging it or needing it to be some other way right now. Know that if it feels difficult at that moment, it's OK. We all encounter strong or troublesome feeling states sometimes. Though it may be challenging, giving ourselves the chance to *feel* without getting entangled in any storylines or resistance becomes a natural part of our healing process. If you find any painful or bristly feelings bubbling to the surface, first offer yourself a few moments of gentle care, laying your hands on your heart, saying, "*Whatever it is, it's OK.*"

In times that feel unsettling and uncertain, metta is a transformative gift we give to the world. Lovingkindness helps us offer every situation, good or bad, and every person, friendly or not, the very best of who we are. This, in turn, provides them the opportunity to experience the very best of who *they* are. This deep, genuine care for one another is the ever-expanding energy of metta: fundamental loving connection, without condition, circulating and sending itself endlessly outward in all directions. Metta is our truest nature.

Guided Technique 1: Cultivating Lovingkindness with the Metta Bhavana

In the following guided meditation, we'll explore a Metta Bhavana variation with six stages, offering the energy of lovingkindness to different people within each. Experiment with reordering the stages or adapting the meditation to include various people, maybe someone who has nurtured you, teachers or mentors, mother earth, or distinct communities, to name a few. You also have the option of adjusting the duration of the stages.

Should you have limited time for your meditation session, pick just a couple of stages to work with. Make the commitment to always include yourself, though – your happiness is central in your desire to help others be happy. As the Buddha wrote in the *Sedaka Sutta*, "Looking after oneself, one looks after others. Looking after others, one looks after oneself." Offering loving attention to yourself is just as important as any other stage. We need healthy self-love and appreciation to be happy and give and receive love.

> Suggested Time: Start with two to three minutes per stage and extend as desired
>
> Suggested Use: Lovingkindness practice is a quieting and heart-ful way to begin a Yin Yoga & Meditation session or to weave throughout the class, sprinkling the stages into any of the more restful, supportive poses or counterposes. Aids such as mudras and stories are ways to ground and enhance the exercise. This metta practice also makes a wonderful standalone practice to regularly integrate into your meditation schedule.

INSTRUCTIONS:

Stage 1: Someone beloved, unconditionally loving

Bring to mind someone you open to effortlessly, someone you care for, someone who's always been there for you, like a grandmother or beloved friend, or maybe a cherished pet. Picture this precious being. Take time to bring their beautiful face fully into your heart-mind. Imagine giving them a present or see them doing something that brings them great delight. Perhaps visualize being on a fun adventure or doing something silly together, or maybe the two of you sitting peacefully in a favorite place.

Breathe naturally as you enjoy this image in your mind. With your heartfelt energy behind the intention, inwardly repeat these phrases during your exhales:

May you be safe...

May you be happy...

May you be healthy...

May you be filled with lovingkindness...

Use these affirmations or choose phrases of your own. Say them slowly with the out-breath. Pause between breaths to feel the effects and stay receptive to whatever you're feeling. Feel how wonderful it is to extend these loving thoughts to someone so treasured. Letting the phrases fill with feeling, allow each to echo in your heartspace.

Stage 2: Yourself

Remember a moment you felt really happy or, if you prefer, imagine what would make you happy. Is there a place you'd like to go, a new experience you'd like to have?

Take some moments to bring vivid details to mind: sights, sounds, smells, anyone who is with you. How does it feel? Allow a soft smile to form, smoothing any tension in the face. Savor this moment.

As you breathe out, offer yourself prayers of lovingkindness, letting each be spacious and sincere:

May I be safe...

May I be happy...

May I be healthy...

May I be filled with lovingkindness...

Give yourself space to feel the effects of each affirmation as you say them to yourself. If you feel any resistance to receiving your loving affection, it's OK, and there's no need to judge.

Maybe place the palms of your hands over your heart to soften the inner landscape and quiet any self-judgment or doubting that you are worthy of these blessings. Tenderly remind yourself that you want and deserve to be happy. As you continue with these self-blessings, see in your mind's eye how people who love you look at you and smile.

Stage 3: Someone Undergoing a Difficult Circumstance

Consider someone you know who is moving through a particularly challenging circumstance. Maybe it's due to a health or financial situation, racial and social inequities, or maybe grief around a difficult loss. While it's not always possible to take away someone's pain or resolve their difficult circumstances, one thing we can always do is offer the blessing of lovingkindness and compassion.

Bring your attention to the person who is experiencing this difficult time. Let the door of your heart open to the pain they're feeling. With your heart available to them, they will not need to suffer this challenging circumstance alone.

May you be safe...

May you be happy...

May you be healthy...

May you be filled with lovingkindness...

Even if you are not near this person right now, feel how the energy of lovingkindness you send reaches them. Nothing is capable of stopping metta. No landscape is too wild, no distance too great. Maintain your concentration on sending them these loving wishes...sense it go to them and surround them, like the supportive arms of a caring friend.

Stage 4: A Neutral Person

The next stage invites you to now take your focus to a neutral person, someone you don't know well or have strong positive or negative feelings toward. The neutral person is someone you might normally disregard or not pay much attention to, like someone standing in line with you, a person stocking shelves at the market, someone beside you on a bus or subway, or someone walking down the street. Sending loving attention to a neutral person helps us recognize that strangers are not so strange. They, too, share a fundamental desire to be happy and free. We connect to our humanity by affirming theirs.

Bring a neutral person to mind, letting whoever arises take shape in your mind.

Use the same metta phrases in the same way, slowly with your out-breath.

May you be safe...

May you be happy...

May you be healthy...

May you be filled with lovingkindness...

Here we are planting seeds of love and watering them on behalf of even those we don't know. Lots of feeling might not blossom right away, and that's OK. The seed does not need to flower immediately. Plant, trusting that your gardening will be successful.

Stage 5: A Person You Have Some Difficulty With

Now think of someone you have difficulty with in your life. No need to begin with your biggest enemy, just someone you don't see eye-to-eye with, someone you disagree with, or maybe someone you'd like to forgive. The teachings say this is the person who sits on the bridge between conditional and unconditional caring. This vital stage stretches our ability to recognize that even those with whom we're experiencing difficulty, whether small or large, want to be happy and without suffering. This stage gives us a chance to wish that for them, too. Remember, metta isn't pretending, it's gardening. We're not pretending we think they're great or that we have rosy feelings for them, we just recognize that, like us, they too want to be happy.

Bring your concentration to this person. If you experience some measure of resistance, recognize that it feels hard right now and know that it's OK. Try to steady your heart with your breath. If possible, reflect on any good qualities you've ever seen in this person, perhaps a kind act they've done for someone or a kind word they've offered.

Repeat these same metta phrases slowly and know that you're not denying or disregarding the reality of the problem. You're simply focusing on something good right now.

May you be safe...

May you be happy...

May you be healthy...

May you be filled with lovingkindness...

If you notice opposition or objection in the heart, offer yourself loving attention because you're suffering right now. There is enough gentle caring to share.

Stage 6: All Sentient Beings Everywhere

The final phase is offering lovingkindness to all beings everywhere. Here we wish for all beings, large and small, known and unknown, to be happy and free.

Begin to spread your good wishes outward, imagining them spreading to all of your loved ones and all of their loved ones, too. See the ripples of love extend further and further, rippling outward to include all people everywhere — whoever they are, wherever they are, every person in every town, every state, every country, near and far. Watch as they ripple to all creatures, too: the birds above us, the insects below us, mammals and reptiles on all continents, whales and fish in the ocean. With the out-breath, sending out the energy of deep care and love.

May you be safe...

May you be happy...

May you be healthy...

May you be filled with lovingkindness...

May all beings in every place be safe, happy, healthy, and filled with lovingkindness, free from all suffering.

Feel yourself as a blazing sun that shines warmth and love to all beings equally, wishing them all to be happy and free from suffering. Let scenes of togetherness and peace from around the world come to your mind, seeing metta flowing through their hearts and faces.

As you're sending the energies of happiness, comfort, and safety for all, sense how you're holding the whole world in your heart. Your heart is that big and that spacious. Let this pure goodness fill every part of you.

Post-Practice Reflections:

Stay inquisitive and kind as you inquire...

- Did you notice any differences between the various Metta Bhavana stages and people you chose? Did any of the stages feel more or less accessible than any other?
- How did it feel to offer yourself these well wishes, was there anything surprising?
- How would you describe the sound of your inner voice if your mind wandered or if you encountered internal dialogue?

Guided Technique 2: A Massage for the Heart

Although life has us moving through different circumstances, experiencing different internal emotional weather and landscapes, each of us has a natural capacity to find the peace and healing inherently possible in each moment.

> Suggested Time: Five to fifteen minutes
>
> Suggestions for Use: Explore this heart nurturing technique in a Yin Yoga & Meditation session as a sitting meditation or enjoy anytime during the day to connect with the sacred heart beating inside you.

Instructions:

Find a comfortable meditative seat, enjoy a strong back and open heart.

Allow your breath to be easy and spontaneous.

Just breathing in and breathing out, coming home to this place and this time.

Feel your breath rise and fall.

Begin to notice the harmony that exists between the movements of the body and the breath.

Breathing in – diaphragm moving down, contracting.

Breathing out – diaphragm moving up, releasing.

In-breath and out-breath, one seamless whole.

Your good heart is held by a membrane called the pericardium, there to support your heart. The pericardium connects to your diaphragm.

When you breathe in, diaphragm lowers, pericardium and heart descend.

When you breath out, diaphragm lifts, pericardium and heart ascend.

In this way, each breath, a massage for your heart.

What a good gift your breath gives to your heart.

Just one of many tiny miracles happening this moment, your good body giving this gift to itself.

Heart and breath, loving friends that move as one.

What beautiful generosity to witness.

Breathing in, my heart opens to receive the gifts of each moment.

Breathing out, I send this light and love outward into the world.

May you remember the beautiful, good heart within you.

May it shine naturally outward, touching with kindness everyone you meet.

Continue to breathe in and out, massaging your good heart, for as long as you desire.

Guided Technique 3: A Simple Heart Scan for Working with Difficult Emotions

When we work compassionately with the body, we bring a gentle touch to our mental and emotional states as well. While the work on the mat often ushers in a sense of deep peace and relief, it's not always easy, so remember that there's no one right or wrong way to feel while you practice Yin Yoga & Meditation. If a difficult emotion surfaces, remain gentle with it, observing its effect within you with tenderness.

It's not always the right moment to feel an unpleasant or challenging emotion. Should you encounter something you're not sure you're ready to feel or release, it's absolutely OK to take a break from the exercise and focus on something or someone that brings you comfort. Give yourself permission to simply rest with your natural, easy breath rhythm for as long as you need. Feel your way forward in your experience without rushing, without judgment, and without forcing. Know that you can trust yourself to discover what you most need.

If we encounter a difficult emotion, our yin guardian the breath helps us offer our feelings a warm welcome. In the following heart scan, we train our spirits to offer a difficult emotion a tender hello and understanding.

> Suggested Time: Moments to minutes
>
> Suggested Use: Try this exercise anytime during the Yin Yoga & Meditation session or the course of your day when you encounter a difficult emotion and you'd benefit from holding yourself with some extra tenderness and care.

INSTRUCTIONS:

Request your focus to settle fully inward now, moving quietly into the space of the heart.

Remember, there's no perfect way to feel or be in this moment.

Say these words softly or silently to yourself:

Breathing in, I recognize this feeling is present in me right now.

Breathing out, it's OK.

Breathing in, this feeling is present.

Breathing out, OK.

Whatever feeling it is, can you name it? Not with judgment or resistance, just recognition. Let it show its face to you. Do you sense any spaciousness and release that comes with just this little bit of allowing?

Continue to use your awareness to soften the muscles all through the body.

Say to this feeling: I see you. It's OK that you're here.

Let the breath help you hold it. Inhale, the feeling is here...exhale, it's OK.

If this is hard, acknowledge that it's challenging right now. Some emotions are more difficult to host than others.

If there is any unhelpful commentary creeping in, look at that with kindness, too. Keep a light touch as you remind yourself that no feeling is right or wrong. Feelings are just feelings. Keep breathing and know it won't always be this way.

Stay curious and watchful. See if it's possible to notice the emotion showing itself in the body. Is how you're feeling accompanied by any physical sensations? Is there a knotted stomach, tension in the shoulder shoulders, a tight chest, or a clenching jaw?

What happens if you send your breath to that part of your body as a messenger of kindness, release, and love? Maybe there's an easy flow of in-breath and out-breath, a wide-open chest, relaxed temples, and softened eyes.

As you continue to breathe deeply and relax the body, does this influence how you feel?

Sense what happens as you hold yourself and this feeling with tender care.

Breathe here for as long as you'd like. In...Here, Out...OK. Held in this moment, body, mind, heart, all safe, all together, all loved.

Guided Technique 4: Concentrating on the Thankful Heart

Consciously welcoming the energy of gratitude into our practice helps us recognize and enjoy the good gifts its energy brings. Gratitude encourages us to pause and embrace the many wonders surrounding us, whether on the mat or in our day, and becomes a gift we offer by extension to all those around us. This meditation creates a simple sacred moment to breathe well and connect with the energy of gratitude in appreciation for the many sweet blessings in our life.

> Suggested Time: Two to three minutes
>
> Suggested Use: This heart-ful concentration exercise is an inspiring and loving way to seal your Yin Yoga & Meditation session journey with a few moments of quiet, supportive reflection.

INSTRUCTIONS:

Come into a comfortable seated position.

Bring your hands together into a prayerful position in front of the heart, creating Anjali mudra.

We touch the palms of our hands in this way as an act of care and connection, bringing near what is far apart, what is separate, together. We do this at our heart center, a fundamental gesture of wholeness and gratitude.

Open a slight place between the palms, creating room for space and air.

It's been said that forming Anjali mudra is like holding a tiny innocent bird in your hands. It's that soft and gentle.

In this moment, allow something to surface in your mind and heart that you're grateful for. Someone you love, a joyful memory, something about your body, whatever arises. Inhale slowly, allowing this blessing to fill your hands.

Imagine your hands holding this precious thing of beauty safely in front of the heartspace. Hold it with tenderness and appreciation in your hands as if cradling a precious little bird close to your heart.

Let your head bow. Exhale slowly, gratitude emanating from the place of your heart.

Allow your hands to open and let the precious wings of your heart fly free, a gift of gratitude to all.

Hear the sweet and soft words of thank you, thank you as they grace the air around you...thank you, thank you, thank you.

Guided Technique 5: Reclaiming Your Preciousness from the Inside Out

Pausing to take a few moments each day to reconnect with and reclaim our preciousness is an uncomplicated, heartfelt way to offer ourselves and the world around us a bit more of the comfort, joy, healing, and peace we all deserve.

> Suggested Time: Five minutes
>
> Suggested Use: The reclaiming preciousness meditation fits especially well as a sitting meditation and could also be enjoyed during your day anytime you feel like reconnecting with your precious and sacred nature.

Instructions:

To begin, wherever you are, start there.

Look toward the sky and smile, then take three intentional, nourishing breaths...

Identify one precious thing about yourself. Maybe it's the instinctual kindness of your heart, how you reach out to others, how you listen well, or how you give freely of your time and energy. Maybe it's the strength of your body and your dedication to its health, how it moves you so effortlessly through your day. Or maybe the clarity and curiosity of your mind, how it engages with the world and allows you to express yourself fully.

Reflect for just a few moments in appreciation for this one precious thing...seeing and feeling how it supports you, your loved ones, and the wider world around you...how this one thing spreads itself beautifully out into the world.

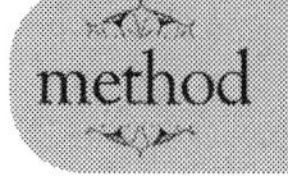

Breathing in...sense how it feels to acknowledge and appreciate this precious thing about you, let the feelings of goodness seep into every cell of your body.

Breathing out...sending that gentle appreciation and beauty outward to touch all those around you.

Identify now something precious about your life, about your family, your circumstances, environment, career, or your larger circle of loved ones. Breathe in and out; allow the appreciation of this preciousness to fill you and then move itself outward into the world.

Now call to mind one precious thing about the world – this living and loving planet that so gently hugs you close, and this grand universe of which we all are a part. Breathing in this preciousness...breathing it out as a gift back to the world.

Allow yourself to rest in these feelings for a bit of time, breathing in, breathing out...steeping fully in the preciousness of this beautiful moment.

Yoga Nidra-Inspired Methods

Another aspect of our Mandala Map, the collection of meditative methods below is inspired by the Yoga Nidra tradition. Yoga Nidra techniques invite us to intentionally release unconscious muscular tensions, clearing the pathway for the stresses of the Yin Yoga exercise to sink below the surface of the body and be more readily absorbed by the targeted yin tissues. These Yoga Nidra-inspired techniques soothe our central nervous system and encourage our attention to focus on what we're experiencing inside. As we train in easefully observing all that arises, whether sensations, thoughts, or feelings, we build our ability to respond skillfully and compassionately to our experiences and coach the mind to maintain a relaxed focus, regardless of the circumstances.

Research has shown that many of these integral Yoga Nidra body and breath awareness methods provide what is called a "generalization effect," producing long-term benefits extending off the mat and into the rest of life.[2] With consistent practice, our mind sharpens, we sleep better, and we feel happier and more at ease. In addition to systematically peeling back layers of physical and mental tension, Yoga Nidra employs the aids of guided imagery and visualization to refine our inner eye and access our pure potential to realize our heart's highest desires.

In addition to integrating them into your Yin Yoga & Meditation practice, you might also enjoy any of these guided techniques on their own while in a relaxing position, such as any of the Savasana pose variations (see Savasana Yin Asana Spotlight, p. 179). Practice them in any safe space that allows you to comfortably close your eyes and internalize your awareness.

Whole-Body Release with Autogenics

Using our intentional attention, we uncover our capability to call up physical relaxation through mental suggestion. Known as Autogenics, Johannes Schulz and Wolfgang Luthe developed this practice in the mid-20th century. Autogenics involves silently repeating restful messages directly to your body to promote ease and deliver a host of other benefits. Studies have shown the Autogenics technique to be effective in treating mild to moderate hypertension, asthma, anxiety, and sleep disorders and assist with pain management.[3]

The repeated messages often begin with physical sensations like heaviness (e.g., "my arm feels heavy") or temperature (e.g., "my body is growing warmer") and then move on to physiological processes typically controlled by the autonomic nervous system, such as stabilizing the heartbeat, soothing the stomach and GI tract, and so on. Autogenics helps bring automatic, unconscious physical reactions under conscious control by repeating the basic instructional statements softly until the desired outcome occurs. Each of the following Autogenics guided relaxation techniques focus on aiding the release of tensions through the whole body.

Guided Technique 1

Suggested Time: Five to ten minutes

Suggested Use: Experiment with this Autogenics exercise as part of your Savasana experience at the end of your Yin Yoga & Meditation session or enjoy it as a standalone exercise while in a comfortable resting position of choice.

Instructions:

Close your eyes now, if you'd like, to guide your attention inward.

Breathe slowly as you relax. Inhale...pause. Exhale...pause. Very smooth and slow.

Squeeze your closed eyes, holding them like that for a few seconds, then let your eyes totally relax. Do this a few times.

Now bring your awareness to your arms and repeat these phrases silently to yourself...

My arms are getting very relaxed and heavy...

My arms are more and more relaxed, getting very heavy...

Repeat this to yourself a few times, letting the feeling of relaxation and heaviness absorb into your arms. Feel the insides of the arms getting heavier. Heavier and heavier from the inside out.

Say to yourself: My arms are very relaxed and getting heavier.

Simply stay aware...allow the experience to be natural and unrushed.

Now bring your attention to your legs, and repeat these phrases silently to yourself...

My legs are getting very relaxed and heavy...

My legs are more and more relaxed, heavier and heavier...

Keep repeating this softly to yourself several times...

Feel the sensations of relaxation and heaviness settle into your legs. Feel the insides of the legs relaxed and heavy.

Say to yourself: My legs are very relaxed and getting heavier.

If any distractions pull you away, simply bring your mind back to your body and the increasing sense of heaviness in your arms and legs.

Next, bring your awareness to your whole body as you repeat to yourself: My whole body is getting more and more relaxed.

My whole body feels heavier and more relaxed.

My whole body is very heavy, very relaxed.

Keep letting the sensations of relaxation and heaviness settle, feeling the weighty sensations filling your whole body from the inside.

The earth is holding your whole body to its side; there's nothing for you to do but notice the sensations now.

Whole body heavy, whole body held. Just noticing.

Aware of any mental activity, now repeat these phrases silently to yourself...

My mind is spacious and relaxed.

My mind is very spacious and relaxed.

Keep repeating this message softly to yourself several times.

Feel the relaxation spread through your mind, with more and more space between each thought. Notice how spacious and relaxed your mind is becoming.

Scan your whole body with your awareness now, sensing how relaxed and open it feels.

Rest for a few moments to a few minutes, enjoying this soothing, tranquil state.

Guided Technique 2

Suggested Time: Five to ten minutes

Suggested Use: Experiment with this Autogenics exercise as part of your Savasana experience at the end of your Yin Yoga & Meditation session or enjoy it as a standalone exercise anytime you could benefit from some extra ease. It can be abbreviated to a handful of moments to encourage relaxation while holding a pose or during your resting counterpose time.

INSTRUCTIONS:

Feel your breath becoming more relaxed and gentle.

Feel the crown of your head relax.

Relax the brow and feel both the temples relax.

Feel the places around the eyes soften and relax.

Expand the feeling deeper behind your closed eyes, letting pure relaxation spread into the brain.

Sense the space within the brain, open and relaxed.

Relax the cheekbones.

Relax the tongue and allow it to fall from the roof of your mouth.

Relax the lips.

Relax the jaw.

Feel the whole face and head relax.

Relax the throat and feel the neck relaxing.

Let the shoulders relax and release.

Relax now the right upper arm, the right forearm.

Relax all the way down through the right arm and into the right palm. Relax all five fingers.

Relax the left upper arm, the left forearm.

Relax all the way down the left arm and into the palm of your left hand. Relax those fingers too.

Relax the upper back and its shoulder blades.

Relax the entire front of chest. Feel the heart relaxing, nestled within the chest.

Let the muscles of the abdomen relax. Feel the middle of the back relaxing.

Keep relaxing the breath.

Feel relaxation filling the bowl of the belly, relaxation spilling over and flowing into the lower back.

Feel the hips now relaxing.

Relax the right leg – its thigh, knee, ankle. Relax the right foot. And the right toes.

Now relax the left leg – thigh, knee, ankle. Relax the left foot. Relax those toes too.

Feel the whole body free from any tension or gripping, your entire body, relaxing.

Bring your awareness to the heartspace, settling your attention there for a bit now.

Awareness deep in silence and stillness, resting fully in the space of your heart.

Sense your heart open, safe, as spacious as the sky, calm, expanding infinitely outward in all directions.

Enjoying being the beautiful, miraculous spirit you are, stay here for as long as you need, entirely at ease and relaxed.

Melting Away Tension Using Progressive Muscle Relaxation

Progressive Muscle Relaxation (PMR) uses a yang-like contraction of the muscles to experience tension, then enjoy its opposite, yin-like relaxation, upon release. This kind of yang-yin muscular cycle helps us grow keenly familiar with how both tension and relaxation feel, sensitizing us to the differences between them. Because much of the tightness we carry in our bodies is often unconscious, being adept at noticing when an area is tense gives us an added chance to intervene, soften, and relish the relief.

In PMR, we consciously bring tension to a group of muscles for a few seconds, then release it, allowing the area to relax completely. This systematic tensing and releasing helps shed the armor of long-standing tensions and stress, bringing relaxation to the musculature. PMR has been shown to aid recovery from a host of medical and psychological conditions, with the potential to offer relief from depression, fatigue, anxiety, headaches, insomnia, pain, panic attacks, and negative emotions, overall enhancing quality of life and sense of wellbeing.[4]

When practicing PMR, the instructions are to tighten a specific group of muscles using about half of your available strength, enough to notice the tension but never painful. After five to ten seconds of a moderate squeeze, release and pause for ten to twenty seconds to rest before beginning to tense again. As you begin to squeeze each set of muscles, inhale slowly. Depending on what feels best for you, choose to hold the breath during the period of contraction or simply breathe naturally. In either case, as you release the muscular tension, practice simultaneously releasing the breath. Aligning the letting go of physical tension with your slow, long exhale enhances the relaxation. Whether the muscle group is tense or released, maintain awareness of the sensations that emerge. As you focus on each muscle group, do your best to let the rest of your body remain loose. For a more complete circuit, methodically work your way through the entire body, exercising each major muscle group at least once in this tense-release cycle. Rescan the body, and if you find any particularly tight muscles, you may choose to repeat the process with those.

Guided Technique 1

Suggested Time: Moments to minutes

Suggested Use: This abbreviated version of PMR is a short and sweet way to relax and soften a bit more into your poses. Integrate a whole-body squeeze and release cycle just after settling into the shape or maybe a focus on the areas of sensations part way through the pose. Both are great options.

Instructions:

As you inhale slowly and deeply through the nose, moderately engage all of your muscles. Be sure to find them all, each and every one. Take your time. Squeeze your toes and feet, legs, buttocks, belly, fingers, hands and arms, shoulders, all the muscles of the face.

Hold this full body squeeze, keeping all the muscles activated for a few seconds. Feel them all squeezed at the same time.

Then, slowly exhale out of the nose as you relax all the muscles simultaneously...letting them all go.

Breathe naturally as you give your full attention to the sensations of ease spread through you.

Perhaps now you spend a few moments moving your attention back through the body, slowly scanning with kindness to look for any places where tightness remains.

If you come upon any areas that are still holding on, emphasize that tension by squeezing those muscles as you breathe in, hold the contraction a few seconds, then on the out-breath, release that tension, letting the muscles completely relax.

Continue with this technique once or twice more by locating any other areas of tension, perhaps focusing on the places being stimulated by the Yin Yoga exercise.

For each area, inhale to tense, lengthening the contraction hold time to five to ten seconds, then on the exhale, let any tension or holding fall away as you rest with muscles disengaged.

Attune to the effects as you rest in the pauses for a few seconds between the cycles.

Notice how you feel after you've completed this technique. What has your experience been like? What changes do you sense?

Guided Technique 2

Suggested Time: Ten minutes

Suggested Use: Depending on your intention and how much time you have for your day's practice, use this whole-body PMR method as a way to arrive to the mat and settle the body before entering your poses. Try this exercise as a lead-in to your Savasana experience at the end of your Yin Yoga & Meditation session.

Practitioner's Tip: If you're using this technique as entry into the Savasana experience, providing plenty of time to rest in silence at the end of the exercise is quite nurturing, offering the chance to steep quietly in the bountiful gifts of the practice.

INSTRUCTIONS:

If you'd like, now practice tensing and releasing the different parts of your body. The basic instruction is to inhale and methodically tighten all the muscles in each part, hold mild tension there while you hold the breath or simply breathe naturally, then release slowly the breath along with the muscular tension, relaxing that part wholly.

As you tense and release, keep full awareness on this part of the body and the sensations you're experiencing. Throughout the exercise, breathe fully and easefully so you're not over-exerting in any way.

Begin now with the face. Breathe in and tense all the muscles in your face, including those of your mouth, cheeks, forehead, around the eyes. All the muscles tense. Feel the tension, the holding.

Now with full awareness, release the breath and the muscles within the face. Feel the relaxation now in your face.

Let your head rock from side to side slowly, sensing the slight pressure in the muscles of the neck. Pause and allow the head to return to the center in stillness. Feel the muscles release.

Inhale and tense your shoulders now, pulling them up and up toward your ears. Hold for just a moment, then with a long exhalation, release, pausing to enjoy whatever sensations relaxation brings.

Bring tension now to your entire right arm as you breathe in, tense all the way from the shoulders to the tips of your fingers. Create a closed fist and even raise your arm slightly away from the floor, bringing tension into the muscles of your whole arm. Pause.

With full awareness, breathe out as you release to your right arm. Feel the tension and tightness evaporating, right arm relaxing.

Make your left arm tense now in the same way as you inhale, the whole of the left arm, with a tiny fist and scrunched up fingers, let the arm lift slightly. Pause.

Now release the breath and all those muscles. Feel the relaxation as tensions fade.

Breathe in to help squeeze the muscles of your torso now, feeling tension increase in the chest and the abdomen as you gently pull the navel toward the spine. Tension arising through all of your center. Pause. Let go with the breath and feel the release.

Inhaling now, tense the right hip and buttock. Pause...exhale and release.

Inhale and tense the whole of the right leg, all the way down into the feet as you scrunch the toes. Let the tension lift the leg slightly up. Pause. Release with the out-breath. Continue to maintain full attention on the muscles as they tense and then as they relax through the exhale.

With the in-breath, tense the left hip and buttocks in the same way...and release. Feel relief spreading further and further, hips and buttocks relaxing.

Breathe in slowly and tense the whole of the left leg, down your thigh to your calves, feet, and scrunched up toes. Let the left leg come up slightly away from the floor. Pause. Exhale slowly and release.

Let the whole body relax. Feel pure relaxation arising within you...everything in the body absolutely relaxed.

Keep your open, curious focus on the sensations you feel as you scan one last time from the tips of your toes upward all through the body...sliding the awareness slowly up the inner legs, through the hips, along the arms and all the way back to the face.

Let your awareness rest lightly for some moments between your eyebrows, relaxing the inner vision on the inside space behind closed eyes, feeling the whole body at peace and serene.

Sounds for Whole-Self Relaxation and Healing

Conscious breathing brings us home to the place of peace that lies within us. Here we experience a body awareness technique called the Relaxation Response developed by Harvard researcher Herbert Benson which explores the effects of specific sounds.[5] Physically relaxing helps center the mind and allow us to be more fully present, so if we feel nervous, tense, anxious, or edgy, using this simple breath technique very naturally and almost instantly triggers the relaxation response.

Guided Technique 1

Suggested Time: A few moments

Suggested Use: Experiment with this technique to help create relaxation at the start of your Yin Yoga & Meditation session or while holding any low to the ground pose that allows you to safely close your eyes and visualize.

Instructions:

Close your eyes if it's comfortable and imagine for a moment you're on a boat floating down a lazy river on a beautiful summer's day.

See yourself stretched on your back as the soft waves lap against the edges of the hull.

A warm breeze brushes lightly over your body as you float contentedly down the river under the dappled light of the leaves above you.

In this moment, you're floating smoothly along without a care in the world. Sense your body comfortable and at complete peace.

Feel your breath. Take a long gentle breath in through your nose, and as you exhale slowly through the mouth, make the luxuriating sound of...*ahhhhhh.*

Once again, inhale, and exhale like a sigh...*ahhhhhh.*

Notice, how does this feel for you? Feel it on your inside a few more times. Do you sense how the whole of your body vibrates with the sound and sensation of *ahhhhhh*...filling you with calm and relaxation?

Let your breath move now without any effort on your part, natural and flowing gently like a river.

Guided Technique 2

Suggested Time: A few moments

Suggested Use: While in any pose, experiment with this inquisitive sound to evoke your natural curiosity.

Instructions:

Begin by bringing your awareness to an area in your body where you're experiencing physical sensation, any part of the body that the posture is stimulating.

Keeping your awareness on this place, inhale through the nose, and as you exhale back out through the nose, create the sound of *hmmmmm.*

Repeat this a few more times, and each time you exhale, sense for the vibration of the sounds on the inside, filling the area of sensation with *hmmmmm.* Let the sound resonate through the tissues and the sensations there.

Staying attentive to your body, what do you feel? Do the sensations change as you watch them?

As you repeat this, sense how the sound of *hmmmmm* helps to keep the attention curious as you observe any internal response to its energy.

Practitioner's Tip: Whether before an important conversation with a loved one, in preparation for big meeting, or just while waiting in a long line, try using the stress-relieving sounds of *ahhhhh*... or *hmmmm*... to help bring relaxation to the body within moments.

Greeting Opposites for Experiencing Both Sides of the Coin

Greeting Opposites is a technique that helps us foster a nonjudging, welcoming presence for the whole of our emotional landscape. Through a fundamental willingness to feel, we come alive to the whole of our beautiful and complex human experience. This applies to basic physical sensations, such as temperature, and also to our emotional landscape. As we know, every emotion is another emotion's opposite, like two sides of a coin. As we practice opening to one feeling, we simultaneously expand our ability to experience its opposite.

Guided Technique

Suggested Time: Fifteen to twenty minutes

Suggested Use: This exercise fits well as a sitting meditation to begin a Yin Yoga & Meditation session or perhaps as an entryway into Savasana at the end of class.

Instructions:

Evoking Heavy/Light Sensations:

If you'd like, take a moment to elicit the physical sensation of heaviness and sense how heaviness in the body feels. Heavy limbs...heavy arms, heavy legs.

Feel them heavy on the ground as though covered with a weighted blanket.

Heaviness in your feet and legs, heaviness in your torso and head.

Feel it spread through you, like it feels when you're falling into a deep sleep...

Let the heaviness begin to lift now, and allow a feeling of lightness to happen in the body.

Let a feeling of lightness and weightlessness spread from your head, through your trunk and arms, down through your hips and legs all the way to your feet.

Sense how all the parts of your body are floating like a cloud is beneath you, and you're rising up and up, away from the floor.

Nothing is holding you down, just floating with ease and lightness.

Evoking Uneasy/Relaxed Feeling Tones:

Let's move on to eliciting an emotion...you're now invited to bring into your mind a feeling of uneasiness, a little bit of anxiousness.

Nothing too distressing, please, just a little unease. The kind of feeling when maybe you're not sure where something is, like when you're running late but can't find your keys, or perhaps when you have an important meeting coming up.

Envision yourself as if you're experiencing this situation of mild unrest at this moment...

Feel how this might bring tension into any parts of the body. Maybe how the shoulders tighten, how the forehead crinkles and jaw clenches, how the breath changes, how there may be a fluttering or tightness in the stomach.

Sense anywhere the uneasiness travels in your body now, how it moves and changes...

Let go of the unease now and bring into your mind the feeling of being relaxed, totally at ease, carefree, without a concern or worry.

To help, think of a time you felt utterly relaxed, without a worry in the world, not a bit of tension. Maybe it was a welcome vacation with loved ones or a long weekend away from work and its daily responsibilities.

Feel how loose everything feels all through the tissues of your body, no tension, no worries, no problems or constraints.

Feel this sense of ease spread all through your forehead, your shoulders, your stomach, your legs...the whole body.

Sense all of you now feeling completely relaxed and comfortable, light, and calm.

Evoking Sadness/Happiness Feeling Tones:

Now you're invited to bring to mind a time when you felt sad. Not deep grief or sorrow, just when you felt a little blue or discontent.

Let that feeling tone arise in your mind, and let it move outward into your physical tissues.

Feel it as it spreads, feel what it does in your face, what it does in your shoulders, does it show up anywhere else? Is it reflected in the breath?

Allow the sadness to release now and instead bring to mind a time when you felt elated – maybe when someone special looked into your eyes and told you they loved you, the birth of your child, a time you attained an important goal, or when you received a pleasant surprise. If nothing comes to mind right away, that's OK. Imagine an experience that would fill your heart to the brim with joy.

Let the energy of this happy moment settle itself within your face, maybe bring a smile to your lips.

Notice how quickly this happiness expands all through you – is there a buoyancy? What do you feel? What sensations does this feeling of happiness bring with it? Where do those happen?

Closing the practice now, let yourself rest a few moments here, returning to this moment, finding once again the easy flow of your breath. Spend a little time reflecting on this exercise and any insights that may have presented themselves.

Traveling through the Inner Body Using Rotation of Consciousness

Rotation of Consciousness is a Yoga Nidra technique that encourages the withdrawal of the senses from the external world to help relax the physical tissues, quiet the mind, and harmonize the flow of our inner energy. Known as Antar Mouna, or inner silence, this practice is rooted in Tantra Yoga, where traditionally, different parts of the body were physically tapped while speaking various mantras. In the following exercises, the awareness is carried through a relatively rapid and systematic mental tour of the body, often in the areas called marma points. Marma points are areas in the body where two or more tissues meet, such as bones, muscles, ligaments, nerves, and veins, and are considered primary energetic intersections.

While a wide variety of approaches to the Rotation of Consciousness exist, the person leading the exercise typically names the part of the body while inviting the practitioner to place their awareness there without any physical action required. To aid the movement of the attention, you could use sound or visuals such as a small star, a little point of glowing light, a sound such as OM, or by directing the breath through that space.

Guided Technique 1

Suggested Time: Ten to fifteen minutes

Suggested Use: This Rotation of Consciousness exercise is a relatively uncomplicated but profoundly relaxing technique to use as a lead-in to a restful and refreshing Savasana at the end of class. As a standalone exercise, it's an effective way to prepare for a restful night's sleep.

INSTRUCTIONS:

You're welcome now to take a mental trip through your body to free the flow of inner energy and spread relaxation into the tissues of the muscles, bones, and organs.

As you mentally scan the body, take your time to sense very deep into the body and bring relaxation there.

Begin by letting the attention settle into the head.

Move the awareness next behind the forehead and behind the eyes, deep into the head.

From the center of the brain, slowly sweep your awareness down now through the bones of the face, down through the jaw and neck.

Let your awareness slide into the bones of the right shoulder joint. Relax all of the right shoulder.

Awareness traveling through the bones of the right upper arm, down through the elbow joint into the forearm. Sense the bones of the lower arm, the right wrist, the right hand, and fingers.

Awareness moving back up the bones of the right arm to the right shoulder joint.

Attention traveling to the left shoulder now, sensing the bones in the left shoulder joint, relaxing, relaxing.

Awareness moves down through bones of the left upper arm and elbow joint into the left forearm. Allow a relaxed focus as you sense the bones of your arm. Sense now the left wrist, left hand, left fingers.

Let your awareness slide back up through the left arm to the left shoulder joint.

From the shoulder, move the awareness slowly down into the torso and into the lungs, where the breath goes in and out.

Bring the awareness now into the heartspace, to the beating heart in the chest. Feel the heart beating.

Move the attention from the heart into the liver, the gall bladder, and the stomach. Let the awareness move slowly now into other inner organs of digestion and detoxification, the pancreas, spleen, small intestine, large intestine.

From the large intestine, split the attention and go simultaneously to each of the kidneys on either side of the spine.

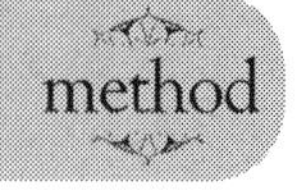

Slip the awareness down into the bones of the right hip joint, awareness to the right hip.

Sense the right thigh bone, then the right knee joint, go to the knee. Then through the bones of the right shin, pass the attention through the lower leg.

Aware of the right ankle joint, the right foot, and right toe bones.

Returning now up the bones of the right leg and into the right hip joint.

Cross the awareness now to the left hip joint.

Sense the left thigh bone, then the left knee joint, go to the knee. Then through the bones of the left shin, pass the attention through the lower leg.

Aware of the left ankle joint, the left foot, and left toe bones.

Return the attention up the bones of the left leg and into the left hip joint.

Now place the awareness at the base of the spine and allow it to slowly glide upward through the center of each vertebra of the spine. Bring the awareness through each bone of the spine until you reach the head.

Awareness settling into the center of the head, relaxed, relaxed, relaxed at the center of the head. Let the awareness stay in this place of ease and calm for some moments more, resting in the relaxed spaciousness of your true nature.

Guided Technique 2

Suggested Time: Fifteen minutes or more, depending on length of time you choose to rest in silence at the end of the meditation. Take as much time as you need.

Suggested Use: Spread sparkling healing light all through the body. This Rotation of Consciousness exercise incorporates the use of visualization and is able to be used at the start of Yin Yoga & Meditation session or as a lead-in to a restful and refreshing Savasana. Choose to enjoy this guided meditation as a standalone exercise while in a comfortable resting position, whether in your personal practice space or in preparation for a restful night's sleep.

Instructions:

Let us prepare now for deep rest and rejuvenation.

As you lie on your back, give the weight of your body to this good earth, let it hold you.

Relax all parts of you.

Let yourself settle and steady yourself as you rest here...the legs relax, the abdomen and upper torso, the arms, the head...sense the whole body relaxed.

Mentally tell the whole body it's OK to release more and more.

Allow the breath to flow with ease. Follow its sensations as the breath moves through you, flowing through the throat to the abdomen and back to the throat again.

Let it be natural, just as it is. There's no need to force or manage its movement in any way.

If it feels comfortable for you, close your eyes so that you are more able to perceive in the subtle realms.

Straight above you, see a glowing green sparkle of light descending.

A gift from the universe giving itself to you, the light nestling softly now into your third eye center, gently and with great love.

See it shining there, feel its healing warmth and comfort.

Now we'll take a mental journey through the body.

Simply move your awareness from part to part of your body as you hear it. You don't need to move the body, just rest your awareness there.

Right Side:

Bring your attention to the right hand
Feel the right-hand thumb
Second finger
Third finger
Fourth finger
Little finger
The palm of the right hand, see a droplet of healing green light glimmering, in the right palm.
Go to the back of the hand
Then wrist
Forearm
Elbow joint
Upper arm
Shoulder joint
Underarm
Right-side waist
Right hip joint

Front of right thigh
Knee joint
Calf
Ankle joint
Heel of the foot
Sole of the foot
Top of the right foot
Right toes: first toe, at its tip, second toe's tip, third toe's tip, fourth toe's tip, tip of the little toe

Left side:

Feel the left-hand thumb, see there a tiny green light twinkling at the tip of the left thumb
Second finger
Third finger
Fourth finger
Little finger
The palm of the left hand, a droplet of healing green light glimmering in the left palm.
Go to the back of the hand
Then wrist
Forearm
Elbow
Upper arm
Shoulder joint
Underarm
Left-side waist
Left hip joint
Front of the left thigh
Knee joint
Calf
Ankle joint
Heel of the foot
Sole of the foot
Top of the left foot
Left toes: first toe, at its tip, second toe's tip, third toe's tip, fourth toe's tip, tip of the little toe

Front side:

Go to the top of the head.
Top of the head, a droplet of shimmering green light
Crown of head
The whole of the forehead
Right eyebrow
Left eyebrow
Third eye, situated at the eyebrow center, a green light shining
Right eye
Left eye
Right side of the jaw
Left side of the jaw
Right ear
Left ear
Right side of the nose

Left side of the nose
Right cheekbone
Left cheekbone
Upper lip
Lower lip
Chin
Throat
Right side of the collarbone
Left side of the collarbone
Right upper torso
Left upper torso
Middle of the chest, see a tiny drop of healing green light shining at the middle of the chest
Belly button
Lower belly
Right upper thigh
Left upper thigh
Right knee joint
Left knee joint
Right shin
Left shin
Right ankle joint
Left ankle joint
All of the right toes, at once
All of the left toes, at once

Back side:

Now move to the back of the body
Sole of the right foot
Sole of the left foot
Heel of the right foot
Heel of the left foot
Right calf
Left calf
Back of the right knee joint
Back of the left knee joint
Back of the right upper leg
Back of the left upper leg
Back of right hip joint
Back of left hip joint
The whole of the spine
Attention gliding along the whole of the spine
Right shoulder blade
Left shoulder blade
Back of the neck, back of the head, top of the head

Main Parts:

Now go with your attention to all of the main parts of the body
The whole right leg
The whole left leg
Both legs, collectively

The whole right arm
The whole left arm
Both arms, together
The whole of the back, collectively
The whole of the head and shoulders, collectively
The whole of the front, collectively
The whole body, all together
Awareness of the whole body, all together
Feel the whole body, all at once, all together.

[Repeat 2 complete rounds of the Main Parts]

With eyes closed, see your whole body glowing with a shimmering green light, lit from part to part until you glow completely and seamlessly from within.

Rest now, your whole being bathing in light, a divine healing energy from the universe.

Remain here as long as you'd like, communing, completely relaxed, and held.

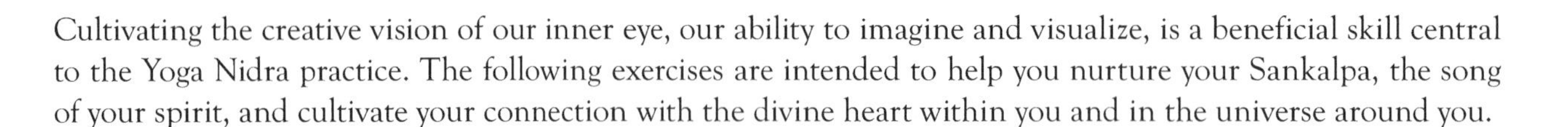

Discover and Super-Charge Your Sankalpa with Visualization

Cultivating the creative vision of our inner eye, our ability to imagine and visualize, is a beneficial skill central to the Yoga Nidra practice. The following exercises are intended to help you nurture your Sankalpa, the song of your spirit, and cultivate your connection with the divine heart within you and in the universe around you.

Guided Technique 1

Suggested Time: Twenty to twenty-five minutes

Suggested Use: Longer in duration than some of the other techniques, this self-discovery meditation is a delightful complement to a workshop-style program that allows for more time for integration. Abbreviate it for use at the beginning of a class to focus on your intention or in Savasana to help plant your Sankalpa in the fertile soil of the relaxed and quieted mind.

Instructions:

Begin by finding a comfortable meditation posture of your choice, sitting in any seated position you find relaxing or lying down. Choose whatever posture feels easeful and best sustains your meditative awareness. Take the moments you need to make any adjustments to your position or props.

Let your breath flow naturally now, fully and calmly, without striving to manage it. Simply allow it, enjoy it, and let it happen as it will.

As you settle onto the earth, close your eyes as long as this feels appropriate for you.

Let your body relax more and more deeply into each in-breath and each out-breath. Let your mind be unencumbered here in the present time.

Give your spirit space in these moments to unfold, unfurl, expand beyond the lines of your body for these moments. Feel it fully, this inner flame that lights your whole self.

Bring your awareness now to the open space between your eyes, your third eye, the source of your inside sight.

You are a precious, energetic being made of stardust and light. When our internal energy is harmonious and flowing well, we move more freely from 'I wish' to 'I am.' In aligning our energies with our intention, we actively design our life. Awareness changes everything.

Smile with warmth and loving friendliness into your heartspace.

As you send this energy of lovingkindness to your spirit, inquire: What guides the compass rose of your heart? What brings you light and joy, your truest happiness?

Open your heart to whatever arises...what do you hear, feel, see?

Can you name it?

Be relaxed and attentive as you watch, and listen...what is your spirit presenting to you?

Your Sankalpa already exists within you, so you can trust whatever answer arises in your mind. Listen inwardly as your spirit speaks. You don't have to rush, it will come.

Whatever arises, just let it arrive. It could be a single word or a short phrase.

Trust...openness...compassion...being of light...spreading peace...I am love...I am joyful...I am whole...I embrace all...whatever it might be.

With your attention resting into the space behind closed eyes, let this sacred inner space be a blank canvas upon which your spirit will write.

In bright and shining letters, allow the answer, your Sankalpa, to appear letter by letter. Allow this intention and aspiration to write itself in shimmering silver letters. Watch as it appears.

Transform this word or phrase now into mantra through repetition of sound, the energy and the power of sound. Start repeating it to yourself, softly, slowly, again, and again. Allow this word or phrase to nestle itself into your heart, held with care in the sacred space of your heart. Hear the sound of these words moving in time with the beat of your heart.

When we plant a seed, we know it has its own magic inside it, that as we plant it with care and create favorable conditions, this seed will manifest. Just as an acorn turns into a majestic oak tree, Sankalpa is like this.

Visualize planting your seed now into the innermost resolute parts of yourself, confident in its innate wisdom, its natural magic. Know that in its time, the seed of Sankalpa will grow and grow. It must manifest up, up, and out, just as a tree rises from the earth, spreading its magnificent limbs in all directions, a source of blessing to creatures above, creatures below, to all beings on earth.

Feel the seed sending roots down now and allow the energy of manifestation to draw upward through them, rising through each area of your spine and filling you with a confident peace.

The powerful energy of manifestation rising up and up into your heartspace, filling your chest with soft glowing light, the light of joy and peace and purpose.

See all the goodness you bring to the world. Let yourself steep in this blessing.

Rest in the knowledge that you serve the whole through the gift of your spirit.

Gently begin to deepen your breath, letting it fill and relax the whole of your body.

Your body, your heart, full of natural magic.

Your face, confident and shining.

Coming home to this moment.

With every breath in...coming home.

With every breath out...coming home.

Here, present in this moment, holding fast to the sure knowledge that you are a powerful spirit on the earth, here to flourish and to thrive. Take a deep breath in and send a long breath out...hearing a quiet voice within you whisper...may it be so...may it be so...thank you.

Guided Technique 2

The Vajrapradama mudra is a lovely way to strengthen the highest commitment of our heart, our Sankalpa. This mudra is a simple but impactful aid that immediately directs our attention and feeling into the heartspace. Working regularly with this mudra, we move forward, confident that the winds of grace will support us as we bring our deepest desires to fruition.

> Suggested Time: A few minutes daily
>
> Suggested Use: Vajrapradama mudra is easily explored in a sitting meditation practice or while in a relaxing supine pose in which the hands are free.

INSTRUCTIONS:

Hold your hands in front of your chest, elbows out, with thumbs up and palms facing toward you. Point right and left fingertips at one another.

Begin to slide the hands closer together so that fingers interweave to form a flat crisscrossing lattice, palms still facing the chest. Rest your joined hands in this Vajrapradama mudra onto the heartspace and breathe slowly as you feel each heartbeat.

Sense for anything shifting as you breathe in and out, your hands woven together, a symbol of strength and connection.

This mudra reminds us that we have everything we need inside us and can trust the beauty and design of the universe to support the realization of our most heart-felt intentions.

Breathe in, opening yourself to receive the loving universal support you deserve and softly speak the words: I am...

As you breathe out, speak your Sankalpa...sending it out onto the winds of grace which are sure to carry it to fruition.

Repeat this a few more times...Inhale: I am...

Exhale...speaking your Sankalpa, sending it out.

Sensing and trusting that as you speak this highest intention of your heart, it is already manifesting in the universe.

When ready, close the practice by bowing head to heart and hands. Breathe in and out a few times, allowing the energy of gratitude to gather in your heartspace.

Practitioner's Tip: To further energize your Sankalpa, write it on a piece of paper and post it somewhere where you'll encounter it during the course of your day. Whenever you see it, pause a few moments to visualize it as if manifested in the present time. How do you feel, what do you see and experience?

Post-Practice Reflections:

Remember to maintain a compassionate, kind attention as you reflect. There's no right or wrong answer, it's just information for your contemplation.

- As you reflect on the Yoga Nidra-inspired techniques you've explored here, are there ways you feel led to incorporate any of the exercises in your daily life? Is there one exercise, however short or simple, that you'd like to practice on a daily basis to encourage relaxation?
- As you continue with your Yin Yoga & Meditation practice and exploring these meditative techniques, are there any specific yin qualities you'd like to cultivate, such as self-compassion, patience, or permission to be just as you are? Are there any experiences, techniques, or approaches which could help strengthen this quality?
- Do any of these techniques renew the connection you feel to your most natural self, the loving, wise, joyful essence of who you are?

Taoist-Inspired Energy Cultivation Methods

Yin Yoga & Meditation invites us to explore and support all layers of our being, and the mysterious unseen energetic network flowing within the connective tissues below the skin is no exception. When we *yin*, we go *in*, accumulating and improving the flow of Qi to nourish all aspects of ourselves. By nature, Yin Yoga is a Qi cultivation practice that supports the vital life-force energy Taoists consider to be the animator of body, mind, and spirit. The shapes we create with our body twist, compress, and decompress the connective tissues where these tiny rivers of energy trace, helping to stimulate, re-balance, and enhance the quality and movement of Qi within us.

The relative stillness and longer hold times of the poses also offer built-in time for us to fine-tune our internal perception. The Yin Yoga practice is another opportunity to learn to work intentionally with our energy network as a skillful alchemist and Qi cherisher. As we're training our attention ever inward, we encourage our sensing self to arise, feeling and intuiting our way below the surface of the skin. Sensing energy's flow is the starting point in harnessing its power. When we feel energy, we're more able to consciously direct it. If we sense flow is sluggish or restricted in some area of our body, for example, bringing intentional attention into that place helps to bolster it.

Liquid Flowing Palms

To truly know our energy is to feel it, and the Liquid Flowing Palms technique offers the chance to turn inward and practice doing just that. In this brief energy awakening exercise, we attune the awareness to the qualities of the flowing Qi within us.

Practitioner's Tip: If you are newer to subtle energy work, keep in mind that sensing energy flow is a skill often developed over time, so if you don't feel anything right away, that's OK. Stay with it, free yourself from judgment, and be confident it will come.

Guided Technique

> Suggested Time: Two to five minutes
>
> Suggested Use: This exercise could be explored as you arrive to the mat. It also serves well as preparation for a lengthier sitting meditation practice to help attune the awareness to the energy within, sensing the Qi that is you.

Instructions:

Join your hands together in a prayer position in front of the heart center.

Close your eyes, if you wish, and bring your awareness to your palms.

Briskly rub the palms back and forth against each other until you feel a little bit of heat arising from the palm centers.

Still the palms and then separate your hands slightly so they're about an inch apart.

Rest your attention into the space between the palms.

Begin to create slow, small circular movements, cycling the hands like the pedals of a bike, keeping the palms facing one another. As you circle the palms, keep the one-inch space between them.

Notice as you continue this circling motion any sensations arising in the atmosphere between the palms.

What do you sense in this space? Do you feel a weightiness, a lightness, vibration, tingling, or pressure?

Slowly, in a wave-like motion, begin now to pull your hands apart several inches away from each other, then press them toward one another in the same slow manner until they're almost touching. Repeat this slow meditative motion, like you're playing an energetic accordion, twenty times or so with your awareness resting in the open air between the palms.

Continue to let your sensing self perceive by feeling. Are there any feelings of warmth, a pulling or pushing magnetic-like sensation between them? Any pulsation, flickering, or fluttery feeling? Stay sensitive to the sensations.

You are an energetic being, Qi flowing within and around you. Between your hands, what you're feeling is...You.

Qi Bop, An Energy Shifter

Qi Bop is a favorite Taoist energy practice for the way that it frees and stimulates the flow of blood and Qi within and releases whole-body tension. A lighthearted energy-shifter, Qi Bop helps relieve tightness in the low back, supports joint wellness, and promotes a balanced flow of Qi to help us feel more centered, present, and vibrant. It also offers a rebalancing remedy for clearing the energy of lethargy, restlessness, or mind fog in support of a relaxed meditative awareness.

Guided Technique

Suggested Time: Five to seven minutes

Suggested Use: If you're looking to add a little yang to your yin, you might position Qi Bop at the beginning of the Yin Yoga & Meditation session where it can help open the body, loosen areas of constriction, and lay the groundwork for the enhanced energy work in the poses. Try Qi Bop anywhere, anytime, on your own or with family and friends.

Instructions:

Stand with feet hip-width distance apart with the crown of the head floating toward the sky.

Feel as though there is a cord rising from the earth to the heavens running upward along your spine and through your top of your head, offering support as you stand tall and at ease.

Settle the weight evenly between both feet and just a bit behind the balls of the feet so you're neither on toe tips nor heels.

Slightly drop the tailbone, so the lower back opens and relaxes a touch more.

Bend your knees just enough to unlock the joints.

Allow the shoulders to release down and away from the ears and dangle the arms loosely by your sides.

Rest your attention in your body, letting any mental distractions fall away as you take a few moments to feel yourself breathing.

Suspended by the energetic cord keeping you upright with minimal muscular effort, feel a pleasant sense of buoyancy imbue your entire body.

Begin to lightly bounce your whole body up and down while keeping your feet connected to the earth and your joints relatively soft.

Breathe in through the nose, then let the breath go out the mouth, making the sound of...*Hah, Hah, Hah...* loose and light.

Feel surface tensions begin to release, gently shaking free.

Continue to breathe multiple short, staccato-like *Hah* exhales as you bounce to call relaxation into the body.

As you keep bouncing, take a mental tour through your body by moving your awareness to each of your joints.

Start with the toe joints and, in your own time, work your way methodically up to the jaw and all the way to the crown of your head. As you scan through your body, continue to lightly bounce to loosen and aid the release of any tensions. Pause your attention at each major joint to help mentally relax each area. Use the exhales to emphasize the release, *Hah, Hah, Hah.* Sense relaxation and lightness as you gently bounce and pause at each joint.

Once you've completed the joint scan, let your attention go anywhere you still feel tenseness or holding. Keep bouncing lightly and breathing the *Hah* breath.

After you've completed your whole-body circuit, pause with your awareness in the heart center. Inhale through the nose, then exhaling through the mouth, make the Taoist healing sound for the Heart, *Hawwww*, releasing any emotional tensions or stress. *Hawwww* is made as a round, opening sighing sound at the back of the throat. Shake free any blockages as you continue to bounce. Repeat *Hawwww*...letting any sticky or heavy feelings release that might be weighing you down. Again, *Hawwww*...feel the sound calming the heart and quieting any whirling or twirling in the mind.

When you're ready to end the practice, allow the body to begin to slow down naturally.

Close the eyes and let the outer layers of your body become still.

Feel any ripples of movement on your inside. What sensations are there? Do you feel energy streaming and flowing? Any warmth, renewed sense of lightness or spaciousness in the body, mind, or heart? Keep the attention open and inquisitive as you notice any effects on all layers of yourself.

Recharging Our Battery with Dan Tian Breathing

This Dan Tian Breathing technique employs the breath and the expansion and contraction of the belly to build up the reserve of energy within the lower abdomen. Low belly breathing calms the central nervous system and promotes relaxation throughout our musculature. Creating more space for our lungs to expand, breathing from the belly allows blood and Qi to circulate more freely.

Guided Technique

method

Suggested Time: One to five minutes

Suggested Use: This exercise could be explored as you arrive to the mat or intermittently during poses or counterposes to deepen the breath and build energy stores. Try this anytime during the day you're ready for a recharge.

Instructions:

Place your hands lightly over the lower abdomen and on top of the navel with one stacked on top of the other.

Bring your awareness to rest behind your hands and into the reservoir of the low belly known as the energetic center of the Lower Dan Tian.

Let your attention reside there as you breathe naturally through the nose.

With a slow and steady pace, bring the breath into the lower belly.

Feel the breath filling and expanding the belly in all directions, sending the air of your breath to the front, the back, right, and left of the lower abdomen.

Breathe out effortlessly through the nose, feeling the whole of the belly soften and contract toward the spine as the air slowly releases.

Again, inhale fully and feel the low belly expanding, lifted by the in-flow of the breath.

Exhale easefully and completely, feeling the low belly softening and falling with the out-flow.

Stay with this breath practice for a bit of time, watching and feeling the breath at the belly as you power up your internal energetic battery. After a minute or two of this relaxed deep belly breathing, notice if your breath naturally smooths and lengthens.

When ready, release the exercise and pause with curiosity to sense the effects of your breathing practice.

Qi Tapping & Massage to Clear and Refresh All the Qi Channels

Think of Qi Tapping as sending an energy infusion straight to your Organ Systems, keeping them nourished and functioning well. By tapping with awareness along the primary yin-yang energy channels, we loosen stuck energy, clear congestion, and revitalize the flow of Qi throughout our entire subtle energetic network.

Practitioner's Tip: Where attention goes, energy flows! Use your attention like a magnet for QI as you tap, keeping a focused awareness on the tapping palm and the sensations arising beneath it.

Guided Technique 1: Heart, Pericardium, & Lung Qi Channel Pairs

Suggested Time: Two to three minutes

Suggested Use: This Qi Tapping & Massage technique is relatively simple and fits well at the beginning of a Yin Yoga & Meditation session and after the static hold of a posture to help open and promote the circulation of blood and Qi. It can be done standing or in a comfortable seated position.

Instructions:

To clear and harmonize the Heart-Small Intestine, Pericardium-Triple Burner, and Lung-Large Intestine Qi channels, start by placing your open right hand at the center of the chest just below the collarbone.

With your right palm, begin to tap gently and rhythmically at the center of your chest for a few moments.... tap...tap...tap...tap... Bring your awareness to your palm and the area of your body beneath it as you tap.

In hand-width increments, slowly tap with your right hand across to the upper left chest, continue tapping gently across the front of the left shoulder and down the left inner arm...tap...tap...tap...tap...tap all the way to the palm of hand...tap...tap...the palm of hand. Then turn your arm to tap the back of your hand and continue tapping your way up the back of your left arm...tap...tap...tap to the back of left shoulder...tap... tap...tap...several times on the back of left shoulder... then tap across to the upper left chest...tap...tap...tap and back to the center of the chest. Tap the chest center for several moments.

Now switch sides and with your left hand, repeat this same tapping pattern. Start with the center of the chest, then tap along the upper right chest, shoulder, and arm. Find a balanced rhythm and light intensity that feels energizing.

Once you complete one full loop, return to the left side to begin the entire left to right loop a few times.

When finished with the tapping cycles, allow yourself to rest and experience any reverberating sensations of energy movement on the inside.

Guided Technique 2: Kidney, Liver, & Spleen Qi Channel Pairs

Suggested Time: Two to three minutes

Suggested Use: This Qi Tapping & Massage technique is relatively simple and fits well at the beginning of a Yin Yoga & Meditation session or after the static hold of a posture to help open and promote the circulation of blood and Qi. This can be done standing or while in a comfortable seated position with the legs extended in front of you.

Instructions:

To activate the Kidney-Urinary Bladder, Liver-Gall Bladder, and Spleen-Stomach Qi channels, start with hands placed on the lumbar area of the spine and the Kidney of Door of Life at the lumbar vertebra L2-L3 region. Gently tap this place with your open palms and finger pads for a minute or two.

Next, begin to move the hands toward outer hips and legs, tapping every few inches with a gentle staccato pressure, tap...tap...tap. Continue tapping down the outer leg line of both legs simultaneously and once you reach the outer ankles, transition to the inner ankles, inner legs tapping up the inner shins and inner upper legs to the upper front of thighs, to the lower belly where the Lower Dan Tian sits, tap...tap...tap mindfully for several moments on the lower abdomen. Then tap your hands back to the lumbar spine. Tap the area of the Kidney Door of Life for some moments, tap...tap...tap.

Repeat this lower body cycle a few times to help clear the tiny Qi channels and enliven the energy flow. Stay sensitive to any sensations arising with your body as you gently tap loose any energetic blockages.

When you're finished, pause in stillness for a few moments to listen to your body's internal response.

Guided Technique 3: Sweeping all the Qi Channels

> Suggested Time: Two to three minutes
>
> Suggested Use: This Qi Massage technique uses the palm like an energetic broom to clear and harmonize the Qi channels. It fits well at the beginning of a Yin Yoga & Meditation session and after the static hold of a posture to promote the flow of blood and Qi. This can be done standing or in a comfortable seated position with the legs extended in front of you.

INSTRUCTIONS:

Start with your open right palm resting on your upper left chest.

Inhale, and as you breathe out, slowly sweep your palm in one continuous movement to the front of the left shoulder and down the entire surface of the inner left arm all the way to the tips of the fingers. As you breathe in once again, slowly sweep the palm up the outer left arm to the back of left shoulder, over the top of the shoulder, and then return the palm to the upper left chest.

Repeat this loop a few times on the left side, coordinating your breath with the sweeping palm. Watch these inner areas closely as you sweep.

When you've completed a few sweeping loops on the left side, switch hands and switch sides. In the same way, sweep on your right side in time with your breath as it moves in and out.

After a few loops on the right side, place both palms on your lower back. Gently massage the entire area of your lower back and Kidneys with your palms for several breaths as you slowly inhale and exhale through the nose.

If you need some extra tension-easing power, try creating the soft whisper sound of *Chooooooooo* to speak directly to the Kidney energy. *Chooooooooo* is made by pursing the lips as you exhale, touching the tip of your tongue to the front top of the mouth to create a nearly silent breathy sound as though saying the beginning of the word "choose." Repeat this sound a few more times as you massage the area of the Kidneys.

Next, place the palms on their respective outer hips. Breathe in, and as you breathe out slowly, sweep the palms down the outer legs to the feet and to the toes.

Breathe in and sweep the palms up the inner line of the leg to the upper front of thighs and front hips, then return to the lower back. Repeat this lower body cycle a few times, creating slow continuous sweeping motions in unison with your breath.

Pause at the end of your sweeping to feel any inner energy sensations, fluttering, flickering, pulsing, or temperature variations.

Guided Technique 4: Revitalizing all the Qi Channels

> Suggested Time: Five to seven minutes
>
> Suggested Use: This combination of tapping and sweeping techniques helps to clear and balance all the Organ System Qi channels in support of whole-body energetic harmony. It fits well at the beginning of a Yin Yoga & Meditation session and after the static hold of a posture. This can be done standing or in a comfortable seated position with the legs extended in front of you.

INSTRUCTIONS:

To cleanse and refresh all the Qi channels of the subtle energy body, simply combine in consecutive order the following Qi Tapping & Massage exercises: Guided Technique 1: Heart, Pericardium, & Lung Qi Channel Pairs, Guided Technique 2: Kidney, Liver, & Spleen Qi Channel Pairs, and Guided Technique 3: Sweeping all the Qi Channels. Instructions for all techniques are included above.

Create Breathing Room with the Emptying Breath

Did you know the typical exhale leaves a fair amount of air sitting stale in the lungs? Even a great big satisfying *aaaahhhhhh* won't necessarily empty the lungs completely of air. There's an easy breath technique called the Emptying Breath that soothes the central nervous system as it clears outs old, stagnant air and creates space for a fresh new breath in just a few seconds.

Guided Technique

Suggested Time: A few moments

Suggested Use: This brief technique can be used as preparation for a more prolonged breathing practice, at various intervals throughout your Yin Yoga & Meditation session, or during the day to help maximize the flow of oxygen coming in and carbon dioxide moving out.

INSTRUCTIONS:

Feel how the belly moves in time with your breath, rising in collaboration with in-breath and falling alongside your out-breath.

Without straining, begin to deepen your breath a bit, breathing slowly and deeply into and out from the nose a few more times.

Now at the very bottom of your next exhale, through the mouth slowly blow out any leftover air as gently and completely as possible, as though you're blowing out a candle without splattering the melted wax at all.

Repeat this again. Breathe in fully through the nose, then breathe out through the mouth as slowly and entirely as possible....*whoooooo*...gently blowing out the candle.

Breathe in this way a few more times to be sure to make plenty of room for more pure, fresh oxygen to fill your lungs.

Microcosmic Orbiting

The Microcosmic Orbit is a cornerstone Taoist practice used to balance our yin and yang energies. This energetic orbit helps refine Qi and strengthens its flow within us. In this meditative exercise, we circulate Qi through the two energetic superhighways of the body, the Governor and Conception Vessels.

The effects of this exercise could feel like a warm and energizing wheel of energy turning within the body as we refresh the flow of Qi and saturate our Organ Systems. To sense the energy movement, you could choose to close your eyes and visualize the Qi as a golden light flowing. By re-supplying these two reigning vessels with energy, we're more able to easily lead our Qi to where it's needed.

Guided Technique

Suggested Time: Ten minutes or more

Suggested Use: This technique makes a wonderful sitting meditation at the start or end of class.

INSTRUCTIONS:

With your intention on alert relaxation, arrange yourself in a comfortable position so that the whole of your body feels at ease.

Breathe in mindfully, then back out...easy breath, free breath, enjoying this moment.

Allow the breath to flow naturally in and out as you arrive into the here and now.

Place your attention in the lower belly, the place where the Lower Dan Tian serves as a primary storehouse of life-force energy. Open your awareness to any sensations as they arise while you tune into this energetic battery of your body, the Lower Dan Tian.

Keep breathing easefully through the nose as you feel for energy collecting in this space. Visualize it as a pool of golden light. With our attention and intention, we influence the flow of Qi through the body, strengthening and balancing it.

After some moments of focusing on this area, inhale and use the breath to draw this stream of golden energy from the lower belly down to the pelvic floor and then upward through the spine along the back of the body, the pathway of the yang Governor Vessel. Pull the energy up through the lower back, the Door of Life behind the navel, and along the spine behind the Lungs and Heart. Continue moving it up through the back of the neck, the occipital bone of the skull, up to the crown of the head, then over the crown through the forehead to the space between the eyebrows of the third eye center.

With the pause of the breath, rest the attention in the third eye center, letting the golden light of energy pool there, saturating, saturating. Feel for any sensations that arise...see the bright golden light of energy... pooling, pooling.

Exhale slowly and deliberately, then draw the stream of Qi downward along the front of the spine, a golden line of energy flowing down through the throat and the center of the chest, collecting any energy that has dissipated. Keep tracing the energy along the Conception Vessel, the yin superhighway flowing down the front of the body.

At the end of the exhale, return your attention to the lower belly. See the golden light shining there, sensing how Qi gathers when you train your attention on this place, collecting, collecting in the Lower Dan Tian.

This circulation of energy and light through front and back of the body is one full orbit.

To repeat the orbit, start once again with the attention in the Lower Dan Tian, exhale, then inhale to begin pulling the energy down to the pelvic floor. Move the energy then up the entire length of the back of the spine, a strong stream of golden light drawing up and up with the breath. Gently pull it all the way up to the top of the head, seeing its light shine through the forehead and the third eye center.

Pause the attention in the third eye center, seeing golden light glowing in this place between the eyebrows. Feel for any warmth, buzzing, spiraling, pulsing or tingling.

As you exhale, send the energy again downward, a shower of Qi through the front of the spine riding the winds of the out-breath as you refill and refine the Conception Vessel. Notice if there is any brightness or sense of inward sensations as you're exhaling the Qi back down to the Lower Dan Tian.

At the end of the exhale, return your attention to settle once again in the lower belly. With the pause of your attention and the breath, sense what follows this flow of Qi.

Continue this orbiting a bit longer, inhaling Qi up the back of the body. Sense a current of light flowing up and up, filling the Governor Vessel running along the back of the spine. Rest with the pause of the breath at the third eye center in the pool of golden light. Then, exhale and send Qi down the front of the spine and into the lower belly, pause to gather the energy there. Remain relaxed and keep a soft yet focused attention as you sense and move energy along this microcosmic orbit a few more times.

When you're ready to end the technique, let your attention rest in the low belly once again and pause to absorb any aftereffects.

The Peaceful Lake of the Mind

Nature serves as both steadfast mentor and mirror. As we learned, Taoism teaches that emulating nature's wisdom is one effective pathway to wellbeing. In this technique, we'll concentrate our attention on imagery from nature and the visualization abilities of the inner eye.

Guided Technique

> Suggested Time: Ten minutes
>
> Suggested Use: This guided visualization can help settle the spirit during a sitting meditation at the start of class or as a lead-in to Savasana at the end of the Yin Yoga & Meditation session.

Instructions:

Find a comfortable meditative posture of choice.
As you settle here, let your breath flow without any effort on your part.

Close your eyes if you'd like, or perhaps cover them with an eye pillow or light kerchief.

Imagine you're sitting beside a vast lake in the mountains. It is evening, and the air is warm. Golden summer sunlight streams all around you and sparkles along the surface of the lake. You are cradled where you sit by thousands of soft pine needles, their earthy aroma hanging in the air. You know you are safe here in this place, steeped in nature's silence and simplicity.

Your eyes trace the water spread before you. The lake is deep and very still. The surface is so still that it offers a near-perfect reflection of the mountains and trees around you. The cool liquid displays trunks of cedar, oak, birch, and aspen dappled through with the shoulders of huge rocks. All is clearly visible as though you were looking into an enormous mirror...pure vision, pure stillness.

Off to your right, movement appears. You shift your gaze in its direction: a bubble has broken through the surface and promptly disappears. Pure stillness, sudden disruption, then purely still again.

Scanning the surface, you see more occasional bubbles rise, thoroughly disrupt the mirror of the lake, then disappear. Perfect cedar tree reflecting...then swirling, twirling cedar with rings of energy rippling through it...then perfect cedar again. On and on it goes, this yin-yang cycle of stillness-movement-stillness, each phase lasting only for a few moments.

As you continue watching this peaceful lake of the mind, consider that each of us has disruptions rising like bubbles in our lives, some major, some minor. Like the bubbles bursting through the surface of this mountain lake, if we zoom in to see the tossing and turning of that three inches of water, we see only the cedar tree disintegrating into rings of energy for those moments. Yet as we draw back and expand our view, we observe how these disruptions diffuse over time and space, and the lake naturally resolves into calm once again.

With a broadened lens, we see that no matter how strong these disruptions appear initially, they're temporary. We're reminded that calm will return to the lake of our mind, reflecting the serene beauty of our true nature as we rest in timeless, effortless peace.

The Inner Smile and Energetic Self-Love

Inner alchemy, the ability to transform, is central to Taoist practices. Taoism teaches that one cause of unease and potential illness is the unconscious accumulation of negative emotions in our Organ Systems. The Inner Smile technique is used to cleanse our Organs and balance our emotions by bathing the body in the energy of lovingkindness from the inside out. By intentionally infusing our Organs with attentive affection and love, we aid the transformation of harmful emotions into compassionate healing energy to help restore our balance and wellbeing.

Guided Technique

Suggested Time: Twenty to twenty-five minutes

Suggested Use: Integrate this technique into a sitting meditation as you arrive to the mat or at the end of a Yin Yoga & Meditation session to seal the practice. Explore it as a standalone exercise, practiced in any safe space that allows you to comfortably close your eyes and internalize your awareness.

INSTRUCTIONS:

Let's start by closing the eyes, if it feels comfortable, and relaxing all the muscles of the body.

Feel your whole body relaxed...your breath smooth and slow, flowing in and out with ease.

Feel yourself relaxing, letting go a little bit more with each out-breath.

Bring your attention to the third eye center, that invisible place of opening and insight between the two eyebrows.

Now invite in the sense of quiet joy by bringing a peaceful, happy scene to mind. Maybe from a time you spent with someone you loved, a tranquil moment in nature, the smiling face of your child...any experience that immediately filled you with authentic happiness.

Allow this joy to collect behind your eyes as you take these few moments to feel it fully, steeping in the instant contentment it brings you.

Let this bright, happy feeling form itself into a smile on the inside, the energy of an inner smile. Feel this inner smile as a collection of loving life-force inside you that you will now share with your whole body.

As we bring the inner smile to the Organs, you're welcome to rest your hands lightly over them as we focus on each one. The hands, the motor organs of the heart, serve as a tangible delivery system for this joyful energy.

Smile first to your mind – the brain, control center of the entire body, making everything about your life possible. Muscle control, sensory perception, speech and cognition, creative thinking and emotions. Rest your palms on your temples and your fingertips lightly atop your head here, spending these few moments offering a loving smile of appreciation for this miraculous organ.

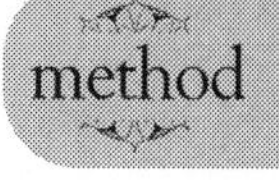

Moving down through the body...as the inner smile passes through your face, let a half-smile settle on your lips, gently lifting the corners of the mouth just slightly into a subtle, sublime smile. Serene, settled, joyful. Perhaps you'll touch the edges of your lips with your fingertips and sense how your half-smile softens your eyes, all the muscles of your face. Spend a few moments in appreciation for all of the ways your face helps you connect with the people around you.

Place the tongue on the roof of the mouth just behind the upper teeth to connect the energy circuit of the primary yin and yang pathways, the Governor Vessel running through the back of the body and the Conception Vessel through the front of the body.

With the jaw relaxed, sense your inner smile touch your throat, your vocal cords. Offer them loving gratitude for allowing you to communicate in this world, to share your truth and celebrate the truth of others. Rest your hands gently along your neck as you send appreciation to your vocal cords for all the sounds they make possible.

Rest your hands, one over the other, on your chest now, as your Heart beats strong and sure. Smile to the Heart, full of gratitude for how it serves you. Smile a love letter to your beautiful Heart in this moment, feel it soften, expand, and glow...the healing color of red emanating from its center. Let your smile radiate from the center of your Heart inherently happy, connected, loving...releasing any hurt, impatience, or sense of otherness. Focus on loving energy.

Send your inner smile into the Lungs now...spanning your chest, these critical Organs receive essential oxygen and Qi from the air and release toxins from the body to keep us harmonious and healthy. Perhaps you spread your hands across your chest as it rises and falls with each breath. Letting go of any grief or sadness that keeps us captive, welcoming connection, joy, and love in its place. Imagine your Lungs filling with a bright white light and offer deep appreciation for the good work they do.

Send your inner smile now to the center of the chest where the thymus gland sits. Visualize it flowering outward as it supports the body's health, strengthening our immunity and ability to heal.

Let your smiling energy travel now to the Liver lying on the right side of the upper abdomen. Place a hand here as you smile. Processing the blood, breaking down fats, filtering out toxins, the Liver works very hard to keep us healthy.

Smile to the Liver tenderly, seeing it emanate a deep green color...full of gratitude for its deep wisdom. See it filling with green and releasing any anger and resentment with the outbreath, receiving kindness and forgiveness with the inhale.

Now bring your inner smile to the abdomen where the Stomach, Spleen, Small Intestine, and Large Intestine do their good work, making nourishment by food and water possible. What a wonderful gift they give to us each day. Let your hands rest on your abdomen for a few moments. Releasing worry and any anxiety, see these Organs glowing a golden yellow light as you inhabit this moment centered in clarity, nourished with faith in the universe to support you.

Moving now to the Kidneys, offer them your loving smile for filtering blood and balancing water, releasing now any stress...grateful to the Kidneys for giving us the confidence and willpower to live from our convictions. Clearing any blockages in the Kidneys as they glow a bright blue color.

Now let your inner smile encompass the skin, the largest organ of the body. Thank it for covering you, protecting you, holding you together in this precious body that moves you through the world with safety and ease and allows you to connect authentically with the earth and with one another. Maybe you envelop yourself in a kind hug...letting it serve as a whole-self embrace. Bathe all of you with the energy of self-love and appreciation.

Breathe in and out fully, smiling appreciation and warmth to the whole of the body now, thankful to these tissues that keep you thriving in this world.

Slide your smiling energy upward through all of the spine and extend golden light out through every nerve in your body and up to the crown of your head. Sense this smiling energy cascading down now through the body filling and bathing you in radiant loving energy. Bask in this serene energetic embrace for some moments.

Allow now the energy to flow back to the space between your eyebrows behind your closed eyes, where it pools and glows, a golden light of life and love.

Inhale, and move this smiling light down to the navel. Place stacked hands over the navel and gently circle the palms in a slow clockwise movement to spiral and store the smiling energy you've gathered. Allow the inner smile to settle nurturing at the navel, held safe and precious here...just like you.

A Meditation for Preserving Sacred Space 

An old Taoist adage advises us that when we add things back in, their meaning will be clear. Experiencing the space of emptiness can be quite enlightening in this busy, often cluttered world. Training in offering ourselves space supports our presence on and off the mat. Space gives us the chance to notice happenings and habits. Space offers the opportunity to simply be and experience the moment more fully. What if you spent a few minutes every day noticing space? See only the space where something is not... Look around the room you're in – where isn't something? How does that empty space impart value? Considering no-thing helps illuminate the value of what is present. If a vase wasn't empty, how would it present the beauty of flowers to us? Looking for what isn't, listening for what doesn't happen, and enjoying what isn't offers new information about and appreciation for what is.

Guided Technique

Suggested Time: Five minutes or more

Suggested Use: Integrate this technique into a sitting meditation as you arrive to the mat or as a standalone exercise, practiced in any safe space that allows you to comfortably close your eyes and internalize your awareness.

INSTRUCTIONS:

Settle the mind as you sit here, centering your attention to the place where you are.

If it's comfortable for you, close your eyes to train your gaze inward and behold yourself with your inside eyes.

Sense how you are sacred space. Your home is sacred space. Your mind, sacred space. Your heart, sacred space. You are space, the stuff of potential and endless possibilities...

Imagine the space of you fully open, emptied of all things.

Sense how this inner space infuses purpose and value. Observe the beauty in all this space. All notions, all ideas, all commentary, allowing them to fall away. Free of mental chatter, of cycling thoughts.

Now, consider – what things would you like to bring back in? What would you retrieve and add? What nourishes you and waters the seeds of your happiness?

What if this day, and every day, you whispered, "This exact day and its beautiful opportunities will never come again"? What would you bring into such an auspicious, momentous time?

Allow yourself to adorn the space of you with that which nurtures, inspires, and empowers. Construct in your mind the who, the what, the where, the why. As you consider your invitations, ask: What has earned its place in you? What helps you love what you love?

This body, this spirit, never to happen precisely this way again. This moment, singular, finite, fertile with countless possibilities. This is true of every sight we see, every conversation we have – each one, a sacred place, a sacred space, never to come again in the same way.

How can we help ensure we treat each moment this way, in our bodies and in our minds?

As you breathe in, sense how your body takes in oxygen and transports it along specified paths to specified places. As you breathe out, sense how your body gathers and sends out what is no longer important to it. Feel your body taking good care of itself as sacred space.

Consider this moment not just another minute of the day, but a slice of sacred space.

This slice of sacred is yours to savor, spend, and serve.

75-MINUTE YIN ASANA FLOWS FOR WHOLE-SELF ENERGETIC HARMONY

Each Yin Yoga pose is an opportunity to maintain the wellbeing of our energy body, a tool for energy cultivation and balance based on the yin-yang Organ and Qi channel pairs we want to target. Here are some sample Yin asana flows for a whole-system Energetic Harmony Yin Yoga & Meditation Series that is designed to stimulate each Organ System-Qi channel pair. See Yin Asana Spotlights (p. 135) for pose instructions.

As you practice these sequences, you have the option of sensing and moving energy along the channels with your awareness and breath. Breathe naturally and fully. As you relax and remain in each pose, sensitize to what's happening below the superficial tissues. Slowly and inquisitively pass your inner eyes through the parts of the body, feeling for the sensations of moving energy. Attention attracts energy, so you may use this time to recruit your awareness like an assist to guide and gather energy into any areas that feel tense. Sense how your calm inner focus creates energetic flow within you. Like the physical stresses of the Yin Yoga postures, compassionate attention nourishes these lines of energy. In your approach, continue to be good company for all parts of yourself.

Practitioner's Tip: Use your breath like an energy brush, letting the soft brush of your breath walk slowly along the inner tissues where the Qi channels flow and into any sensations arising there.

Guided Technique 1: Liver-Gall Bladder Flow, Wood Element

The following Yin Yoga sequence helps open, clear, and revitalize Liver-Gall Bladder Qi and the energetic pathways flowing through the inner legs and lateral sides of your ribcage, and outer hip/leg areas. From the Taoist perspective, Liver energy supports joint strength and removes unwanted toxins from the body. By re-strengthening Liver Qi, we maintain a connection with our inherent patience and ability to be present for what's happening with greater grace and ease. Harmonious Liver Qi reduces emotional reactivity, allowing our natural kindness and compassion to arise.

> Suggested Time: Seventy-five minutes, includes counterpose hold times of one to two minutes. Can be adapted for sixty- or ninety-minute classes by reducing the number of poses or slightly increasing or decreasing pose/counterpose hold times and modifying meditation timing.
>
> Suggested Use: For your home practice or teaching. Make it your own to best meet your needs. Remember to try out variations of the poses to find your expression of each shape and to swap with substitutions as the body requests.

INSTRUCTIONS:

Arrive to the Mat: Seated, w/meditative method of choice (5min)
Wide Knee Beetle (5min)
Cp: Closed Knee Beetle and Cat's Breath
Lying Crescent Moon (5min), Cp, then do the other side
Cp: Savasana
Sukhasana or Square w/upright twist (3min), then forward bend + side bend (2min), Cp, then switch cross of legs and do the other side
Cp: Savasana

Dragonfly w/side bend over straight leg (1.5min), then forward bend between legs (2.5min), CP, then do the other side
Cp: Savasana and Tipped Beetle
Supine Lingering Windshield Wipers w/overhead binding (5min), Cp, then do the other side
Cp: Tipped Beetle
Savasana (10min)
Close with meditative method of choice (10min)

Guided Technique 2: Heart-Small Intestine/Pericardium-Triple Burner Flow, Fire Element

The poses in this Yin Yoga sequence focus on the upper back and chest, shoulders, neck, and arms, all areas where the Heart Qi channel runs. As you clear away any stagnant energy and amplify the Heart Qi's natural flow in this session, practice meeting the whole of your experience with compassion and allowing attention. Offer yourself lovingkindness, the vibrant energy of the Heart. You'll remember, the Heart Organ is considered a seat of Shen, our highest spirit energy, the home of unconditional love, warmth, connection, and delight. You might choose to close your practice by extending the Heart energy you've cultivated on the mat as an offering of loving compassionate energy to all beings everywhere: *May you find ease and wellbeing, may you be happy, safe, and free-hearted.*

> Suggested Time: Seventy-five minutes, includes counterpose hold times of one to two minutes. Can be adapted for sixty- or ninety-minute classes by reducing the number of poses or slightly increasing or decreasing pose/counterpose hold times and modifying meditation timing.
>
> Suggested Use: For your home practice or teaching. Make it your own to best meet your needs. Remember to try out variations of the poses to find your expression of each shape and to swap with substitutions as the body requests.

INSTRUCTIONS:

Arrive to the Mat: Seated, w/meditative method of choice (10min)

Wide Knee Beetle w/prayerful hands (2.5min), then unbind arms and reach forward (2.5min)

Cp: Closed Knee Beetle

Melting Heart (5min)

Remember option of doing one arm at a time (2.5min ea)

Cp: Wide Knee Beetle or Closed Knee Beetle

Mayfly (2.5min), Cp, then do the other side

Cp: Prone Penguin

Shoelace w/cow-faced arms with or without forward bend (2.5min), then unbind arms with or without forward bend. Press pinkie tips to the earth where these Qi channels start and end (2.5min), Cp, then switch cross of legs and do the other side

Cp: Heart Beacon and Savasana

One Twig Twist w/overhead binding (5min), Cp, then do the other side

Cp: Tipped Beetle w/knee circles

Angel Fish (5min)

Cp: Sideways Beetle

Extended Savasana, w/optional Yoga Nidra-Inspired method of choice (15min)

Guided Technique 3: Spleen-Stomach Flow, Earth Element

The focus of the physical stresses in this session is on the fronts of the legs and torso to help replenish and balance the Spleen-Stomach Qi. This Qi helps us notice mental loops and cycles of anxiety or mental chatter. Supporting the release of the "monkey mind," Spleen-Stomach Qi clears the way for clarity, insight, and creative thought. Because these are the main Organs of digestion and nourishment, when their channels are clear and energy flow is reinvigorated, we feel energized, full of vitality, and enthusiastic about life.

> Suggested Time: Seventy-five minutes, includes counterpose hold times of one to two minutes. Can be adapted for sixty- or ninety-minute classes by reducing the number of poses or slightly increasing or decreasing pose/counterpose hold times and modifying meditation timing.
>
> Suggested Use: For your home practice or teaching. Make it your own to best meet your needs. Remember to try out variations of the poses to find your expression of each shape and to swap with substitutions as the body requests.

INSTRUCTIONS:

Arrive to the Mat: Seated, w/meditative method of choice (10min)

Closed Knee Beetle (3min)

Cp: Cat's Breath

Baby Dragon (2.5min), then Dragon Pulling Its Tail (2.5min), Cp, then do the other side
Cp: Down Dog
Proud Swan (1.5min), then Sleeping Swan w/single threaded needle option (1.5min), unthreaded (2min), Cp, then do the other side
Cp: Closed Knee Beetle
One-Legged Saddle or Saddle (5min), Cp, then do the other side
Cp: Gentle Fish
Cat Pulling Its Tail (5min), Cp, then do the other side
Cp: Tipped Beetle and Savasana
Savasana (10min)

Guided Technique 4: Lungs-Large Intestine Flow, Metal Element

Through these Yin Yoga poses, we focus on the Qi supporting the Lungs-Large Intestine Organ Systems. This energy flows through the upper body, shoulders, and arms to the thumb and index fingertips. Balanced and healthy Lung Qi supports a healthy breath and a healthy body. Through the Lungs we take in natural air Qi to replenish and nourish the whole network of Qi in the body. Working together, this Qi strengthens and multiplies everything that is good for us and encourages the letting go of what isn't. Through the Lungs, we reconnect with our inherent value. We're empowered to release what gets in the way of living our life as an expression of our truest self. Reclaiming our natural spaciousness helps us fill back up and re-nourish the yin and yang energies that support our soul's aspiration, our Sankalpa.

> Suggested Time: Seventy-five minutes, includes counterpose hold times of one to two minutes. Can be adapted for sixty- or ninety-minute classes by reducing the number of poses or slightly increasing or decreasing pose/counterpose hold times and modifying meditation timing.
>
> Suggested Use: For your home practice or teaching. Make it your own to best meet your needs. Remember to try out variations of the poses to find your expression of each shape and to swap with substitutions as the body requests.

INSTRUCTIONS:

Arrive to the Mat: Seated, w/meditative method of choice (15min)
Butterfly w/forward bend (3min), then Bow Tie Butterfly (2min)
Cp: Windshield Wipers
Walrus w/wrist press, flexion (2min), Cp, then do Walrus w/wrist press, extension
Cp: Pinwheel Hands
Caterpillar (5min)
Cp: Reverse Table or Slide and Savasana
Prone Rolling Cactus (2.5min), Cp, then Prone Rolling Wing (2.5min), Cp, then do the other side
Cp: Prone Penguin
Sphinx or Seal (5min)
Cp: Stay a While Crocodile
Shoot the Moon (5min), Cp, then do the other side
Cp: Savasana
Supine Square w/hugging arms (1.5min), then do the other side
Cp: Tipped Beetle
Savasana (8min)

Guided Technique 5: Kidneys-Urinary Bladder Flow, Water Element

This spine and legs sequence helps stimulate the Kidney-Urinary Bladder channels flowing through the body's inner legs and entire backside. Kidney Qi keeps our bones strong and, because it rules Water, it supports hydrated and supple joints. This energy assists the filtering function of the Kidneys, keeping the body cleansed and clear of toxins. This is the Qi of personal power and confidence, helping us move through anxiety and fear to connect with our natural wisdom, confident in our ability to manifest our desires.

> Suggested Time: Seventy-five minutes, includes counterpose hold times of one to two minutes. Can be adapted for sixty- or ninety-minute classes by reducing the number of poses or slightly increasing or decreasing pose/counterpose hold times and modifying meditation timing.
>
> Suggested Use: For your home practice or teaching. Make it your own to best meet your needs. Remember to try out variations of the poses to find your expression of each shape and to swap with substitutions as the body requests.

INSTRUCTIONS:

Arrive to the Mat: Savasana posture of choice, w/meditative method of choice (10min)

Supine Butterfly (5min)

Cp: Sitting Beetle

Twig Twist of choice (5min), Cp, then do the other side

Cp: Supine Windshield Wipers

One-Legged Butterfly w/forward bend over straight leg (5min), Cp, then do the other side

Cp: Heart Beacon and Savasana

Sphinx or Seal x2 (2.5min), Cp, then repeat the pose

Cp: Resting Crocodile

Dragons: Baby Dragon (1.5min), stay in Baby Dragon or morph into Crouching Dragon (1.5min), then Crouching Dragon Hidden Toes Squat (1.5min), Cp, then do the other side

Cp: Down Dog

Diving Dragonfly (1.5min)

Bridge (5min)

Cp: Constructive Rest and Tipped Beetle w/knee circles

Savasana (10min)

Post-Practice Reflections:

After practicing the yin-yang Organ flows, consider journaling to reflect on each of your experiences. With a warm open attention, jot down whatever comes to mind. Here are few ideas to get you started:

- Day of the week, time of day, length of your practice session.
- How were you feeling before the Yin asana practice? How do you feel afterwards? Consider contemplating each layer of your being: body, mind, energy, and heart.
- Are there poses that felt particularly accessible? Any poses that were inaccessible? In what ways, specifically? Did you find any substitute poses useful? If so, which ones?
- Did you experiment with any guided techniques? If so, which ones? What went well? Is there anything to change or adjust for next time? Is there anything you wish to build upon in your future practices?
- How would you describe your approach to your Yin asana session? What about your approach would be of benefit to continue to cultivate? Is there something to do differently next time?

- Did any tendencies of the body, the mind, energy flow, or the heart come to light?
- Are there any guided techniques you'd like to incorporate as stand-alone practices in your daily life to reinforce the good work you're doing on the mat?
- Is there a skill you've grown or an awareness or insight you've gained as a result of your practice time that you'd like to carry with you into the rest of your day or week? Anything that might benefit you in how you respond to yourself, loved ones, or daily life circumstances?

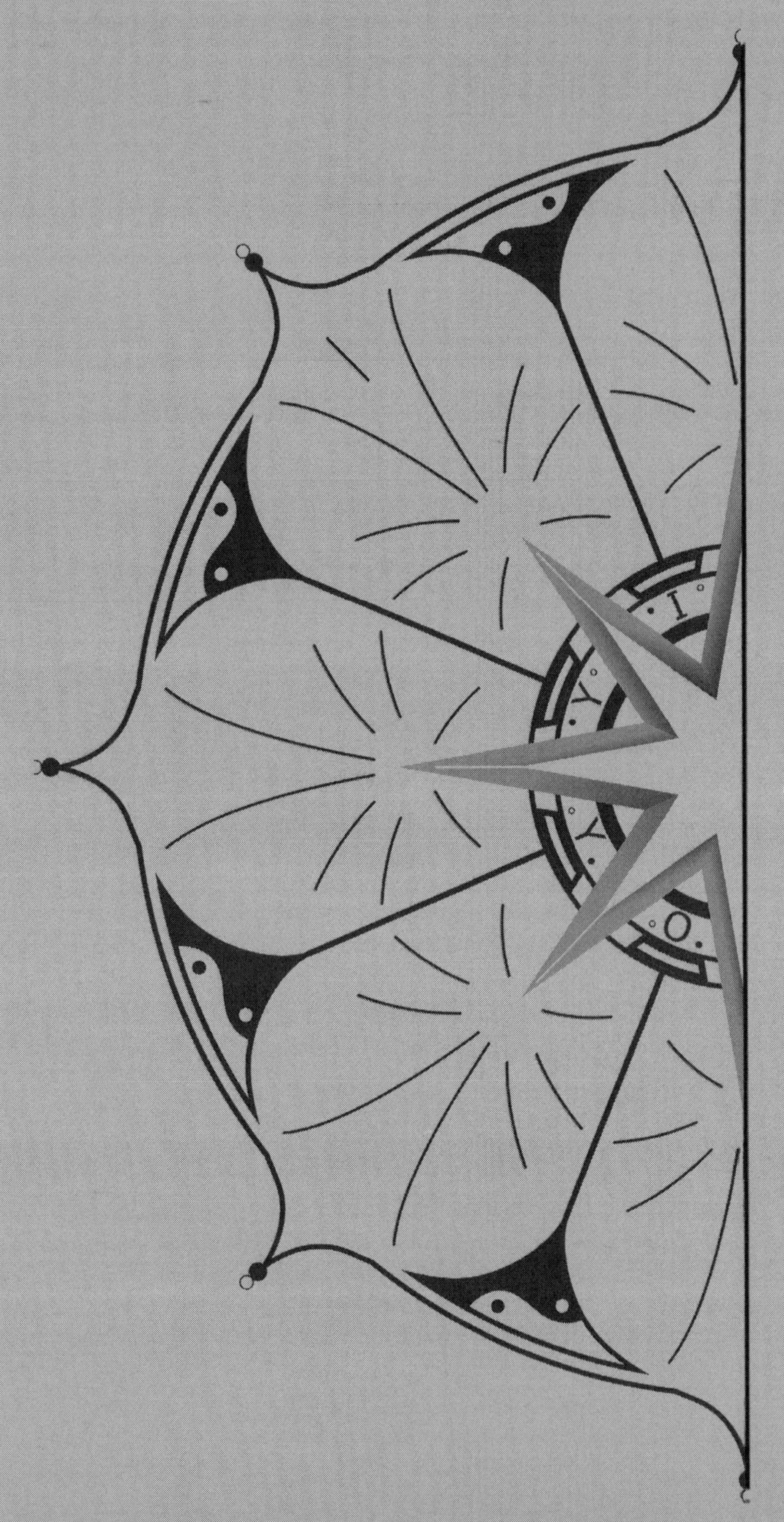

• Part Three

Mapping Your Way

Chapter 12
Meditative Mandala Mapping for Practice, Teaching, and Beyond

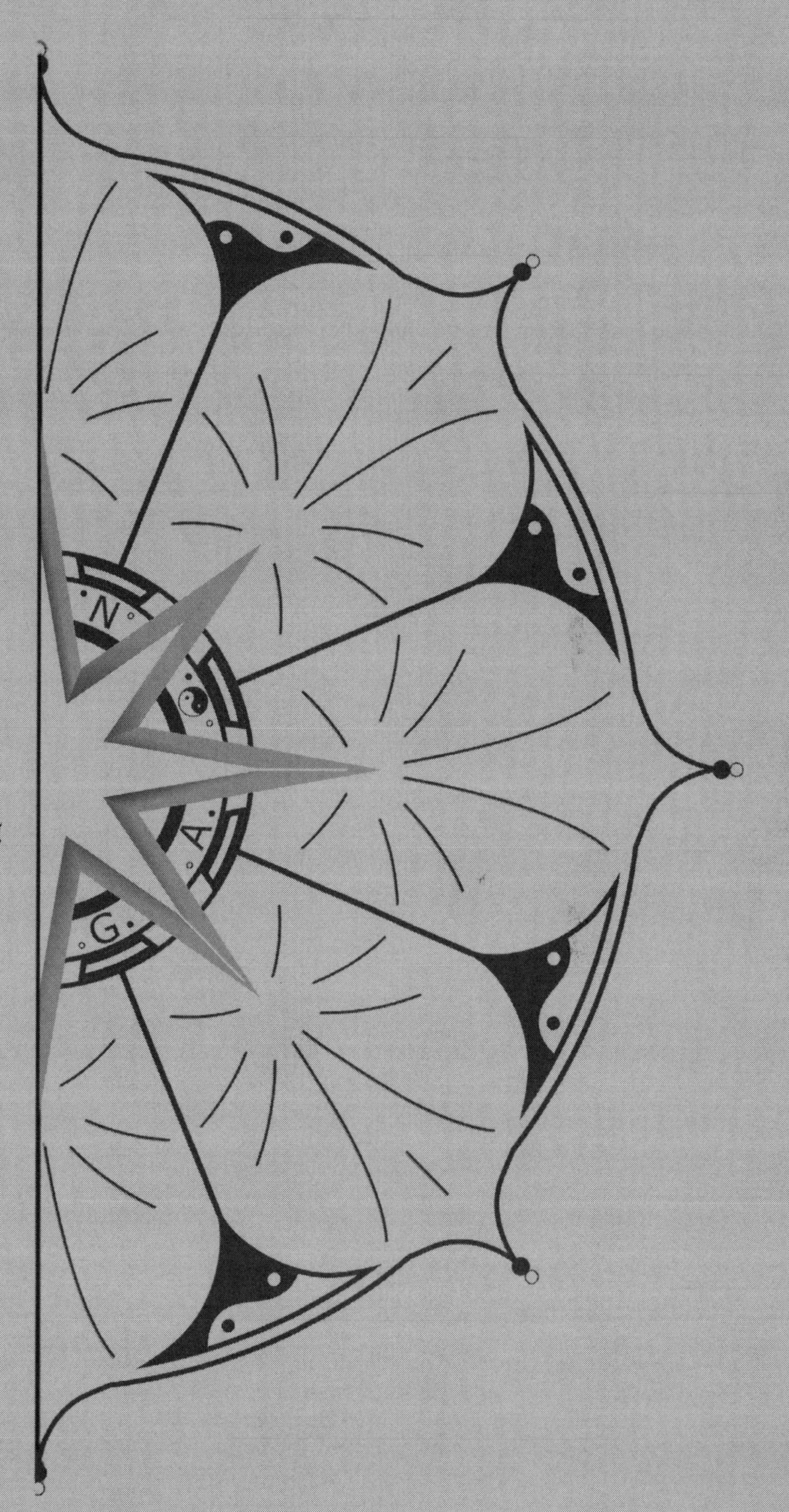

illuminate
inspire
transform
cultivate
Y I N Y O G A
inspire
transform

Chapter 12

Mandala Mapping for Practice, Teaching, and Beyond

Throughout this book, we've journeyed through the elements of a safe, effective, and transformative Yin Yoga & Meditation practice. Each is rich with possibility for insight and inspiration in support of our presence and whole-self wellbeing:

- Layers of Our Being
- Practice Principles
- Jewels of Encouragement
- The Yin and Yang Wings of Present Moment Awareness:
    - Awareness Anchors
    - Yin Guardians
    - Yin Qualities
- Yin Asana
- Meditative Methods
- Yinquiry
- Intention and Inner Wisdom

These elements form the core attributes of the traceable Mandala Map to aid your meditative contemplation and intuitive investigation, whether for practice or teaching. Let's now take a more in-depth look at the Mandala Map's design as well as some guidance and inspirations for use.

At the heart of the Mandala Map, you'll find the compass rose, the element that represents the place of your ever-present inner knowing calling you home. You can place your practice intention here.

The eight pointers of the compass rose serve as open pathways inviting you on an experiential journey further inward. Each pointer leads to a core element of the Yin Yoga & Meditation practice held within a petal of the mandala.

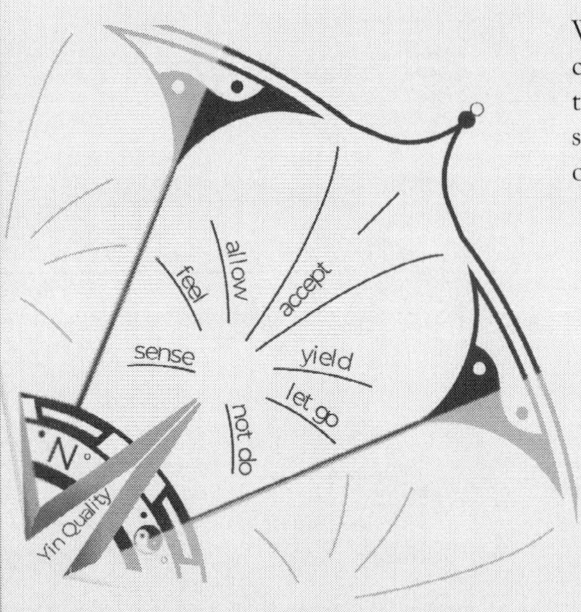

Within each of the petals, you'll encounter various aspects, or facets, of that particular practice element. Consider if there are any aspects of your own that you'd like to add.

The outer rim pathway of prompting Yinquiry words seals the mandala and connects practice elements to one another, enabling a continuity of flow as you trace between them.

Use the Yinquiry words to stimulate internal connections or insights as you integrate the practice elements in your meditative explorations and mat time. Consider if there are any Yinquiry words you'd like to add to spark your inner contemplation.

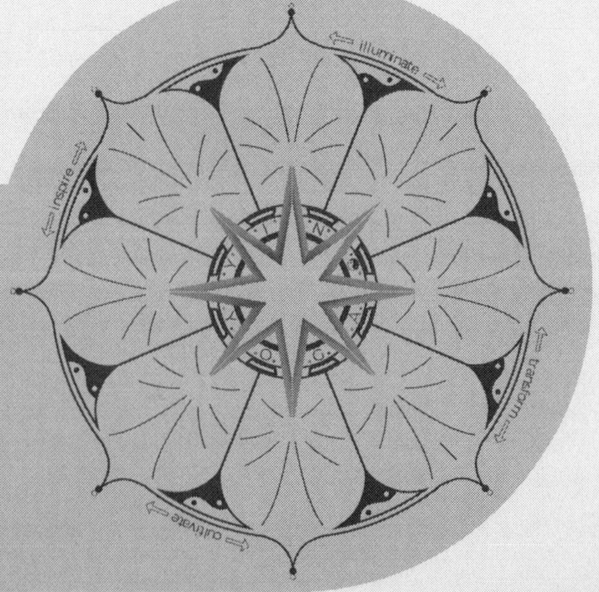

Mapping Your Way

The Mandala Map can support your Yin Yoga & Meditation sessions, whether for personal home practice planning or preparing to teach others. Using this tool, you can create a personalized guide for your practice based on your needs.

Following is some general guidance for getting started on your meditative mapping journey, but there's no one right way to use the Mandala Map. As you continue to engage with the mandala, let the flow of your individual process organically unfold within you.

You could choose to use a pencil, your finger, or simply the spotlight of your mind to trace your way through the Mandala Map. Select whichever feels best for you each time you use it.

1. **Place your intention in the center of the compass.** Write or imagine your intention in the center of the mandala. You might find yourself circling back to adjust or refine your intention as your session evolves. If you don't happen to have a specific intention at the moment, no problem! Just go to the next step and see if one arises. You could also try the "Guided Mandala Map: Inhabiting the Blue Sky of Your Mind" (p. 291) to help jump-start your journey inward.
2. **Choose a pointer of the compass rose and trace from the center through it and into its connecting petal.** Consider the various aspects of this practice element and select any that you'd like to explore in your session; it could be one or more. If none call your attention, go to the next step.
3. **If you'd like, follow a pathway to another petal to continue to craft your practice session.** In this petal, are there any aspects of this element you'd like to focus on? Do any specific facets complement your intention or blend well with the previous element? In what ways might they work together?
4. **As you trace along the outer rim pathway, note any Yinquiry words that speak to you.** Do they prompt any insights or connections between the practice elements? If so, in what ways?
5. **Continue to trace through the pathways of the Mandala Map until you feel you have what you need for your session.** Follow any pathways that request your investigation, moving through the petals, outer rim, and the pointers of the compass. Linger any place in the mandala that invites you to pause, asking yourself: *How may this be of benefit to me and support my intention?*

Additional pointers for your mandala mapping:

- As you contemplate the practice elements, you may find it helpful to revisit the chapter discussing that element for a refresher or for further inspiration. For ease of reference, pages covering the elements are indicated with a corresponding label.
- You can start your mapping in whichever space of the mandala that speaks to you.
- Consider as many or as few practice elements as you prefer. You may discover multiple practice elements in the map serve you in your voyage Yinward one day, while at a different time, just one generates all the clarity and resources you need. Trust your curiosity to guide you onward and inward for as long or as briefly as desired.
- While you're mapping, attune to any thoughts, feelings, or sensations arising within you to help you build on your intention or further tailor your session.
- When ideas or "aha" moments surface, feel free to jot them down on the map or in your practice journal.
- You could also incorporate additional facets of your own into the map. For example, you might add a meditative method that you're studying, like Reiki or Ayurveda, or a jewel of encouragement from another wisdom tradition that speaks to you. You'll find several unannotated Mandala Maps at the end of this section to use as you'd like.

Each time you arrive to the Mandala Map, just as to your mat, your approach and experience will be different, so enjoy letting your individual internal journey naturally manifest.

Exploring Inspirations for Use

Here are just a few specific ways the Mandala Map can help you in your practice or teaching:

- Clarify your practice session intention.
- Develop your practice session based on your intention, for example, specific areas of the body to target, skills to cultivate, meditative methods you'd like to integrate, or energetic benefits you'd like to explore.
- Craft a class theme based on any element or combination of elements.
- Create a Yin Yoga & Meditation class series for your home practice or teaching highlighting a particular idea or need, for example, a deep dive into directed breathing techniques, fostering yin qualities, stimulating Organ-Qi channel pairs for whole-self energetic harmony, or certain Mindfulness Meditation practices.

Perhaps there are other ways you feel the map may support you in your practice or teaching – feel free to list any ideas here:

-
-
-

Mandala mapping can also help open new intuitive pathways for presence and wellbeing in daily life. Here are just a few of the many possibilities to use this tool off the mat:

- Unearth an insight or inspiration for daily personal reflection or journaling.
- Enjoy some quiet contemplation and cultivate a nugget of wisdom for the day ahead.
- Ground yourself for a difficult conversation or an upcoming performance or presentation.

- Develop a weekly plan for something you'd like to strengthen, perhaps pairing a few elements to nurture greater presence, balance, and relaxation, or to support loving relationships.
- Strengthen the habit of compassionate response and decrease reactivity.

You might spend a few moments considering some other circumstances where the map may benefit you in the course of a day and record any thoughts here:

-
-
-

Guided Mandala Maps to Support Your Practice and Teaching

In this section, you'll find several guided Mandala Maps to support your Yin Yoga & Meditation practice or teaching:

- A Yin Yoga & Meditation Practice of Stress Relief
- A Qi Cherishing Yin Yoga & Meditation Practice
- Inhabiting the Blue Sky of Your Mind
- Yin Asana Flows
  - Wholly Hips – Keeping It Low with an All-Supine Flow, 75-minute
  - Full Body TLC Rebalance Remedy Flow, 90-minute
  - Yin Basics – A Delightfully Simple Flow, 60+-minute
  - Deep Breath Refresh – A Mini Flow for Anytime, 20-minute
  - Yin-Nidra Duo Flow – Finding Your Bliss, 60-minute

These themed guided Mandala Maps offer a starting point for crafting unique practice sessions for yourself or others. All include:

- A brief introduction to the practice session theme.
- Step-by-step instructions inviting you to trace the annotated mandala pathways on your contemplative journey into different practice elements and make selections that align with your focus.
- Inquiry prompts to spur personal insights as you consider the aspects of each element and ways you might blend them to build your practice session.
- Mapping variations you could try while staying aligned with the same general theme.

When considering which poses to include, remember to try out variations and modifications to find your expression of each shape and swap with substitutions as your body requests. As you explore the guided Mandala Maps, keep in mind that there's no right or wrong way to travel through the mandala. Let this be a process of discovery!

illuminate
transform
cultivate
inspire
acknowledge
recognize
notice
greet
watch
feel
allow
accept
sense
yield
let go
not do
energy
physical
heart
mind
kindness
curiosity
breath
spaciousness
nature
gratitude
smile
relax & remain
transition
arrive
watch & welcome
mild sensation
continue
rest
Y
I
N
Y
O
G
A
Layer
Anchor
Yin Quality
Principle
2
Yin Guardian
Asana
Jewel
Method
safe
effective
pose
counterpose
yinpression
release
balance
impermanence
imperfection
interconnection
1
breathwork
yoga nidra
concentration
3
qi cultivation

Guided Mandala Map: A Yin Yoga & Meditation Practice of Stress Relief

It can be easy to unconsciously accumulate and carry tensions and stress in all layers of our being. As a practice for stress relief and self-care, Yin Yoga & Meditation offers many opportunities for us to release these unhelpful tensions and enjoy the peace of real relief.

1. **To begin your mapping, rest your attention on the Jewels of Encouragement element. Select: Releasing Tensions for Real Relief**

   Arising from the sacred wisdom roots of Yoga Nidra, the jewel of releasing tensions for real relief encourages us to heighten our perception of patterns of holding to consciously, systematically, and compassionately invite their release to experience long-lasting stress relief. Serving as a touchstone for this practice, let's allow this jewel to inspire this session's intention.

2. **Go to the center of the Compass Rose, the home of intention. Select: Relieving Stress and Tension**

   Take a few moments to reflect on this session's intention of *relieving stress and tension* and notice the first five to ten words that come immediately to your mind. Feel free to write them on the map or in your practice journal.

   - Inquire: Reflect on the words you've chosen. What sort of practice suggestions or guidance for your session would support your intention and help you nurture yourself?

3. **Chart to Meditative Methods. Select: Yoga Nidra-Inspired Methods: Progressive Muscle Relaxation (PMR) Technique**

   Whatever we're doing, we're training in something. Yoga Nidra-Inspired methods give us many effective options for conscious relaxation. The Progressive Muscle Relaxation (PMR) technique allows us to experiment with transforming tensions into relief and polish the skill of using our senses to discern the differences between tension and relaxation. Regularly scanning the body helps us watch and feel the physical sensations arising and observe any physical effects of the PMR practice.

   - Inquire: Consider when you could incorporate the PMR method during your Yin Yoga session, perhaps in your arrival, the poses or counterposes, or Savasana. Call to mind two science-backed physical benefits of the PMR technique and how they support greater calm and relaxation both on and off the mat.

illuminate
transform
cultivate
inspire
5
4
Y I N Y O G A
Anchor
Yin Quality
Yin Guardian
Method
Jewel
Asana
Principle
Layer
acknowledge
recognize
notice
greet
watch
feel
allow
accept
sense
yield
let go
not do
kindness
curiosity
breath
spaciousness
nature
gratitude
smile
breathwork
yoga nidra
concentration
qi cultivation
release
balance
impermanence
imperfection
interconnection
safe
effective
pose
counterpose
yinpression
watch & welcome
arrive
transition
relax & remain
rest
continue
mild sensation
physical
energy
heart
mind

Guided Mandala Map: A Yin Yoga & Meditation Practice of Stress Relief, cont'd

4. **Now, track to Yin Asana. Select:** Poses for a Whole-Body Yin Asana Flow
   Ponder a Yin Yoga pose selection that would blend well with the intention of relieving stress and tension. To help ensure you're reaching all the major areas of any potential tensions, assemble a diverse, whole-body Yin asana flow. Here are a few considerations:

   - Include at least one pose for each primary part of the body: hips/legs, chest/shoulders/arms, and spine. You might also consider incorporating a pose or Yinpression for the feet, ankles, and/or wrists. Choose a simple class-opening pose to share the practice principles for safety and efficacy. Here's an example of a brief summary of the practice principles:

     > "Practice embracing your Yinside as you move mindfully toward mild sensations that are sensation-ful but stay-able and never painful, so avoid any sharp, burning, or localized sensations, or anything that doesn't allow you to breathe well. Let yourself relax and remain in relative stillness, making intentional adjustments as your body requests...Go in and watch and welcome whatever's happening inside you, sensations, thoughts and emotions, energy flow...Give yourself space to feel before you follow. Stay kind to yourself in your approach, transitioning out of each pose as slowly as you transitioned in. Be sure to offer yourself plenty of permission to rest whenever rest is needed...If you get distracted, practice beginning again, coming back to the intention you set when you first arrived to the mat."

   - Sketch out your sequence and timing, reflecting on the class length and the approximate number of poses and counterposes including hold times. Remember to factor in time for arriving to the mat, a sitting meditation, any other meditative methods you'd like to include, Savasana, and the class closing.

   Staying aware of contraindications and body diversity, consider specifying one safety precaution and substitute posture per pose.

5. **Now, follow the pathways to Yin Guardians. Select:** Kindness and Compassion
   The illuminating energy of kindness and compassion shines a gentle, revealing light on tensions and facilitates their release.

   - Inquire: How might you use this yin guardian to inspire relaxation and stress relief during your practice? Is there a way to blend the PMR technique with the energy of kindness and compassion? For example, can you speak loving words in your mind to the part of your body as you're tensing and relaxing during the technique?

illuminate
transform
cultivate
inspire
6
7
acknowledge
recognize
notice
greet
watch
allow
feel
accept
sense
yield
let go
not do
kindness
curiosity
breath
spaciousness
nature
gratitude
smile
breathwork
yoga nidra
concentration
qi cultivation
release
balance
impermanence
imperfection
interconnection
safe
effective
pose
counterpose
yinpression
watch & welcome
relax & remain
transition
arrive
mild sensation
continue
rest
physical
energy
heart
mind
Y
I
N
Y
O
G
A
Anchor
Yin Quality
Layer
Principle
Yin Guardian
Asana
Jewel
Method

Guided Mandala Map: A Yin Yoga & Meditation Practice of Stress Relief, cont'd

6. **Now trace to Yin Qualities. Select: Letting Go**
   To enrich your experience of the internal landscape of the body's tissues, consider infusing the energy of kindness and compassion with the yin quality of letting go during your Yin Yoga & Meditation session.

   - Inquire: How might this yin quality-guardian duo guide your awareness and help transform tensions into relief in your practice approach? For example, letting go of judgments or storylines that can cause tension and planting seeds of kindness and understanding in their place.

7. **Follow the pathway to Practice Principles. Select: Continue to Cultivate**
   We can invite whatever we're practicing on the mat to follow us into the rest of our day to continue to benefit us.

   - Inquire: Is there a brief reading you'd like to use to close your practice that honors the importance of taking time to let yourself relax? Are there any times during the day you'd benefit from incorporating the PMR technique? If so, would you like to commit to trying this technique occasionally over the next week, including perhaps a few moments to journal any observations?

Continue mapping as you feel led...

Try Mapping a Variation

Using this guided map, replace the selected jewel of encouragement with another of your choice as the starting point and uncover the many ways this practice can support your whole-self wellbeing.

inspire
illuminate
transform
cultivate
1
2
3
physical
energy
heart
mind
recognize
acknowledge
notice
greet
watch
feel
allow
accept
sense
yield
let go
not do
watch & welcome
relax & remain
transition
arrive
mild sensation
continue
rest
kindness
curiosity
breath
spaciousness
nature
gratitude
smile
safe
effective
pose
counterpose
yinpression
release
balance
impermanence
interconnection
imperfection
yoga nidra
breathwork
concentration
qi cultivation
Layer
Anchor
Yin Quality
Principle
Yin Guardian
Asana
Jewel
Method
Y
I
N
Y
O
G
A

Guided Mandala Map: A Qi Cherishing Yin Yoga & Meditation Practice

To help you nourish and rebalance the energy body, one option is to harmonize your Qi with nature's cycle of seasons. As you'll remember, each season is ruled by one of the Five Elements and associated with the yin-yang Organ pair that's most active during that time.

1. **To begin your mapping, go to the Layers of Being element. Select: <u>Energy Layer + Your Season of Choice</u>**
   Choose either the current season or the one you're transitioning into as your focus for this Yin Yoga & Meditation session. Write down the Taoist Element and yin-yang Organ pair corresponding to your selected season.

   - Inquire: Is there anything you can do to immerse yourself in this season and its corresponding Taoist Element? For example, is there an opportunity to spend some time outside to experience it? If not, consider using nature music or visualization, which can be just as effective. Let yourself really soak in this season and its characteristics. What sensations and feelings arise when you're surrounded by this season? How do you experience this Element in the natural world? How does it shine its presence within you?

2. **Next, trace to the center of the Compass Rose. Identify: <u>Your Session Intention</u>**
   To help you identify your intention for your session, consider the various qualities and characteristics of your chosen Element, yin-yang Organ pair, and season.

   - Inquire: Do any of these qualities or characteristics call your attention? Are there any you'd like to strengthen, cultivate, or balance in yourself? If so, which ones? Do you sense an intention arising for your practice session?

3. **Move to Meditative Methods. Select: <u>The Yin Asana Flow for Your Yin-Yang Organ Pair + another Meditative Method of Choice</u>**
   Revisit "Taoist-Inspired Energy Cultivation Methods" (p. 255) to locate the Yin asana flow that targets your season's yin-yang Organ pair. Feel free to make adjustments to the posture sequence. Also consider incorporating any other energetic meditative methods that align with your practice session intention.

   - Inquire: Because it's often difficult to feel what we can't see, is there a directed breathing technique, internal body scan, visualization, or another meditative method to help you sense Qi while you're practicing this Yin asana flow?

illuminate
transform
cultivate
inspire
4
5
acknowledge
recognize
notice
greet
watch
feel
allow
accept
sense
yield
let go
not do
kindness
curiosity
breath
spaciousness
nature
smile
gratitude
breathwork
yoga nidra
concentration
qi cultivation
balance
release
imperfection
impermanence
interconnection
pose
safe
effective
yinpression
counterpose
rest
continue
mild sensation
watch & welcome
arrive
transition
relax & remain
mind
heart
physical
energy
Y
I
N
A
G
O
Y
Anchor
Yin Quality
Yin Guardian
Method
Jewel
Asana
Principle
Layer

4. **Next, travel the pathway to Awareness Anchors. Select:** 1 or 2 Awareness Anchors of Choice
   To know our inner energy is to feel it.

   - Inquire: Which of the awareness anchor words could help you steady your inside eyes and present moment attention on sensitizing to and feeling your internal flow of energy? Consider choosing one or two to help anchor your attention during your practice session.

5. **Now, go to Jewels of Encouragement. Select:** Cultivate Balance for Energetic Harmony
   Flow cultivates balance and balance cultivates flow.

   - Inquire: What are a few benefits of harmonizing the flow of Qi to this yin-yang Organ pair? Note some potential effects of imbalance. How might balancing this internal energy flow support your wellbeing and sense of peace on the mat and in daily life?

Continue mapping as you feel led...

Try Mapping a Variation

Using this guided map, trace the same pathway again, only this time swapping the season and its associated Taoist Element and yin-yang Organ pair with another. Continue mapping for all five seasons to create a Qi Cherishing Yin Yoga & Meditation practice series to harmonize your whole energetic system. You might choose to use the provided Yin asana flows for energetic harmony in "Taoist-Inspired Energy Cultivation Methods" (p. 255), or perhaps create your own pose flows. Revisit "Yinpression: Qi Charting" (p. 132) and the collection of Yin Asana Spotlights (p. 135) to help you build your pose sequence.

illuminate
transform
cultivate
inspire
acknowledge
recognize
notice
greet
watch
allow
feel
accept
yield
let go
sense
not do
spaciousness
curiosity
kindness
breath
smile
gratitude
nature
concentration
breathwork
yoga nidra
qi cultivation
interconnection
imperfection
impermanence
balance
release
pose
safe
effective
counterpose
yinpression
watch & welcome
relax & remain
transition
arrive
mild sensation
continue
rest
physical
energy
heart
mind
Y
I
N
Y
O
G
A
Anchor
Layer
Yin Quality
Principle
Yin Guardian
Asana
Jewel
Method

Guided Mandala Map: Inhabiting the Blue Sky of Your Mind

Turn your awareness to your breath for some moments and let the stream of any mind chatter to begin to quiet. Enjoy simply sitting in the company of the vast expanse of who you are, allowing your spacious attention to naturally settle. You might choose to use this map to illuminate or clarify your practice session intention. As you trace your way through the mandala, you might annotate the pathways you follow.

1. **To begin your mapping, sit in a comfortable position with your Yin Yoga & Meditation Mandala Map in front of you.**

2. **Meditate on the whole Mandala Map.**
   Allow the eyes to soften on the whole of the map shape. Broaden your gaze rather than focusing on any one aspect or element as you welcome it all into your awareness. Let the breath be natural and the body at ease. Let your attention be entirely absorbed in the space and shapes of the map, staying receptive and relaxed. Let the breath flow effortlessly and listen inwardly as the doorway to your natural wisdom opens wider and wider. Allow your awareness to slide toward whatever element speaks to you at first glance. As you're looking, inquire: *Is there something I want to cultivate? What matters most to me right now for this session?*

3. **Next, let your intuition lead you.**
   After a couple of minutes of meditating on your Mandala Map, let your intuiting self lead you as you place your finger somewhere on the map. Perhaps the place it lands will help further guide your intention for your session.

   - Inquire: Is there anything writing itself on the space of your mind in this moment?

4. **Identify your starting point.**
   See which map element you've selected as your potential starting point.

   - Inquire: Allow this element to float into the vast blue sky of your mind. Are there any resonances as you sit with this element of the practice and its various facets? Give it space to be and breathe in the peaceful expanse that is you. Feel for any responses reverberating in your mind, body, and heart. What arises? Any thoughts, any physical sensations, interconnections, or feeling tones?

illuminate
transform
cultivate
inspire
acknowledge
recognize
notice
greet
watch
feel
allow
accept
sense
yield
let go
not do
kindness
curiosity
breath
spaciousness
nature
gratitude
smile
breathwork
yoga nidra
concentration
qi cultivation
release
balance
impermanence
imperfection
interconnection
safe
pose
effective
counterpose
yinpression
watch & welcome
relax & remain
transition
arrive
mild sensation
continue
rest
physical
energy
heart
mind
Y
I
N
Y
O
G
A
Anchor
Layer
Yin Quality
Principle
Yin Guardian
Asana
Jewel
Method

Guided Mandala Map: Inhabiting the Blue Sky of Your Mind, cont'd

5. **Go to the opposite side of the Mandala Map**
   Now trace on your Mandala Map to the element directly opposite your origination point. What interconnections and inspirations present themselves to you?

   - Inquire: Consider using visualization to invite a helper from the natural world. What from nature presents itself as a helpful companion, messenger, or teacher? What insights might it bring you?

6. **Trace the outer rim pathway two elements in a clockwise direction.**
   Journey two map elements clockwise, and as you trace, notice the Yinquiry words in the outer circle that you encounter along the way. Do any speak to you or bridge connections between the elements? As you arrive, pause in the second petal and open your awareness to any inspirations it might spark.

   - Inquire: How could this new element transform your approach? Which facet(s) within it are you drawn to?

Continue mapping as you feel led...

Try Mapping a Variation

Turn your Mandala Map 180 degrees and begin again by softening your gaze or closing your eyes. Place your finger on the map to select your starting point. Open your eyes and instead of tracing clockwise, trace counterclockwise as you reconnect with your inner spaciousness.

illuminate
transform
cultivate
inspire
1
2
3
Y
I
N
Y
O
G
A
Anchor
Yin Quality
Yin Guardian
Method
Jewel
Asana
Principle
Layer
acknowledge
recognize
notice
greet
watch
sense
feel
allow
accept
yield
let go
not do
breath
kindness
curiosity
spaciousness
smile
gratitude
nature
breathwork
yoga nidra
concentration
qi cultivation
balance
release
imperfection
impermanence
interconnection
pose
safe
effective
yinpression
counterpose
rest
continue
mild sensation
watch & welcome
arrive
transition
relax & remain
mind
heart
physical
energy

Guided Mandala Map: Wholly Hips – Keeping It Low with an All-Supine Flow, 75-minute

This Wholly Hips sequence is a great option whether you're feeling fatigued or just want to reclaim your energy at the end of a long day. This all-supine set contains simple postures with very few transitions and limited up-and-down movements. It has the advantage of moving the hip joints through all directions of movement.

Arrive to the Mat: Savasana pose of choice (5min)
Tipped Dragon (2min), then do the other side
Cp: Savasana
Supine Eye of the Needle (2.5min), then Supine Twisted Needle (2.5min), Cp, then do the other side
Cp: Savasana
Supine Shoelace (3.5min), Cp, then do the other side
Cp: Savasana
Two-Legged Tipped Dragon (3min)
Cp: Tipped Beetle
Drawbridge (5min)
Cp: Constructive Rest
Supine Square (5min), Cp, then do the other side
Cp: Supine Calf-Hamstring Opener
Supine Lingering Windshield Wipers w/overhead bind (5min), Cp, then do the other side
Cp: Tipped Beetle
Savasana (10min)

(includes counterpose hold times of 1-2mins)

1. **To begin your mapping, go to the Yin Guardians element. Select: A Yin Guardian**
   - Inquire: With the intention of relieving any long-held tensions, what yin guardian would be a good companion for you to invite into your experience on the mat in this supine sequence?
2. **Next, trace to Layers of Beings. Select: A Layer**
   - Inquire: In addition to focusing on the physical layer as you exercise the hips, what other layer of being would you like to spotlight in this nurturing flow? Are there any interconnections between the layer you selected and the physical body that support your intention and practice approach?
3. **Next, go to Meditative Methods. Select: A Meditative Method of Choice**
   - Inquire: Given the easeful transitions and long holds of this Yin asana flow, what meditative method could you recruit to provide some extra relaxation?

Continue mapping as you feel led...

inspire
illuminate
transform
cultivate
1
2
3
4
physical
energy
heart
mind
recognize
acknowledge
notice
greet
watch
feel
allow
accept
sense
yield
let go
not do
breath
kindness
curiosity
spaciousness
nature
gratitude
smile
breathwork
yoga nidra
concentration
qi cultivation
release
balance
impermanence
interconnection
imperfection
safe
effective
pose
counterpose
yinpression
arrive
transition
relax & remain
watch & welcome
rest
continue
mild sensation
Y
I
N
Y
O
G
A
Anchor
Yin Quality
Yin Guardian
Method
Jewel
Asana
Principle
Layer

Guided Mandala Map: Full Body TLC Rebalance Remedy Flow, 90-minute

This lingering, rebalancing full-body Yin asana flow will leave you feeling nurtured from the inside out and head to toe. Includes an extended pause before Savasana to attend to all layers of your being.

Arrive to the Mat: Seated, w/meditative method of choice (5min)
Bridge (5min)
Cp: Savasana
Pixie Toes Squat w/shoulder-arm bind of choice (2.5min), Cp, then switch arms and repeat pose
Cp: Tabletop with gentle tops of feet taps and Closed Knee Beetle
Foot Cradle (2min), then do the other side
Cp: Tabletop
Supine Calf-Hamstring Opener (1.5), Cp, then do the other side
Watchful Deer (2min), then Sleeping Deer (3.5min), Cp, then do the other side
Cp: Savasana
Caterpillar w/forward bend + hugging arms or twisted branches shoulder-arm bind (2.5min), Cp, then switch arms and repeat pose
Cp: Savasana
Sleeping Crescent Moon (5min), Cp, then do the other side
Cp: Savasana
Supine Butterfly (5min)
Cp: Tipped Beetle
Waterfall (1.5min)
Cp: Sideways Beetle
Seated, w/meditative method of choice (10min)
Savasana (10min)

(includes counterpose hold times of 1-2mins)

1. **To begin your mapping, go to the Layers of Being element. Select: All Layers**
   - Inquire: Consider the benefits of nurturing all layers of your being as you enjoy this full-body flow.
2. **Next, move to Practice Principles. Select: A Practice Principle of Choice**
   - Inquire: Is there a practice principle you'd like to emphasize to support your journey into all layers of your being? For example, the "*Watch and Welcome What's Happening Inside You*" practice principle might inspire you to pay particular attention to what's happening in every part of yourself and observe the way each layer influences another.
3. **Now go to Meditative Methods. Select: Internal Scan**
   - Inquire: How might you integrate an internal scanning technique to serve your whole self in these poses? Are there any other techniques or complementary aids you'd like to experiment with to grow your awareness while on the mat?
4. **Trace to Yin Qualities. Select: A Yin Quality of Choice**
   - Inquire: Mutually reinforcing and balancing, yin and yang energies enliven and balance all things in the universe. Which yin quality could you invite into this practice session to cultivate and strengthen the same harmonic balance within you?

Continue mapping as you feel led...

inspire
illuminate
transform
cultivate
1
2
3
4
Y
I
N
Y
O
G
A
Anchor
Yin Quality
Yin Guardian
Method
Jewel
Asana
Principle
Layer
acknowledge
recognize
notice
greet
watch
physical
energy
heart
mind
sense
feel
allow
accept
yield
let go
not do
breath
kindness
curiosity
spaciousness
nature
gratitude
smile
breathwork
yoga nidra
concentration
qi cultivation
release
balance
impermanence
interconnection
imperfection
safe
effective
pose
counterpose
yinpression
arrive
transition
relax & remain
watch & welcome
rest
continue
mild sensation

Guided Mandala Map: Yin Basics – A Delightfully Simple Flow, 60+-minute

This back-to-basics Yin asana flow offers plentiful space to introduce newcomers to the fundamentals of a safe, sustainable, and effective Yin Yoga & Meditation practice. Consider expanding the class by offering an extended Savasana experience with a guided Yoga Nidra-Inspired method of choice (20-25min) as a fun introduction to Yin Yoga and Yoga Nidra as practitioners enjoy a state of bliss.

The simple nature of these poses allows for relatively uncomplicated technical pose instruction, giving a generous amount of time to become familiar with the Yin Yoga shapes and explore the many ways to use props to modify the poses as needed. Shorter hold times help prevent over-stressing the yin tissues as students build body awareness of the sensations they're experiencing.

Arrive to the Mat: Seated, w/meditative method of choice (10min)
Butterfly (3.5min)
Cp: Windshield Wipers
One-Legged Butterfly w/forward bend over straight leg (3min), Cp, then do the other side
Cp: Savasana
Resting Crocodile or Sphinx (3min)
Cp: Stay a While Crocodile, both sides
Leaning Swan (3min), Cp, then do the other side
Cp: Closed Knee Beetle and Down Dog
Two Twig Twist (3min), Cp, then do the other side
Cp: Tipped Beetle w/knee circles
Gentle Fish (3.5min)
Cp: Sideways Beetle
Savasana (10min
Seated Close (3-5min)

(includes counterpose hold times of 1-2mins)

1. **To begin your mapping, go to the Layers of Being element. Select: Physical Layer**
   - Inquire: Focusing on physical sensations helps us become acquainted with the effects of the Yin Yoga shapes and learn the principles of a safe and effective practice. How might you integrate careful attention of sensations into instructional pose guidance for yourself or others?
2. **Next, trace to Meditative Methods. Select: An Internal Body and/or Breath Scan**
   - Inquire: How might you employ your chosen scan(s) to help improve awareness of the state of the physical body and encourage present moment awareness? Would periodically revisiting the scan(s) be of benefit while holding the Yin Yoga poses or at any other time during the session?
3. **Now, move to Yin Qualities. Select: A Yin Quality of Choice**
   - Inquire: Newcomers to the practice may be unfamiliar with yin qualities. Is there a yin quality you'd like to better acquaint yourself with or introduce to your students? How could it help ground the attention in physical sensations and observing the effects as you practice?
4. **Travel to Practice Principles. Select: Continue to Cultivate**
   - Inquire: Reflecting on the benefits of our practice serves as a healthy motivator to return to the mat, especially when we're starting something new. What are some ways to acknowledge and honor the gifts of this practice time?

Continue mapping as you feel led...

illuminate
transform
cultivate
inspire
2
1
acknowledge
recognize
notice
greet
watch
feel
allow
accept
sense
yield
let go
not do
kindness
curiosity
breath
spaciousness
nature
gratitude
smile
breathwork
concentration
yoga nidra
qi cultivation
balance
release
imperfection
impermanence
interconnection
safe
pose
effective
yinpression
counterpose
watch & welcome
arrive
transition
relax & remain
rest
continue
mild sensation
energy
physical
heart
mind
Y
I
N
Y
O
G
A
Anchor
Yin Quality
Layer
Principle
Yin Guardian
Asana
Jewel
Method

Guided Mandala Map: Deep Breath Refresh – A Mini Flow for Anytime, 20-minute

This Yin Yoga mini fits into almost any schedule. With the support of twisting and side-bending, it effectively opens space through your chest and rib cage to build a better breath.

Arrive to the Mat: Seated (3min)
Wide Knee Beetle w/side bend (2min), then do the other side
Cp: Bear Rolls
Sukhasana w/upright twist + one arm behind the back bind (2min), then forward bend (2min), Cp, then switch cross of legs and do the other side
Cp: Leg Reviver and Lying Full Body Stretch
Savasana (3min)

(includes counterpose hold times of 1-2mins)

1. **To begin your mapping, go to the Meditative Methods element. Select:** <u>A Meditative Method of Choice</u>

   - Inquire: Given the relatively brief time frame of this session, which directed breathing technique could help you consciously attune to your breathing apparatus and enjoy an expanded breath?

2. **Move to Awareness Anchors. Select:** <u>An Awareness Anchor of Choice</u>

   - Inquire: Which awareness anchor would you like to use to ground your compassionate awareness on the breath, allowing you to relax and remain more easefully in the poses?

Continue mapping as you feel led...

illuminate
transform
cultivate
inspire
2
1
acknowledge
recognize
notice
greet
watch
allow
feel
accept
sense
yield
let go
not do
kindness
curiosity
breath
spaciousness
nature
gratitude
smile
breathwork
yoga nida
concentration
qi cultivation
balance
release
imperfection
impermanence
interconnection
safe
pose
effective
yinpression
counterpose
watch & welcome
arrive
transition
relax & remain
rest
continue
mild sensation
energy
physical
heart
mind
Y
I
N
Y
O
G
A
Anchor
Yin Quality
Yin Guardian
Method
Jewel
Asana
Principle
Layer

Guided Mandala Map: Yin-Nidra Duo Flow – Finding Your Bliss, 60-minute

This Yoga Nidra-inspired Yin Yoga & Meditation practice begins with poses on the wall for a supportive opening for hips and legs, easing tensions and quieting the mind to prepare for an effortless transition into the sweet bliss state of Yoga Nidra.

Arrive to the Mat: Wall Caterpillar w/overhead binding (5min)
Wall Butterfly (5min)
Cp: Wall Caterpillar
One-Legged Wall Butterfly w/side bend (5min), then do the other side
Cp: Wall Caterpillar
Wall Eye of the Needle (3.5min), then do the other side
Cp: Wall Caterpillar and Sideways Beetle
Expanded Savasana, w/Yoga Nidra-Inspired Method of choice (25-30min)
(includes counterpose hold times of 1-2mins)

1. **To begin your mapping, go to the Jewels of Encouragement element. Select: A Jewel of Choice**
   - Inquire: Is there a particular jewel of encouragement you'd enjoy using as a touchstone to help you relax more completely to receive the most benefit from this Yin-Nidra session?
2. **Next, trace to Yin Qualities. Select: A Yin Quality of Choice**
   - Inquire: What yin quality might you embody during your practice session to support the process of turning ever inward to commune with the beautiful being of light within you?

Continue mapping as you feel led...

illuminate
transform
cultivate
inspire
acknowledge
recognize
notice
greet
watch
allow
feel
accept
yield
sense
let go
not do
kindness
curiosity
breath
spaciousness
nature
gratitude
smile
breathwork
concentration
yoga nidra
qi cultivation
release
balance
impermanence
interconnection
imperfection
safe
pose
effective
counterpose
yinpression
watch & welcome
relax & remain
transition
arrive
rest
continue
mild sensation
physical
energy
heart
mind
Y
I
N
Y
O
G
A
Anchor
Yin Quality
Yin Guardian
Method
Jewel
Asana
Principle
Layer

illuminate
transform
cultivate
inspire
acknowledge
recognize
notice
greet
watch
feel
allow
accept
sense
yield
let go
not do
kindness
curiosity
breath
spaciousness
nature
gratitude
smile
breathwork
yoga nidra
concentration
qi cultivation
release
balance
impermanence
imperfection
interconnection
pose
safe
effective
yinpression
counterpose
rest
continue
mild sensation
watch & welcome
arrive
transition
relax & remain
mind
heart
physical
energy
Anchor
Yin Quality
Yin Guardian
Method
Jewel
Asana
Principle
Layer
Y
I
N
Y
O
G
A

illuminate
transform
cultivate
inspire
acknowledge
recognize
notice
greet
watch
allow
feel
accept
sense
yield
let go
not do
kindness
curiosity
breath
spaciousness
nature
gratitude
smile
breathwork
concentration
yoga nidra
qi cultivation
balance
release
impermanence
interconnection
imperfection
pose
safe
effective
counterpose
yinpression
watch & welcome
arrive
transition
relax & remain
rest
continue
mild sensation
physical
heart
energy
mind
Y
I
N
Y
O
G
A
Anchor
Yin Quality
Yin Guardian
Method
Jewel
Asana
Principle
Layer

illuminate
transform
cultivate
inspire
Y I N Y O G A
Anchor
Yin Quality
Yin Guardian
Method
Jewel
Asana
Principle
Layer
acknowledge
recognize
notice
greet
watch
feel
allow
accept
sense
yield
let go
not do
kindness
curiosity
breath
spaciousness
nature
gratitude
smile
breathwork
yoga nidra
concentration
qi cultivation
release
balance
impermanence
imperfection
interconnection
safe
pose
effective
counterpose
yinpression
watch & welcome
relax & remain
transition
arrive
rest
continue
mild sensation
energy
physical
heart
mind

May these pages inspire you to follow your innate wisdom as you travel the pathways of presence inside you on your Yin Yoga & Meditation journey. Always remember, you are a guardian of love, made of stardust and light, the stuff of the universe and of magic – powerful beyond measure, peaceful, and wise. With joy in the heart, there can be joy in the world, so continue to lead from your heart and let love flow in you and from you.

ACKNOWLEDGEMENTS

I offer endless gratitude to all who have so generously given their intelligence, kind energies, and time to help bring this book to life. In a process that has been both more challenging and rewarding than I could have dreamed, your contributions helped make these pages possible.

To my beloved partner Kel, thank you for being there for every step of this journey. Your loving and enduring faith in me, insightful editing and conversation, and our beautiful desert hikes in the Sonoran made all the difference. Your spirit and energy were as important in bringing this project to fruition as mine.

To my cherished family, I'm forever grateful to you all for your love and support. Thank you, Dad, for making me laugh even when things felt challenging, lending a listening ear, and encouraging me with your loving and objective perspective. Star, your voice of sincerity and gentle reminders of my inner strength have been an ever-shining light for me. Mom, I miss you dearly and have so much gratitude for your caring heart and for all the ways you shared your love of nature with me, teaching me to see the sacred beauty all around me. To my sister of the moon, Tracy – thank you for believing in magic, our marathon chats, and brightening the day with bunnies and butterflies. To my grandparents Verna and Sam, thank you for always showering me with your unconditional love.

To my dear friends, my heart is filled with gratitude for each of you. For all your care, support, and thoughtful review of portions of this book, my appreciation goes out to: Chris Byrne (Mr. Byyyyrrnne!), Gretchen Campos, Jennifer Cunningham, Molly Donlan, Mary Evans, Andrea Gleason, Cindy Glennon, Benjamin Ho, Jill Kelley, and Dan Panzarella. Many thanks to the talented Katie Strait for your photography and keenly aesthetic eye, and to my dear and dedicated journey companions and pose models, Molly Donlan and Benjamin Ho, for your energy and enthusiasm in helping bring the Yin asana to life in these pages and joy to my heart. In addition to so many others, a special thank you Bill Newton for your commitment to community and always keeping the lamp lit. Nicole French, I'm so grateful for our many years of inspired and inspiring connection. Maryanne Campbell, thank you for being my wonderful mentor and friend for these many years. Your guidance and humor helped me learn to teach and to lead with passion and integrity. And a very kind thank you to my friend and esteemed fellow teacher, Norman Blair. I greatly appreciate your goodwill, insight, and whole-hearted service in the world.

To my incredible editing team, thank you Kelly Mowrer and Dana Alsamsam for your invaluable editing assistance. Thorough and astute, you helped make this book the best it could be. Ivana Mundja thank you for your beautiful illustrations, I'm grateful to have them grace these pages. Predrag Markovic thank you for your partnership in bringing your brilliant design to this book. Your talent is unmatched and you're right, I will miss working with you!

To my esteemed teachers, I offer a deep bow of gratitude and respect to you for your wisdom, support, and generosity of heart. Each is a blessing on my pathway of practice and teaching. Among them: Thich Nhat Hanh, whose teachings have been a beacon of peace and happiness for me since I first began my practice. Bernie Clark, thank you for your enduring dedication to building and supporting the worldwide Yin Yoga community. Your teachings have been invaluable in my yoga journey and remain a steady source of knowledge and insight for me. Gratitude to Paul Grilley and Sarah Powers for sharing this practice with so many. Amy Figoli, owner of

Threads of Yoga, thank you for taking that first call in the airport on your way to Italy. You took a chance on me, encouraged me to press on with my teacher training in spite of a broken foot, and consistently held me in the light.

Jacqui Bonwell, owner of Sacred Seeds Yoga School, my dear friend and universal co-conspirator, thank you for your belief in me and your trust. I have been honored to teach by your side for so many years. Your teachings are a constant guiding light, and your encouragement to do the work that allows knowledge to evolve into wisdom continues to ring in my heart. Thanks also to cherished teachers Tara Brach, Jack Kornfield, Lee Holden, Josh Summers, and ShivaShakti School of Yoga. Gretchen Campos, I have so much gratitude for you. Thank you for seeing and celebrating the teacher in me, and thank you for sharing the teacher in you. Your Tuesday morning classes were treasured moments.

I'm so grateful for the opportunities I've had to partner with such a beautiful and broad yoga community over the years. Thank you to the many dedicated studio owners and their committed students who host and attend my trainings, to Kripalu Center for Yoga and Health in Lenox, Massachusetts, and the Maine Yoga Fest team led by Andrea Gleason, owner of Scarborough Yoga, always so full of vision, persistent optimism, and love for our fellow yogis.

I offer my heartfelt thank you to the ladies of Greener Postures Yoga, Heidi MacVane, Danielle Toolan, and Gretchen Campos. I am immensely grateful to each of you for the blessing of being part of such an amazing team of GPY teachers and bringing these practices to the lovely GPY community. Your commitment to service and spreading the power of these practices is an inspiration.

I send deep appreciation and love to each of my precious students for choosing to sit with me over the years, and for continuing to inspire and teach me. Your trust and commitment are humbling, and it's always a great honor to share in the energy of these practices with you.

Sagel

Endnotes

Preface

Rabindranath Tagore, Indian poet, philosopher, painter, composer, and reformer 1861-1941

Chapter 2 Embracing Yin Qualities in a Yang World

Eckhart Tolle, *The Power of Now* Namaste Publishing 1997

Chapter 3 Root Wisdom Traditions of Yin Yoga & Meditation

Buddha, *Lokavipatti Sutta* (Thanissaro Bhikku translation) dhammatalks.org

Chapter 4 Exploring the Layers of Our Being

1 Hepburn, Case Studies: Contracture and Stiff Joint Management with Dynasplint™ 1987

2 "The Human Respiratory Gate" Dwain L Eckburg, The Journal of Physiology 19 July 2004 and "Effects of Yoga on the Autonomic Nervous System, Gamma-Aminobutyric-Acid, and Allostasis in Epilepsy, Depression, and Post-Traumatic Stress Disorder" Streeter, Gerbarg, Saper, Ciraulo, Brown Med Hypotheses May 2012

3 Nair S, Sagar M, Sollers J 3rd, Consedine N, Broadbent E. Do slumped and upright postures affect stress responses? A randomized trial. Health Psychol. 2015 Jun;34(6):632-41. doi: 10.1037/hea0000146. Epub 2014 Sep 15. PMID: 25222091

4 Luders E, Thompson PM, Kurth F. Larger hippocampal dimensions in meditation practitioners: differential effects in women and men. Front Psychol. 2015;6:186. Published 2015 Mar 6. oi:10.3389/fpsyg.2015.00186, and Hölzel BK, Carmody J, Vangel M, et al. Mindfulness practice leads to increases in regional brain gray matter density. Psychiatry Res. 2011;191(1):36-43. doi:10.1016/j.pscychresns.2010.08.006

5 Trampe D, Quoidbach J, Taquet M. Emotions in Everyday Life. PLoS One. 2015;10(12):e0145450. Published 2015 Dec 23. doi:10.1371/journal.pone.0145450

6 Cowen AS, Keltner D. Self-report captures 27 distinct categories of emotion bridged by continuous gradients. Proc Natl Acad Sci U S A. 2017 Sep 19;114(38):E7900-E7909. doi: 10.1073/pnas.1702247114. Epub 2017 Sep 5. PMID: 28874542; PMCID: PMC5617253

7 Lim D, Condon P, DeSteno D. Mindfulness and compassion: an examination of mechanism and scalability. PLoS One. 2015 Feb 17;10(2):e0118221. doi: 10.1371/journal.pone.0118221. PMID: 25689827; PMCID: PMC4331532

Pema Chödrön, *No Time to Lose: A Timely Guide to the Way of the Bodhisattva* Shambhala 2007

Paul Grilley, March 2020 yinyoga.com

Tom Myers, Huffington Post Interview with Eva Norlyk Smith, Ph.D. https://www.huffpost.com/entry/mind-body-_b_4387093

Archibald MacLeish, *"Bubble of Blue Air," Riders on the Earth; Essays and Recollections*

Hafiz, *The Gift* (Daniel Ladinsky adaptations) Compass 1999

Stephen Mitchell, *Tao Te Ching* Harper Perennial Modern Classics 2006

Tara Brach, Ph.D., dharma talk tarabrach.com

Dr. Richard Davidson, Founder and chair of the Center for Investigating Healthy Minds at the University of Wisconsin. Interview with Joy Trip Project https://joytripproject.com/2012/04/finding-happiness-with-richard-davidson/

Shunryu Suzuki Roshi, *Zen Mind, Beginner's Mind* John Weatherhill, Inc 1983

Helen Keller, paraphrasing her teacher Anne Sullivan in an 1891 letter to Reverend Phillip Brooks

Thich Nhat Hanh, dharma talk

Chapter 5 Yin Yoga & Meditation Practice Principles

Sogyal Rinpoche, *The Tibetan Book of Living and Dying* HarperSanFrancisco, 2020

Swami Kripalu, also known as Swami Kripalvanandji, kundalini yoga master 1913-1981

Shunruki Suzuki Roshi, in a Shoshan Ceremony lecture, http://cuke.com/Cucumber%20Project/lectures/most-important.htm

Kabir, *The Kabir Book: Forty-Four of the Ecstatic Poems of Kabir* (Robert Bly translation) Beacon Press 2007

Thich Nhat Hanh, *The Miracle of Mindfulness* Beacon Press 1999

Lao Tsu, *Tao Te Ching* (Gia-Fu Fen and Jane English translation) Vintage Books 1972

Patanjali, *Yoga Sutras* (Swami Vivekananda translation) Solar Books 2015

Thich Nhat Hanh, *Present Moment, Wonderful Moment* Parallax Press 2002

Chapter 6 Jewels of Encouragement for Our Practice

1 Curran, T., & Hill, A. P. (2019). Perfectionism is increasing over time: A meta-analysis of birth cohort differences from 1989 to 2016. Psychological

Bulletin, 145(4), 410–429) (Hewitt, P. L., Flett, G. L., Turnbull-Donovan, W., & Mikail, S. F. (1991). The Multidimensional Perfectionism Scale: Reliability, validity, and psychometric properties in psychiatric samples. Psychological Assessment: A Journal of Consulting and Clinical Psychology, 3(3), 464–468

2 1. Paik A, Sanchagrin K. Social Isolation in America: An Artifact. American Sociological Review. 2013;78(3):339-360. doi:10.1177/0003122413482919 2. Smink FR, van Hoeken D, Hoek HW. Epidemiology of eating disorders: incidence, prevalence and mortality rates. Curr Psychiatry Rep. 2012 Aug;14(4):406-14. doi: 10.1007/s11920-012-0282-y. PMID: 22644309; PMCID: PMC3409365. 3.Thompson CM, Durrani AJ. An increasing need for early detection of body dysmorphic disorder by all specialties. J R Soc Med. 2007 Feb;100(2):61-2. doi: 10.1177/014107680710000203. PMID: 17277262; PMCID: PMC1790987

Dr. Wayne Dyer, *The Power of Intention*. Hay House Inc 2005

Buddha, *The Avatamsaka Sutra* (Thomas Cleary translation) Shambhala 1993

Chapter 8 Yin Guardians, Trusted Companions in Our Practice

1 Rowland L, Curry OS. 'A range of kindness activities boost happiness.' J Soc Psychol. 2019;159(3):340-343. doi: 10.1080/00224545.2018.1469461. Epub 2018 May 15. PMID: 29702043

2 Wollmer MA, de Boer C, Kalak N, Beck J, Götz T, Schmidt T, Hodzic M, Bayer U, Kollmann T, Kollewe K, Sönmez D, Duntsch K, Haug MD, Schedlowski M, Hatzinger M, Dressler D, Brand S, Holsboer-Trachsler E, Kruger TH. Facing depression with botulinum toxin: a randomized controlled trial. J Psychiatr Res. 2012 May;46(5):574-81. doi: 10.1016/j.jpsychires.2012.01.027. Epub 2012 Feb 24. PMID: 22364892

3 Gould van Praag, Garfinkel, Sparasci, Mees, Philippides, Ware, Ottaviani, and Critchley 2017

4 Emmons RA, McCullough ME. Counting blessings versus burdens: an experimental investigation of gratitude and subjective well-being in daily life. J Pers Soc Psychol. 2003 Feb;84(2):377-89. doi: 10.1037//0022-3514.84.2.377. PMID: 12585811

George Burns, American comedian, actor, and singer. 1896-1996

Norman Blair, *Brightening Our Inner Skies: Yin and Yoga*. Micmac Margins 2016

Thich Nhat Hanh, *You Are Here* Shambhala 2010

Aesop, *Aesop's Fables*

Thich Nhat Hanh, *Being Peace* Parallax Press 2005

Thich Nhat Hanh, dharma talk

Richard Louv, *The Last Child in the Woods* Algonquin Books 2008

Meister Eckhart, Eckhart von Hochheim 1260-1328, German Catholic mystic, philosopher and theologian

Chapter 9 Asana Yinpressions: Patterns and Potentials

1 https://yip.guru

Chapter 11 Meditative Methods for Presence, Possibility, and Wellbeing

1 Fehmi LG, Shor SB. Open focus attention training. Psychiatr Clin North Am. 2013 Mar;36(1):153-62. doi: 10.1016/j.psc.2013.01.003. PMID: 23538084

2 *Clinician's Complete Reference to Complementary & Alternative Medicine* by Donald Novey, 2000

3 Stetter F, Kupper S. Autogenic training: a meta-analysis of clinical outcome studies. 2002. In: Database of Abstracts of Reviews of Effects (DARE): Quality-assessed Reviews [Internet]. York (UK): Centre for Reviews and Dissemination (UK); 1995. https://www.ncbi.nlm.nih.gov/books/NBK69422/ and *Autogenic Therapy*, a six-volume book collection by Wolfgang Luthe and Johannes Shultz 1969-70

4 Jacobson, E 1938 *Progressive Muscle Relaxation* Chicago. University of Chicago Press; Merakou K, Tsoukas K, Stavrinos G, Amanaki E, Daleziou A, Kourmousi N, Stamatelopoulou G, Spourdalaki E, Barbouni A. The Effect of Progressive Muscle Relaxation on Emotional Competence: Depression-Anxiety-Stress, Sense of Coherence, Health-Related Quality of Life, and Well-Being of Unemployed People in Greece: An Intervention Study. Explore (NY). 2019 Jan-Feb;15(1):38-46. doi: 10.1016/j.explore.2018.08.001. Epub 2018 Aug 20. PMID: 30228090

5 Benson, H. 2000. *The Relaxation Response*. New York: HarperTorch

Buddha, *Sedaka Sutta* (Andrew Olendzki translation) accesstoinsight.org

Made in the USA
Coppell, TX
12 March 2024